D1130738

THE SOURCES OF SCIENCE

Number 30

THE SOURCES OF SCIENCE

Editor-in-Chief: HARRY WOOLF

WILLIS K. SHEPARD PROFESSOR OF THE HISTORY OF SCIENCE
THE JOHNS HOPKINS UNIVERSITY

THE CELL IN DEVELOPMENT AND INHERITANCE

THE CELL

in

Development and Inheritance

By EDMUND B. WILSON

Reprinted from the New York Edition of 1896

With a new Introduction by
HERMANN J. MULLER
DISTINGUISHED SERVICE PROFESSOR OF ZOOLOGY, EMERITUS
INDIANA UNIVERSITY
BLOOMINGTON, INDIANA

MEMBER, INSTITUTE FOR ADVANCED LEARNING IN THE MEDICAL SCIENCES
CITY OF HOPE, DUARTE, CALIFORNIA, 1965

VISITING PROFESSOR, UNIVERSITY OF WISCONSIN
MADISON, WISCONSIN, 1965/1966

The Sources of Science, No. 30

JOHNSON REPRINT CORPORATION

New York and London

1966

Introduction© *1966 by*
JOHNSON REPRINT CORPORATION

Library of Congress Catalog Card Number: 66-12710

PRINTED IN THE UNITED STATES OF AMERICA

INTRODUCTION

W ILSON'S GREAT BOOK "The Cell in Development and Inheritance,"
especially in its first edition, here reprinted, marks him as the
most constructive encyclopedist of biological science. Even in those
days, the cellular phenomena that formed the object of his study constituted a rich skein. Yet it was a bewilderingly diffuse one, and at
times it seemed almost impalpable. Wilson carried out no merely
formalistic compilation of all the facts and hypotheses extant concerning this elusive web of life. True, his coverage of all then-known components was a comprehensive one. But—what was far more important
—he brought to bear on this welter of material an insight and an
organizing genius that sharply highlighted the courses and interrelations of its really significant strands. At the same time, he made known
the gaps that needed filling in and he exposed the false leads. In doing
so, he did not allow himself to be ensnared by the pretentious verbiage
then prevalent.

Wilson's combination of analysis and integration, his search for
underlying principles, proved its worth by pointing the way to diverse
observations, experiments, and lines of thought. These, carried out in
no small part by Wilson himself and increasingly, as time went on, by
others for whom he had led the way, have led to an ever deeper understanding of the basic problems at issue. In consequence, the cell science
of 1966, although so enormously deepened and clarified, is still in
essential and surprising conformity with the distant vision descried by
Wilson in the murky dawnlight of 1896.

For Wilson, the study of the cell was the study of life. His interests
were not confined to the cell as such but were centered in the principles
exemplified in it that might furnish clues to the problems of evolution,
development, and heredity, and to the basic distinctions between
living and nonliving matter. That is, he was primarily an all-round
biologist, and the cell was his window into life in general. Yet at the
same time he was deeply moved by the fascinating details of the
microcosm that was coming into view within the cell.

Wilson combined esthetic with scientific perceptivity and expres-
sivity—there being, as he recognized, much in common between true

art and true science. Gentle, restrained, and meticulous though he was
in manner, conduct, and mode of expression, he nevertheless harbored
a powerful inner ardor and drive. These impelled him to plumb the
depths and bind the breadths of his diversified materials into as consistent and meaningful a whole as possible, one that disclosed the order
and beauty inherent in the living world.

Careful not to let words run away with him, he was the better able
to share with his readers and hearers the great experiences involved in
this undertaking, to convey to them his points of view, and to imbue
them with the spirit of adventure that the quest aroused in him. Thus,
throughout his life's long productive period (1880–1937), Wilson
exerted a profound and widespread guiding influence on the education
of increasing numbers and successive generations of biologists. The
latter were thereby led to similarly controlled and critical, yet constructive and sometimes daring, efforts of observation, experiment, and
conceptualization. Since his death in 1939, this influence has continued
to grow, even though with ever less realization, by the successively
newer recruits to science, of the main source from which it had issued.

Prior Biological Developments

To appreciate in perspective the contribution represented by "The
Cell," the state of biological science and Wilson's own activities during
the years preceding the composition of this work should be realized. It
was in 1872, when he was about 17 years old, that Wilson decided to
go into biology. At that time, Darwin's "On the Origin of Species"
constituted as new and engrossing a theme as the Watson-Crick break-
through into molecular genetics does at the time of our present publication (1966), and even Schleiden and Schwann's cell theory was but
20 years its senior. Not until 1875, when Wilson was an undergraduate
majoring in biology at Yale, was it first shown, by Oscar Hertwig, that
just one sperm nucleus joins one egg nucleus at fertilization. And only
in 1878, during Wilson's last year at Yale, did he see for the first time
a picture (taken by Mark at Harvard) of chromosomes and mitosis.
This impressed him profoundly.

By 1883, cell knowledge had ripened enough to allow Weismann to
put forward his theory of germ-plasm continuity and the noninheritance of acquired characters. Soon thereafter, by the mid-eighties,
Weismann and others had been able to deduce, on the ground of a
series of cogent findings, that the chromatin (i.e., the material of the
chromosomes) probably constitutes the basis of inheritance. Biologists
in general were far from agreed on these conclusions. However, Wilson
had in the meantime been drawn increasingly into the main stream

of the biological research of the day, and had spent two rich years (1881–1883) in Europe, at Cambridge, Leipzig, and Naples. He came to view these concepts as the keys for obtaining, through a better understanding of the cell, a deeper comprehension of evolution and of the processes of development. It was in this spirit that, in 1892–1893, the first of his many years at Columbia, he gave a notable course of lectures which, during the next three years, he amplified and updated into the book here reprinted.

The Formulation of a Biological Foundation

Wilson's exceptional insight into biology in general had in the meantime become embodied in a college text, "General Biology." Along with his colleague, W. T. Sedgwick, Wilson wrote the first (1885) edition of this book during a period (1883–1885) when, as a teacher at Williams and then at the Massachusetts Institute of Technology, he had little opportunity for research. Remarkably advanced for its day, it started with a consideration of living matter as a highly complex system that is composed of atoms of the same kinds, working according to the same fundamental laws, as in nonliving things. Unlike the latter, however, according to Sedgwick and Wilson, it is enabled by its special organization to maintain itself in "a shifting state of equilibrium" in adjustment to the changes in its environment. (Nowadays, this concept is sometimes mistakenly regarded as a new one, and is given the pretentious appellation "homeostasis.") Living matter sustains this equilibrium even as it appropriates additional material and energy, reworks them suitably both for these operations and for its growth and reproduction, and eventually relinquishes most of them. Before these operations can be adequately understood, say the authors, there must be much further development in both physics and chemistry.

Having laid this basis in connection with a discussion of the cell, the authors then introduce the student to the workings out of these processes in the case of a multicellular plant, the fern, and after that, of a multicellular animal, the earthworm. Both of these have been chosen to represent an intermediate complexity of intercellular organization, suitable for highlighting the differentiation of functions without a superabundance of detail. The differentiated structures are always interpreted in terms of how they work. It is emphasized that the whole plant or animal is not merely a congeries of its parts, inasmuch as the form and activities of the parts undergo integration when all are present together. Without this integration neither the whole nor the parts can succeed, under natural conditions, in surviving or in reproducing themselves.

It is further made clear that in both of these very different examples, the systems of specialized operations comprised in their vegetative physiology and in their life cycles result in the carrying out, and are themselves the resultants, of the same previously noted general principles concerning the distinctive mode of working of all living matter. As for the great differences between these two types of organism (fern and earthworm), they are shown to be for the most part expressions of the different needs occasioned by their characteristic modes of nutrition. Yet this does not complete the picture, for it is explained that only in the light of their divergent evolutionary histories can the nature of the present-day organizations become really intelligible.

It is true that none of these individual ideas were unique with Sedgwick or Wilson, yet they form a complex that was unusual for its time. Vitalism was still rampant, and a truly physicochemical view of life was widely frowned upon. It was virtually a heresy to state, as they did, that even "the phenomena of consciousness are not known to occur apart from a living material basis with which they appear to be in some way closely connected." As for evolution, Wilson found himself taken to task for daring to teach that theory at Williams College, and left there largely for that reason.

Only recently have many of the beginning texts in biology at last come to recognize the importance of treating the subject along the main lines that were adopted so long ago by Sedgwick and Wilson. Even those texts that now do so, however, often make the pedagogical mistake of not using the "type system." That is, they fail to provide the beginner with unified delineations, detailed yet close knit, of entire organisms of contrasting kinds. Thus they do not make him sufficiently aware of the considerable interdependence of the peculiar characteristics of any given organism's different parts. From an evolutionary standpoint, the picture they present is therefore a confused one.

The present writer, who in 1907 enjoyed the privilege of being introduced to college biology at Columbia through a course (taught by Wilson's former student, J. H. McGregor) for which the 1900 edition of the Sedgwick and Wilson text was used, can testify to its efficacy in imparting not just an enlightening but a truly stirring view of living nature. It was in fact this circumstance that decided the writer, for his part, to enter the same general realm of inquiry. For Wilson, the main viewpoints set forth in this book must have been most important in enabling him to pursue so fruitful and sound a course in his researches and theorizations. Moreover, the same basis has proved itself able to foster and to support the increments supplied by the subsequent investigations of multitudes of biologists.

Wilson's Researches on Morphogenesis and Mitosis

Prior to the turn of the century Wilson's own researches, which dealt mainly with problems of early embryology, including cell division, contributed much to his preparation for writing the first edition of "The Cell," and then for the rewriting that resulted in the second (1900) edition. It is therefore of interest for us to consider these earlier researches here.

After having, at Yale, completed his descriptive studies of the peculiar primitive anthropods known as Pycnogonids, and having then become captivated by mitosis as depicted in the fertilized egg, Wilson decided to direct his efforts to attacking the great conundrum of how the entire individual can lie implicit in, and develop out of, an egg. Here, he realized, lay concentrated not only the problems of ontogeny per se (as well as, more generally, those of cellular organization), but, more ulteriorly, those of phylogeny, inheritance, and even evolutionary mechanisms. At that time (1878), years before experimental techniques were introduced into embryology, observation was the only method used in this field. However, the cytological techniques of high-power microscopy, section cutting, aniline staining, etc., then very new, had been exploited so little as to open up rich new vistas to the observer who applied them judiciously. This young Wilson proceeded to do during his three years as a graduate student at Hopkins (1878–1881), and again, after stays in Europe, at Williams, and at M.I.T., when he was head of the biology department at Bryn Mawr (1885–1891).

His successive studies along these lines, first of the sea pen *Renilla*, a colonial coelenterate, then of the earthworm *Lumbricus*, and finally of the sandworm *Nereis*, gave results from which he was able to draw important conclusions. It was of phylogenetic interest to find that the most primitive of these forms, *Renilla*, although possessed of muscular and mesogloeal cells in the developed animal, has no embryonic mesoderm layer, whereas *Lumbricus* and *Nereis* both have true mesoderm, which develops from two apically-dividing "teloblast" cells, derived from one specific cell of a rather early stage in cleavage. Reviewing in this connection evidence from other forms, Wilson pointed out that in a whole group of phyla, unlike some other phyla, there is a pattern of mesoderm development similar to this. Moreover, the teloblastic phyla (at least those representatives of them that are presumably more primitive in their embryogeny) agree also in having a characteristic "spiral" type of cleavage, during which one or more mesoderm-progenitor cells are set aside in an essentially similar manner. As Wilson later emphasized in a graduate course given at Columbia, this situation indicates an early dichotomy of multicellular animals above the coelenterates into two main stems, characterized by mesoderm that is primitively teloblastic and enterocoelic (derived from pouches of the embryonic gut), respectively.

Yet, despite finding these extensive similarities between the embryogeny of widely diverse phyla, Wilson noted that the pattern of cell division is not entirely fixed in relation to the ontogenetic destiny of the cells concerned, even among individuals of the same population. Thus, in *Renilla*, both the spatial arrangement and the timing of the cytoplasmic cleavages are highly variable, yet the outcome of development is the same. Again, whereas *Nereis* is normally very definite in the arrangements and destinies of its blastomeres, *Lumbricus* is not so precise. Moreover, a comparison of the details of early development found by various investigators in different teloblastic phyla, showed that even in forms with normally strict cell lineage evolution has sometimes accomplished the substitution of the ontogenetic roles of some embryonic cells for those of others.

Going beyond the observation of such "experiments of nature," as Wilson was pleased to term them, he embarked, in the nineties, on experiments of his own on early stages, shortly after Roux, Pflüger, Driesch, the Hertwigs, and Boveri had opened the way to such work. During a second stay at Naples (1891–1892), he found that in the primitive chordate *Amphioxus* the early blastomeres have not just the potentiality of producing a whole individual, as do those previously studied by Driesch in echinoderms. Each separated blastomere of the latter could finally produce a complete embryo, but the process involved in its early stages a kind of regeneration. By contrast, it often happened in *Amphioxus* that each of the separated blastomeres followed, from the moment of its separation from the others, a course of development not visibly different from that of an entire fertilized egg. This indicated the perfect equivalence of these blastomeres to the original egg and to each other.

As for the early-differentiating *Nereis*, Wilson proceeded to find that even here, if he flattened the egg by pressure so as to cause its first three cleavages all to be in the vertical plane (with the result that some nuclei that would otherwise have been destined for the ectoderm came to have an endodermal position, and vice versa), nevertheless the subsequent development was normal in that all the cells with displaced nuclei went on to participate in a regular way in the formation of the parts that their enforced positions would have called for. Thus no ground was left for the hypothesis of Roux, shortly afterwards adopted by Weismann also, that differentiation in general results from the segregation, at successive mitoses, of inherited nuclear determiners into just those cells whose later type of differentiation will depend on those determiners. This hypothesis had rested on Roux's early finding in frogs (1888), later verified by others and extended to other forms and stages, that if one blastomere of the two-cell stage is killed—or, in some forms, even if it separated from the remainder—that blastomere will develop "mosaically," i.e., into the part that it would otherwise have become.

Granted an equivalence of nuclei, however, a theoretical reconciliation was still needed between the seemingly contradictory types of development represented by Driesch's sea urchins and Roux's frogs. This was especially true since in the meantime Wilson had found *Amphioxus* to show an even more precise equivalence of separated blastomeres than do the sea urchins, and since other investigators—including Wilson's student Crampton, working on a sea snail—had discovered forms more precisely and unalterably mosaic than the frog.

Wilson, Dreisch, and O. Hertwig, largely independently, found a way of embracing the most extreme types of both kinds, as well as types showing various grades of intermediacy, under a common "epigenetic" principle. According to this, although the nucleus of each cell contains the hereditary materials that determine the potentialities of its cytoplasm, and although these materials have (with certain exceptions) been distributed by mitosis to all early embryonic cells alike, their cytoplasms become differentiated from each other in consequence of organizing processes that involve interactions between regions of the whole. Often these differentiations are at first invisible. Moreover, they may, earlier at least, be more or less reversible if parts invoked in the interactions are removed.

On this view, it is further held that in the course of time ever more localized interactions, leading to finer differentiations, take place successively, within and between the regions that have already undergone the earlier differentiations. Different types of organisms, such as *Amphioxus* and the frog, differ greatly with regard to the timing of these differentiations in relation to the timing of the cell divisions. They differ also in the timing and the degree of irreversibility attained. Wilson went beyond the others in pointing out also that the interactions and differentiations are to some extent independent of the existence of cell boundaries, and that the factors that call them forth are not merely positional or mechanical, but must often be much more subtle chemical and physical ones, an understanding of which was still remote.

In the years between the first and second editions of "The Cell" and for several years thereafter, and again a quarter century later, Wilson and his students continued to experiment along these lines, and succeeded in confirming and further developing these conceptions. In certain mollusks, for example, even the unfertilized egg was found, on ablation of a particular region, to have had given later developments already "prelocalized" in them irreversibly. On the other hand, in a Nemertean egg such processes commenced only after its fertilization, subsequent to which, as cleavage proceeded, a definite succession of them could be traced. Yet even in the mollusks with the very early prelocalization, evidence was obtained soon afterward (1903) that one of these prelocalized parts (that destined to form the "polar lobe") was still, at the two-cell stage, interacting with another region, for its presence up to that time was required for the formation of a specific organ, the "apical organ," which develops from the other region. This was a discovery, probably for the first time, of the same principle as that much later subsumed by Spemann under the designation of "organizers." It was, however, quite in harmony with Wilson's general scheme, according to which both prelocalization and regulation were consequences of interactions between regions, and were subject to varied degrees of finality.

It must be remembered that although these concepts may seem mere commonplaces or even truisms to us today, they were not readily apprehended in the period we are considering, when so many findings seemed to contradict each other. The difficulty of grasping them at that time is illustrated by the tenacity with which Roux and Weismann long held to their view of somatic segregation of nuclear determiners, in the face of the evidence of widespread regulation in embryos and regeneration in adults (processes that Wilson regarded as the same in principle). It is illustrated also by the later history of Driesch who, even though he had for a time espoused largely the same view as Wilson's, gradually became so baffled by it as to postulate in cells a limited kind of spirit or intelligence, called by him "entelechy," which directs their courses of development so as to coordinate those of the different cells that compose the whole. Along with this, he maintained, the cells possessed a kind of memory that made possible—contrary to Weismann—the inheritance of acquired characters. None of this, according to Wilson, was science.

Realizing the important part played by mitosis in development, reproduction, and cell life in general, and its accessibility to both observation and experiment, Wilson made this phenomenon, which had so kindled his interest as early as 1878, an object of special study. In this he was stimulated, during his stay at Naples in 1891–1892, by his close association with Theodor Boveri, who was of the same generation as Wilson. After early observations by O. Hertwig (1875) and others on the origination of the aster of the fertilized egg in the neighborhood of the entering spermatozoon and preceding its nucleus, Boveri in 1887 had clarified the picture further. He showed that in the round-worm *Ascaris* the centrosome about which this aster develops is brought in by the spermatozoon, that it doubles in the formation of the achromatic part of the first mitotic figure of cleavage, and that it preserves its continuity, with further doubling, to perform the same function at later zygotic divisions. It is this centrosome, not the nucleus, according to Boveri, that is the essential fertilizing element, even though the equivalence of the two parents in inheritance indicates that it must be the nucleus that carries the hereditary endowment.

This view, however, had been challenged in 1891 by Fol (and soon afterward by others), who maintained that there is at fertilization a "quadrille of centers," in which both egg and sperm centrosome persist and double, with a subsequent union of each daughter centrosome of paternal to one of those of maternal origin, so as to give rise to the two centrosomes and asters, each biparental in origin, of the first cleavage figure. In 1894–1895 Wilson, his student Mathews, and Boveri, all working on different species of echinoderms, disproved this "quadrille" concept, and verified and extended Boveri's earlier findings, while the results of other investigators soon fell into line also. When Wilson was in his seventies, he returned to this problem, since it was still arousing controversy. With his former student, Huettner, he showed clearly that in the fruit fly *Drosophila*, which is better suited than echinoderms for distinguishing the central bodies themselves, his interpretation is correct, that is, they originate from the sperm and maintain their continuity throughout development.

Despite this purely paternal derivation of the zygotic centrosome and the degeneration of the maternal one in normal cases, Richard Hertwig had in 1895 described the formation and partial functioning of a maternally derived amphiaster in unfertilized echinoderm cells that had been subjected to abnormal conditions. This finding was soon extended by others and culminated in the artificial parthenogenesis achieved by Jacques Loeb. Experiments and cytological observations designed to investigate these matters were immediately thereafter undertaken by Wilson, in 1901 and 1902.

Although this work was carried out just after the appearance of the second edition of "The Cell," its close relation to that just discussed makes it convenient to review it briefly here. Using the egg of the sea urchin *Toxopneustes*, Wilson discovered that the centrosome and aster, in cases of artificial stimulation of the unfertilized egg, arise not from the nucleus, as was previously believed, but as "cytasters," apart from and independently of the nucleus. Multiple cytasters can form *de novo* in the cytoplasm. Although they can function fully only on becoming connected with a nucleus, they can divide and function to some extent even without one. Amphiaster formation and the doubling and condensation of chromosomes could each occur in the absence of the other, and even in the absence of both there was still a tendency for rhythmic cytoplasmic changes resembling those of mitosis to occur. If, as sometimes happened, a cytaster connected with a nucleus failed to divide, the chromosomes nevertheless doubled and condensed, and they arranged themselves along the incomplete spindle fibers of the "monaster." But, as Wilson showed on interfering in various ways with mitosis, effective separation of the daughter chromosomes into two groups required a proper amphiastral spindle. Moreover, cytoplasmic cleavage, as well as the approach of the sperm nucleus to that of the egg, required normal aster formation.

In addition, Wilson's investigations, even in the early nineties, were concerned with the mechanisms and materials *underlying* the phenomena of mitosis. Were the spindle and astral fibers solid structures, or were they, as Bütschli had thought, lines of flow or of the orientation of particles? Wilson held that the mere contraction of the spindle fibers could not cause the chromosomes to travel all the way to the poles, as he had seen them do, nor account for that growth of material around the central bodies that he had observed to accompany the fiber shortening. Wilson and his students were also conducting investigations at this time into the structure and behavior of both the chromatin and the cytoplasmic "ground substance." All these and the previously mentioned studies of his own helped to provide him with invaluable firsthand experience for the first edition of "The Cell."

Preludes to the Writing of "The Cell"

Wilson's research on the origin of the centrosomes of the cleavage stages, carried out in the years just preceding the publication of his first edition of "The Cell," was considered by him to be an important preliminary to the elucidation of the central problems with which his book was to be concerned. This, as he explained, is the reason why he postponed the book's publication for three years following the delivery of the course of lectures on which it was to be based, for if it had been true, as maintained in 1891 and 1893 by Fol and others in the "quadrille of centers" doctrine, that the centrosomes of the two parents

fuse and then divide as do the nuclei, this finding could have constituted a serious challenge to the conclusion that the nuclear chromatin
is the main seat of inheritance.

As we have seen, Fol's view was thoroughly disproved. However,
the postponement thus entailed led to other difficulties for Wilson's
book: In 1893, during the early days of Wilson's research on the
cleavage centrosomes, an exhaustive *Handbuch* by O. Hertwig, entitled
"Die Zelle und die Gewebe," made its appearance. This circumstance
made it desirable for Wilson to rework his manuscript further before
sending it in for publication, even though he was still to follow in the
printed version the same general pattern of presentation and to arrive
at the same conclusions as in his course of lectures. Wilson in "The Cell"
gives generous acknowledgment of the value of this work of Hertwig's,
and of the help it gave him in elaborating his own book. He explains,
however, that he has not aimed in his treatment to be so all-inclusive
as Hertwig, but has chosen, instead, to concentrate on those aspects
of the subject that might be of potential significance in an understanding of development, inheritance, and evolution.

It was fitting that Wilson should have dedicated his book to Boveri.
For one thing, while in Europe, Wilson had formed a deep personal
attachment to Boveri. Second, Wilson had been greatly impressed by
Boveri's series of major findings in the fields of greatest interest to
them both. Third, he had been strongly swayed, although not always
convinced, by Boveri's zealously advocated interpretations of these
findings.

Among the results and hypotheses that had been contributed by
Boveri (some of them arrived at by others independently) were those
concerning the centrosome of multicellular animals. These included its
persistence in an extranuclear position as a permanent organelle, its
ultimate derivation from the midpiece of the paternal spermatozoon,
and its functioning as a dynamic center in the approach of the sperm
and egg nuclei at fertilization as well as, through amphiaster formation, in the effectuation both of daughter-chromosome divergence and
of cytoplasmic cleavage. More significant still were the observational
and experimental evidences Boveri had obtained, and his cogent arguments—to be referred to more specifically later—in favor of the persistent individuality of the chromosomes. In addition, he had done
interesting pioneer work on the phenomena of meiosis. However
Ascaris, his object of study for that purpose, was ill suited for a
solution of this intricate problem by the techniques then available. He
was thus led to conclude that the chromatin splits (or, as we would
say, doubles) twice at meiosis—a procedure that would seem to be at

variance with the maintenance of chromosome individuality. In *Ascaris* he also discovered the striking but enigmatic elimination of chromatin that regularly occurs in the derivation of its somatic cells. All these studies, although much amplified later, preceded Wilson's first edition and played important roles in shaping it.

Main Themes of "The Cell"

Despite Wilson's disavowal of completeness in its treatments, his first edition of "The Cell" is a model of ordered and succinct comprehensiveness in relation to its main themes. It is thorough in its historical coverage of each of the major subjects and in the credit accorded every significant contributor (positive or negative) to that subject's development. Although this procedure makes necessary a separate chronological account of each topic, the reader is always kept aware of the central issues involved, of the bearings of the individual contributions on them, and of the interconnections between the developing conceptions. Moreover, Wilson never allows his approval or disapproval, no matter how strong, of one or more assertions of a given investigator to bias his judgment concerning other points made by the same person. In fact, it is a characteristically Wilsonian practice to point out nuggets of truth that lie embedded within largely erroneous conclusions, and fallacious or doubtful components of otherwise valid propositions. Unfortunately, however, as we shall see, Wilson sometimes carries to a fault his inclination to give maximum credit to the erring and to maintain a balance between opposed views.

Since the primary object of the book is to consider the cell in relation to development and inheritance, and through these, if possible, to evolution, no attempt is made in it to take up specialized cells, such as those of muscle, gland, nerve, or bone tissue, except as they may carry possible lessons in these connections. Moreover, although there is a sizable chapter (VII) on the chemistry and physiology of the cell, the statement—correct for that time—is made in its opening paragraph that "we have scarcely passed the threshold" of the study of the chemical "changes of a complicated character" that take place among the "mixtures of many complex substances" contained within a living cell. This does not mean that the importance of these processes as forming the basis of the matters taken up in the book is not fully recognized— on the contrary, the interdependence of morphological and biochemical phenomena is given special emphasis. It means only that biology and chemistry had not yet advanced to levels at which specific cross-connections of significance for the problems at issue could be made between them. Most of the researches dealt with in the book therefore employ the techniques of morphological (cytological) study, although they are concerned not just with static structures but, more especially, with the observable changes and with the invisible organizations and mechanisms that might underlie those changes.

As stated earlier, the focus is on reproduction and development—also implying, ulteriorly, inheritance and evolution—as effected by cells. This is the field that has traditionally been that chiefly dealt with by "general biology," as contrasted with the branches of science that have been considered more closely allied to or a part of medicine. In accordance with this aim, the book, after giving an outline of cell structures and their observed interrelations, proceeds to consider mitosis, the mode of formation of the germ cells, fertilization, and "reduction" (meiosis). In the chapter dealing with each of these subjects the theoretical interpretations of the observations described are discussed. In most of the succeeding chapters there is a more comprehensive integration of the aforementioned and of additional material, with the object of throwing further light, where possible, on the nature and activities of cellular components and on the mechanisms of inheritance and of differentiation.

For our purposes here, it is more useful to follow an order that is in part the reverse of Wilson's, by pointing out in the first place the main series of conclusions toward which the reader of the book is increasingly led as he follows the observations and arguments presented in it. Clearly the foremost among these series of conclusions, whether from the viewpoint of 1896 or 1966, are the strongly buttressed inferences that there is a distinct, persistent material that carries the inheritance, and that this material is, or is contained in, the chromatin, as Weismann, O. Hertwig, Köllicker, and Strasburger had maintained in 1884. Less certainly, it is surmised that this hereditary material may consist of the nucleic acid component of the chromatin (this is pointed out in the concluding section of the chapter on cell chemistry). Furthermore, it is concluded, this hereditary material is composed of many qualitatively different parts that are linearly arranged in the chromosomes, as Roux had proposed in 1883 on the basis of their longitudinal splitting. These parts, in early embryogeny at least, are distributed alike to both daughter cells at mitosis (unlike what Roux and Weismann believed), after each of them has, prior to mitosis, undergone "growth and division" by an act of self-reproduction (i.e., doubling). Such equal distribution is stated to be the main function of the complicated mitotic mechanism.

The second major series of conclusions is concerned with the problem of how, in the face of this equidistribution of hereditary materials to all parts of a developing individual (in its earlier stages, at least), these parts nevertheless become differentiated from one another in an orderly way that is somehow determined primarily by the organism's hereditary constitution. As has been pointed out in the discussion of Wilson's own researches on development, he concluded that the ultimate answer to this problem must lie in complex and then remote physicochemical processes. It was nevertheless possible for him to conclude, further, that these processes must be such as to cause the cytoplasm of egg or embryo, under the influences of one or more nuclei like that which had controlled that cytoplasm's construction, to become organized, so as to result in interregional heterogeneity. The regional dissimilarities would at first be interdependent on one another for their continuation or, as Wilson would say, conditioned by the whole, and would later become more fixed.

The type of this differentiation, and the timing of its onset and fixation in relation to egg maturity and to the timing of the zygotic divisions, would normally depend upon the hereditary (nuclear) constitution of the given species. The different conditions these set up in the several regions would be such that then, under the influences of the given hereditary material, further organization would be engendered within them. This would differ from one region to another, and would result in further, finer differentiations of diverse types, in an orderly, sequential manner. Wilson realized that the words "organize" and "organization" covered deep unknowns here, but that they nevertheless represented facts of development, and that underlying these facts mechanisms could and must exist.

Despite this conception, however, Wilson inclined to the view that in later stages of differentiation the hereditary material of some regions, in some higher types of organisms at least, probably became permanently limited in its potentialities, in a manner that differed from one region to another. In this conclusion he followed Boveri (1891). He was led to it, for one thing, by the progressive decrease in the range and completeness of regeneration often obtaining in later stages of development and in adults, especially in those of higher forms. Apparently he did not realize that his conception of the fixation of cytoplasmic differences in some early stages in which the nuclei were still equipotential made it unnecessary to apply an interpretation different from this to later stages.

Wilson's second basis for the belief that somatic nuclei of later stages may have lost a part of their original endowment lay most clearly in Boveri's indisputable cytological evidence for the elimination of some chromatin during the formation of the somatic cells of *Ascaris*. This, thought Wilson, was, supported by reports of chromatin changing into other material in other organisms, and he believed this to provide a more usual pathway in differentiation than actual elimination of the *Ascaris* type. Since at that time heterochromatin, ribonucleic acid, etc., were unknown, it was only natural to conclude that potentially active and permanent genetic material had in these cases been lost. It is noteworthy, however, that even in making this concession to a mosaic distribution of hereditary material, Wilson did not, like Roux and Weismann, invoke a qualitative longitudinal division of the chromosomes in preparation for mitosis.

In the light of modern findings, there are several ways of interpreting fixations in differentiation that can continue through many cell doublings after the original causes that had triggered those differentiations had been removed, short of assuming the loss or irreversible change of a part of the hereditary endowment of the cells in question. One way is to assume that there have been self-priming changes in given cytoplasmic(?) reactions that had at first been open to alternative pathways, such as have been shown in Sonneborn's work on the antigenic composition of the outer layer of *Paramecium*. Second (although this possibility may overlap the first), it could be postulated that the permanently differentiated cells have come to contain a particular type of RNA, produced originally by the nuclear chromatin but now able to reproduce itself indefinitely, as shown, for instance, by Gibson and Sonneborn for their gene-engendered "metagons" of *Paramecium*. Third, given nuclear genes (or, for that matter, nonnuclear ones, where such exist) may have become more or less permanently repressed or de-repressed, in a way that permits this condition to be transmitted through replications. This could happen either as a result of self-priming of the given structure itself, or by that in some other material that had instigated the change. Possible parallels here are some heteropycnotic chromosomes (mammals and coccids), "paramutated" genes (maize), and variegation (maize). Nevertheless, the possibility of directed mutations of some kind in the primary genetic material, although it seems remote in the light of present knowledge concerning mutation, cannot yet be finally ruled out.

In the section (F) "On the Nature and Causes of Differentiation" in his last chapter, Wilson expresses his agreement with a conception put forward by Driesch in 1894, to the effect that each cytoplasmic change that occurs in development has the effect of "reacting upon the nucleus and thus inciting a new change." This postulate would seem to have been an unnecessary one at the time it was proposed. For, in view of the complex reaction-possibilities opened up by the myriads of nucleus-dependent substances that might be present in the cytoplasm, any cytoplasmic differentiations could well be conceived as leading to further ones, even without changes in the nuclear source through which those substances were generated. However, our present knowledge of the more or less lasting repression and de-repression (not the mutation) of genes, as triggered by cytoplasmic substances, does make this idea of Driesch's a highly probable one today. Moreover, theoretically, there would be an advantage, by way of economy of materials and of avoiding the cluttering up of the cytoplasm with substances that were useless in the given cell, in having the nucleus affected by the postulated feedbacks, as they might be termed today.

The Hereditary Material as Depicted in "The Cell"

Many of those unfamiliar with nineteenth-century biology ascribe the establishment of what is called "the chromosome theory of heredity" mainly to the researches on genetics in *Drosophila* conducted by Morgan and his co-workers (1910–1915), as first outlined in full (along with their conclusions) in 1915 in "The Mechanism of Mendelian Heredity." Some, however, might go as far back as Sutton's paper of 1902 on the chromosomes and Mendelism. All such persons would be amazed, on reading the 1896 edition of "The Cell," to see how firmly and soundly founded, although admittedly on indirect evidence, had the identification of the hereditary material with chromatin already become in that pre-Mendelian period. But as yet only the more perspicacious and progressive of nineteenth-century biologists of the English-speaking world, such as Wilson, acknowledged the high degree of cogency of the evidence to that effect then existing.

These latter-day readers would also be struck with the masterful and convincing way in which Wilson set forth that evidence. It is important for them to know, further, that both Sutton and the group who worked with Morgan on *Drosophila* had, as the key portion of their preparation for research, taken courses at Columbia with Wilson, studied "The Cell" thoroughly in its very similar 1900 edition, and been entirely won over by the arguments that he presented regarding the role of chromatin.

The pathway to this conclusion had been made very difficult by the obscurity of the chromatin during two crucial stages. One of these was the interphase of ordinary cells, when in most fixed preparations it appeared to have the structure of branched granules embedded in a network. The other stage was early meiosis, at the very time when, as was not learned until later, parasynapsis, that is, the longitudinal side-by-side apposition of homologous chromosomes, a then unknown phenomenon, sets in.

As for the interphase problem, the observations were thought to show that the chromatic granules, termed chromomeres, had probably been derived from the chromosomes of the preceding mitosis, but that they had become more or less disconnected from one another except for some threads, mainly of a nonchromatic material ("linin"). They were thought at the same time to have sent forth some chromatic branches in various directions or even to have become in part diffused. In preparation for mitosis, the outlying chromatic parts were thought to become drawn in, while at the same time the chromomeres became joined up into line, so as eventually, with increasing condensation of the resulting chromatic threads or "spireme," to reconstitute chromosomes.

It could not then be decided by direct observation whether all individual chromomeres retained their identities throughout interphase, or whether they could undergo dissolution and later condense anew from nonchromatic material. However, the doubling preparatory to mitosis had been noted to occur not only as early as the spireme stage but—by Brauer in *Ascaris* in 1893—shortly preceding this, when each chromomere doubled. This fine-grained doubling, passing over later into the longitudinally split condition of the mitotic chromosomes, seemed to make sense only on Roux's conception, based on the split condition, that all visible parts of the chromosomes were qualitatively differentiated—even, as could now be added, when considered on the scale of greatest optical resolution—and that these minute parts had preserved their distinctive peculiarities throughout interphase.

While accepting this conclusion, Wilson disliked the use of the term "individuality" as applied to this situation. For, as he pointed out, this term might be taken to mean the persistence of the original substance and to exclude a dynamic continuity in which (as in a flame or in a whole organism) the original configuration was maintained or regained through a distinctive type of flux of materials rather than through the continuance *in situ* of the very same objects. Of course it is obvious that to achieve a real doubling there must in fact be an active fabrication of other material into a particular configuration like that of the original "self-reproducing" structure. However, as we now know, by noting the persistence in it of radioactive atoms that were introduced at its construction, the original hereditary material, that is, each parental nucleotide chain, is "conserved," maintaining its own material identity, and the term individuality is in that sense strictly applicable.

More direct evidence that the chromosomes, and even parts of them, maintain their individuality (at least in a dynamic sense) throughout interphase was given in observations by Rabl, Boveri, Häcker, and others, in which chromosomes were found to reappear in sister cells not merely in the same number but even in much the same positions and shapes as at the close of the preceding mitosis, and in cases in which parts or traces of them could actually be identified all through interphase. Uniquely decisive in this connection were Boveri's findings (1888) that whenever by some irregularity of fertilization or mitosis an abnormal number of chromosomes had been allotted to a nucleus the same abnormal number reappeared at mitosis in the descendant cells. All this evidence for chromosome individuality and self-reproduction carries with it a strong case for their being bearers of inheritance, as Wilson points out.

The most massive evidence for these conclusions lay in the findings, concurred in by numerous observers, concerning the history of the chromosomes in the course of the life cycle of organisms in general. For one thing, the chromosomes in most species recurringly show a constant general format and a constant, even number, characteristic of the species and present in the first zygotic division as well as throughout nearly all subsequent cell divisions.

Second, it had in 1885 and subsequently been reasoned by Weismann, on the view of the chromosomes being individualized bearers of heredity, that some division prior to the union of germ cell nuclei must be peculiar in that it causes the halving of the number of chromosomes, or at least of chromomeres, inasmuch as fertilization would then restore the original number. Not long afterward, on the basis of the finding that parthenogenetic eggs of some species give rise to but one polar body (unlike eggs that engage in fertilization, which give rise to two), it was further predicted by Weismann that the postulated halving or "reduction" would be shown to take place at a division just preceding fertilization. The verification, in principle, of this rather far-flung prediction is regarded by Wilson as a most impressive argument for inheritance through the chromatin, and it stands as such to this day, even though the details of maturation are so different from those then conceived. Moreover, he emphasizes, the changes occurring during this period result in the chromatin content of male and female germ cells becoming alike, as shown by their post-fertilization appearance, a likeness that parallels the known equivalence of father and mother in transmitting the inheritance, whereas the differences between their cytoplasmic contents are maximal.

The important problem of just how reduction is brought about was at that time most mystifying, since several quite contradictory-seeming accounts of it, based on different organisms, had been promulgated, none of which embodied the conception of the parasynapsis of homologous chromosomes followed by their segregation. Not only was observation of the critical stage in germ-cell maturation most difficult technically; in addition, investigators had been misled by (even when not accepting) Weismann's speculation that each chromo*mere* contained all the hereditary endowment necessary for a whole organism. For if that were the case, reduction could be accomplished as well by the transverse division of chromosomes as by their end-to-end conjugation and segregation. Weismann had proposed both of these alternatives, on either of which, as presented, the concept of chromosome homology would be meaningless. Still more difficult of interpretation were the descriptions by Boveri and others of two longitudinal "splittings" (doublings) of chromosomes at meiosis. Yet for all this clouding of the picture, Wilson puts the case as of that time clearly. He is also able to conclude that, accepting "numerical reduction" as established, the very peculiarities of chromatin behavior that were known to be associated with it must ultimately prove significant in throwing light on the wider problem of the nature of chromosome individuality. In recognition of this, he and students of his had already been working in this field of cytology for several years.

Although accepting the conclusion that chromosomes maintain their individuality—in the sense, previously explained, of including a dynamic or flux continuity rather than a material one as one possibility—Wilson saw this as probably an expression of a finer-scale chromomere individuality. Following Strasburger, he asked why the phenomenon should not be further subdivisible, since it might well be only the impossibility of achieving greater optical resolution that prevented still smaller self-reproducing units from being distinguished. However, he emphasized, if the analysis could be pursued indefinitely a limit of smallness must at last be reached beyond which the parts would no longer have an organization capable of "assimilation, growth, and division." Although today we should term this process "duplication" or "replication," the basic concept involved here is in either case that of self-reproduction, in that materials from the medium are taken up by the given structures and somehow put into a characteristic pattern— one different from part to part—that matches the existing one. As we now know, these materials in the medium are already-formed nucleotides, and the patterning, considered on its smallest possible scale, consists only in the capturing, by each of two linked nucleotides of any of several types, of their respective complements, followed by the linking of the latter together. Nevertheless, even this relatively simple process does constitute self-reproduction, and thus allows the chromatin to carry the inheritance.

Short of this ultimate structural analysis, although the chromatin—that is, its nucleic-acid component—is now known to be divisible into genes and probably subgenes, marked off by so-called punctuation marks whose chemical nature is as yet undetermined, neither of these units is to be identified with the chromomeres. What then are the chromomeres in the light of modern knowledge?

Leaving aside the fact that they are to some extent coagulation products, and the further fact (recognized by Wilson) that they tend to coalesce as their chromosome contracts, it must be acknowledged that at any given stage the chromomeres are to be found at more or less fixed points along the chromosomes. Moreover, the real existence at interphase of very fine-scale condensations of chromatin in fixed positions is proved by *in vivo* observations of such favorable objects as the extended chromosomes of dipteran salivary glands and the "lamp-brush" chromosomes widely found in oöcytes. In view of the probability that the core of the chromatin thread or chromonema of each chromosome consists basically of one pair of complementary nucleotide chains that is continuous (if we include its "punctuations") and that courses in helices of a number of widths simultaneously, these fine condensations would result from denser coilings of the larger-scale kinds at the given sites.

However, although presumably of some fundamental significance they are usually too large to be individual genes, as was shown by myself and Prokofyeva in 1935. Thus, even if we considered portions of the chromatin as large as genes as the ultimate units of heredity we would have to agree with Wilson's inference that the chromomeres were probably larger than these units.

Attention is called in "The Cell" to still another group of findings that indicate that the chromatin, or at most the nucleus, carries material that determines the nature of the cell's constructive operations. In this group are experiments in which cells of diverse types are artificially divided into portions with and without the nucleus, respectively. Although the latter usually continue for a time in some of their routine activities before disintegrating, they are unable to grow, to replace lost parts, or to form new ones, whereas portions containing a nucleus can carry on all of these processes and survive indefinitely. In line with these findings were other observations on varied kinds of cells, showing that in those having a prolonged concentration of constructive operations in a given region, the nucleus usually lies closer to that region. Going beyond such findings and showing the species specificity of the nuclear influences was a report by Boveri that an enucleated egg of one sea urchin species after fertilization by sperm of a different species developed into a larva ("pluteus") having the paternal characteristics only. Although subsequent work has shown that in still earlier stages the stored gene-products derived from the mother largely shape the development then, Boveri's result on the stage he studied is in harmony with present expectation.

Claude Bernard's view, expressed as long ago as 1878, to the effect that the nucleus is the source of chemosynthetic operations and, through these, of morphogenetic construction, is repeatedly cited, with guarded approval, by Wilson. He cites also, as "a tempting hypothesis," the conclusions of the biochemist Kossel (1891) that "organic synthesis" is somehow dependent on the chromatin ("nuclein"). Declaring that "inheritance is the recurrence, in successive generations, of like forms of metabolism," and granting the self-reproducing ability of chromatin (or at least of nucleic acid), Wilson interprets in these terms the ability of this material to serve as the vehicle of inheritance. He does not, however, insist that all syntheses are carried on within the nucleus, but only the primary ones that somehow control all synthetic, and so, ultimately, all other, activities and all structures of the cell. Nor does he wish to pin his interpretation down to any more specific proposal concerning the individual units of inheritance, such as that they consist of "ferments" (enzymes), as held by Driesch, pangens (de Vries), or other imagined entities. In harmony with his physiological outlook, moreover, Wilson sees no one-to-one relation between the organism's characters and its hereditary units, whatever the latters' structure may be, since developmental and physiological processes involve so many interactions. In all this he was as close as it was possible in his day to come to modern theory.

Nevertheless, certain inconsistencies in Wilson's position regarding chromatin must be noted. On the one hand, as we have seen, he is emphatic in his conclusion that, by virtue of its chemical composition, it constitutes the hereditary material and in the last analysis determines the nature of the rest of the cell. In his concluding chapter he states that this "rests upon a basis so firm that it may be taken as one of the elementary data of heredity." Yet, on the other hand, his great caution and desire to maintain a balanced view lead him also to assert that, as shown by "minute analysis," "all cell-organs, whether temporary or 'permanent' [under which he would include not only the centromere but also the chromatin] are local differentiations of a common structural basis." He then goes on to what he calls the "somewhat doubtful inference," at the end of Chapter VI, that "some at least of the cytomicro-

somes are . . . comparable with those of the linin and chromatin networks, and like them capable of growth and division." Although we
today might in this connection be inclined to think of RNA, he proceeds
beyond even this to admit the possibility of "Brucke's [1861] cautious
suggestion that the whole cell might be a congeries of self-propagating
units of a lower order." However, his position regarding the distinctive-
ness of the chromatin was to become a more decided one in subsequent
years, with the progress of research (in considerable measure that of
himself and of those trained by him) on this and related subjects.

A similarly ambivalent situation existed in Wilson's attitude concerning the mechanism of evolution. In his introductory chapter he
forcefully puts Weismann's case for germ-plasm continuity and the
noninheritance of acquired characters, and says it is "the keystone
between the work of the evolutionists and that of the cytologists. . . .
It is from this point of view that the present volume has been written."
And in the penultimate paragraph of the book we find: "The idioplasm
[i.e., the hereditary material] of every species has been derived, as we
must believe, by the modification of a pre-existing idioplasm through
variation, and the survival of the fittest." Directly thereafter, however,
he continues as follows. "Whether these variations first arise in the
idioplasm of the germ cells, as Weismann maintains, or whether they
may arise in the body-cells and then be reflected back upon the idioplasm, is a question on which, as far as I can see, the study of the cell
has not thus far thrown a ray of light." One may reflect at this point
that at least so far as abnormalities in chromosome number are concerned, work of Boveri's had already shown these to be transmitted
strictly to descendant cells, not across from one cell to another. Moreover, the idea that smaller hereditary units could get across was a
special and unnecessary assumption, being in this respect like Weismann's speculation that a single chromomere of a germ cell contains a
complete outfit of hereditary determiners.

Wilson's skepticism on this point arose in part at least from his
realization that the mechanism of heritable variation constituted as yet
a basic unsolved problem of evolution. However, he failed to realize at
that time that such knowledge is not necessary for interpreting the
existence of the complex adaptations of living things, provided that,
with Darwin, one admits that heritable variations in many diverse
directions do occur. For a few of these, at any rate, would chance to
be adaptive in at least a small way, and these would tend to become
accumulated by natural selection so as to result in ever more numerous
and substantial adaptations. In his hesitation on this matter, however,

Wilson did not go nearly as far as many eminent biologists of the day, such, for example, as Morgan.

Finally, it has become abundantly clear that Wilson—in contrast, for instance, to his contemporary, Loeb, and perhaps to certain physicists of today—was quite right in his last conclusion, that "the study of the cell has on the whole seemed to widen rather than to narrow the enormous gap that separates even the lowest forms of life from the inorganic world," and that "the magnitude of the problem of development, whether ontogenic or phylogenetic, has been underestimated." This realization of his should help to excuse his to us excessive caution. It should also be taken into consideration that he does close on a note of hope that, in view of the great progress made by cellular biology in the preceding period "the way may yet be opened up to an understanding of inheritance and development."

Sequelae

Prior to the lectures of 1892–1893 that led to his volume, "The Cell," Wilson had become increasingly concerned with the nature and workings of the hereditary material, and had seen in the study of chromatin behavior and properties, especially during germ-cell maturation, promising possibilities of finding clues to this problem. As his own researches became concentrated in that direction, so did those of his students. Among these, the most notable before "The Cell" appeared were Calkins and Mathews, and, shortly after it appeared, McClung and MacGregor. In consequence, when in 1900 the rediscovery of Mendelian inheritance was announced by Correns, de Vries, and Tschermak; when in the same year evidence for synapsis (of the parallel type) was reported by Winiwarter; and when in 1901, to cap these findings, Montgomery discovered that the chromosomes are present in pre-reduction nuclei as pairs of homologues; Wilson and his team of that time were ready to apply themselves eagerly to the search for discernible connections between cytology and Mendelism.

In this effort Wilson's student Sutton was eminently successful as early as 1902. Working in the Columbia laboratory, he confirmed the concept of homologous chromosomes and showed that during meiosis the members of each pair undergo some kind of synapsis, and during the ensuing divisions separate from one another. He proceeded, moreover, to show how this behavior parallels that of the Mendelian "factors" not only in the segregation of the members of each pair but also, in all probability, in the random assortment of the members of different pairs, and that it could therefore form the basis for the results obtained with Mendelizing characters. Wilson, after studying the same preparations, satisfied himself of the correctness of Sutton's observations and also of the strength of the inferences that he had drawn.

In the same year (1902) McClung, who had by that time become located elsewhere, pointed out that (granting the individuality of the chromosomes) sex differentiation in insects that have one X-chromosome in the male is in all probability determined by the presence or absence of this chromosome in the two classes of sperm that must be formed. Although he mistakenly thought that the sperm with the X result in a male, and that the female therefore contains no X, nevertheless the general principle of sex determination here involved was confirmed in 1905 for diverse insects by Wilson and by Stevens, working independently. They also set the record straight by showing that the females contain two X-s and that the X-containing sperm therefore result in females. At the same time, they showed that it was commoner for a species to have an X and a distinguishable, smaller Y in the male than to have an X without a partner. These findings went beyond Sutton's in proving not only that the distribution of the pairs of Mendelian factors to the germ cells is *like* that of the chromosomes, but that the distribution of a given pair of segregating (and therefore "Mendelizing") factors—here, those determining sex—is in fact *identical* with that of a given pair of chromosomes. Thus it could be concluded that these chromosomes are causally connected with sex, that is, that they constitute or contain the hereditary factors in question.

In the immediately succeeding years, 1905–1912, when he was 49–56 years old, Wilson carried out the most important researches of his life and wrote his most important papers, including the eight notable "Studies on Chromsomes." During this period he developed the theme of sex determination further. Among other things, he showed that the Y-chromosomes in different species of insects—mainly Hemiptera (bugs)—are of widely different sizes relative to the X, ranging from equal to it down to nonexistent. In some species the X or the Y was found regularly to be in two or more separate parts. He also showed that in rare individuals a normal-seeming female of an XY species can have two X's and a Y, or a male one X and no Y. Such cases he interpreted as having probably resulted from the accidental misplacement of a Y at a previous cell division, a phenomenon for which he and Bridges in consultation (when, much later, Bridges found it in breeding experiments with *Drosophila*) coined the term "non-disjunction."

The foregoing findings led Wilson to infer that the Y-chromosome in the group of insects studied by him has degenerated, or else "contains chromatin that is duplicated elsewhere in the chromosome group," and that the X-chromosome, or at any rate some part of it, qualitatively different from the Y, carries the hereditary material that is active in the differentiation of the sexes from one another. On his conception of 1909, the X does not do so by carrying "femaleness" per se, as had been widely assumed. Instead, the effects of one X, on interacting with the effects of the remainder of a normal outfit of chromosomes, are produced in such measure that the combination results in a male, while the greater effects of two X's, interacting with the same set of other factors as before, results in a female. This is in essence what was later termed the "genic balance" conception of sex determination in these insects, as opposed to the earlier one of "unit characters." It has had wide implications in other areas of genetics also.

Wilson realized that this particular mechanism of sex determination need not be the exclusive one for organisms in general. Thus, in a paper written in 1910, he supported Spillman's 1909 interpretation of sex linkage (as it is now termed) in moths and birds, that British investigators had reported. According to this interpretation, long since generally accepted, both sex and the other pairs of characters studied are in these species based in a pair of sex chromosomes, but here it is the female that has these chromosomes qualitatively differentiated from one another.

Another important theme pursued actively by Wilson in his researches of the same period was that of the persistent individuality of chromosomes and of chromosome parts. For one thing, his results concerning the normal process of sex determination in the insects he studied showed, as he pointed out, that whichever sex chromosome, X or Y, had happened to be carried into the egg, that chromosome reappears in all pre-reductional cells of the developed individual that can be critically examined with reference to this point. Even more striking were his findings, extending those of Boveri's in early embryos, that whenever—presumably in consequence of non-disjunction—an individual has an abnormal chromosome composition, such as XXY or XO in species normally having XY males, or an extra one of the tiny "m" chromosomes, that same abnormal configuration is to be found in all clear views of the somatic and the pre-reductional germ-cells of that individual. Moreover, at maturation an extra chromosome exhibits any special kind of behavior that is to be expected of a chromosome of the given type.

As for chromosome parts, Wilson found indirect evidence for their individuality, on making comparisons of chromosome configurations in different but related species. Thus, where the X was single in the male of one species and double or even more multiple (though all parts in such cases segregated from the Y) in others, the total size of the members, taken together, was about the same as that of the single one in the related species. Similarly, with chromosomes other than the X or Y, comparisons between species indicated that in their past evolution from common ancestors some of these chromosomes had become broken into pieces that had persisted as such, whereas others had become joined together, and that in still other cases a portion had become broken off of one chromosome and joined onto a nonhomologous one. Such chromosome changes, Wilson concluded, could occur without much effect on the organism's characteristics, inasmuch as these were really determined by the interplay of the effects produced by the independently self-reproducing and qualitatively different smaller parts.

In these and other ways, the ground was well prepared by 1910 for prosecuting and constructively interpreting the breeding experiments on *Drosophila*. These began to yield important results in that year, with Morgan's finding of mutations which showed Mendelian inheritance and some of which at the same time showed sex linkage. In the following year came Morgan's finding of recombination among sex-linked genes, which he interpreted on the basis of Janssens' theory of "chiasmatype" (called by him *crossing over*). The year 1911 also saw the full-fledged entry into that work of the group of students who, having previously studied under Wilson, were so oriented (despite a greater hesitation on Morgan's part) as to look for genetic results that would be in line with Wilson's views on chromosomes. Their and Morgan's rapid success in this quest is well known. Wilson was happy about this endeavor, with which he kept in close touch, and gave useful suggestions in connection with it. He very soon became a conspicuous advocate of the main concepts that emerged from it.

Highly relevant to the theory of linear linkage and crossing over to which the *Drosophila* work had already led in 1911–1912 was Wilson's careful restudy at that time of synapsis as seen in several diverse types of animals. Only if the method of synapsis were that of longitudinal pairing (parasynapsis) could the required interchange of homologous chromosome parts postulated by Janssens take place, but in one of the types (grasshoppers) the previous investigator (McClung) had reported that this type of pairing did not occur. However, despite the expected difficulties of observation, Wilson found no escape from the conclusion that in all the types the chromosomes do conjugate in parallel. Thus cytological objections were removed from the inferences derived from the breeding experiments.

At the same time, as Wilson pointed out, contrary to the opinion of Janssens, cytological observations alone could not yet provide actual proof of crossing over. The same reservation would also hold with regard to the corollary of crossing over, the concept of the persistent individuality of reproducing units of chromatin far smaller than the chromosomes. Wilson, however, like the *Drosophila* workers, considered the results of the breeding experiments to be cogent enough, when taken in connection with grosser cytology, to establish these points.

There were other areas in which the conclusions arrived at by Wilson, some of them expressed in "The Cell" in 1896, had a major influence on the development of the *Drosophila* work in particular and on that of genetics in general. One of these was his insistence on the importance of interactions of a multitude of kinds, both within cells and among the different parts of a multicellular organism, in morphogenetic as well as in other physiological processes. This general point of view was already expressed in his "General Biology." Later, his and other investigators' experiments on development, recounted in "The Cell" of 1896, had emphasized this conclusion. It reappears frequently, as for instance in 1912, when Wilson made the following statement regarding Mendelian inheritance: "Many 'unit characters' are known to depend upon a number of . . . unit-factors, in some cases probably upon a large number; and they may be definitely altered this way or that by varying the particular combinations of those factors. But any unit-factor produces its characteristic effect only in so far as it forms a part of a more general apparatus of ontogenetic reaction constituted directly or indirectly by the organism as a whole." Although not a few Mendelians in the period prior to 1920 failed to recognize this truth, the same cannot be said of the workers on *Drosophila* who had received training under Wilson, as may be seen by consulting "The Mechanism of Mendelian Heredity" (1915). Nevertheless, there are some prominent geneticists even today who appear to regard their realization of this principle as a new discovery.

Related to this theme is that of the evolutionary importance of mutations with small effects versus those with large ones. For the fact that the ontogenetic and other physiological reactions of the organism are so highly interconnected would argue for the greater likelihood of small heritable changes rather than large ones chancing to have effects of a useful (adaptive) kind. This was also the position of the younger *Drosophila* workers from the start, although it ran contrary to the then popular "mutation theory" of de Vries, toward which many geneticists, including Morgan, leaned at that time, before decidedly contrary data had been accumulated. As Wilson said in 1915: "We should, no doubt, make a larger allowance for the role of single 'lucky accidents' than did many of the earlier evolutionists. And yet, so far as the essence of the principle is concerned, I am bound to make confession of my doubts whether any existing discussion of this problem affords more food for reflection, even today, than that contained in the sixth and seventh chapters of the 'Origin of Species' and elsewhere in the works of Darwin . . . we have made it the mode to minimize Darwin's theory . . . but . . . we should take heed how we underestimate the one really simple and intelligible explanation of organic adaption. . . ."

Curiously enough, however, Wilson himself, even in his later years, continued to harbor some doubt as to the sufficiency of this process. On the other hand, the group of younger *Drosophila* workers, largely under Wilson's influence, had practically from the beginning become convinced of its full validity, as applied to "small mutations." In this, they differed not only from Wilson but, even more, from many of the other established biologists of that time.

In researches of his declining years Wilson returned to the question, broached in "The Cell," of the extent to which other material of animal cells than their chromatin might contain (or consist of) hereditary material. He studied in this connection mitochondria, Golgi bodies, and neutral-red bodies, as seen in the spermatogenesis of scorpions, which provided favorable material for the observation of these structures. His observations drove him to the conclusion that, unlike the chromosomes, these structures fail to divide, at meiotic cell divisions, in a way that would result in the allotment to each daughter cell of a share of each part (large or small) of the original material. This result, as he noted in 1937 at the age of 81, two years before his death, "may be set down to the credit of the chromosome theory of heredity." It may be noted that long before that time he had given up the lingering suspicion, voiced in "The Cell" of 1896, that all cytoplasmic granules might be self-reproducing and individualized.

However, Wilson did not yet consider the possibility ruled out that some of the specialized bodies in the cytoplasm of cells, even of animal cells, do have a persistent individuality, including a genetic continuity. This had, as he knew, long since been proved to be the case for chloroplastids and some related bodies in plant cells. But in these cells it had been found that there is no mechanism providing for the distribution to each daughter cell of a daughter particle derived from each original particle. Hence there was no way for many different kinds of cytoplasmic particles to accumulate in the course of evolution within any given line of descent. This fact has helped to explain the preponderant role of the nuclear chromatin in heredity and evolution in plants. To this should be added that recent evidence (notably that of

Rabinowitz *et al.*, 1965) has demonstrated the existence even in vertebrates of DNA within their mitochondria, although there is no reason to believe that these bodies are distributed in a qualitatively exact way at cell division. At any rate, Wilson's considerable caution in never making his conclusion regarding the relative unimportance of cytoplasmic inheritance more sweeping has now been vindicated.

Reassessment

The monumental third edition of "The Cell," published in 1925 when Wilson was 69, was widely acclaimed and Wilson received high honors for it. These were well merited, for the subject had advanced and broadened so enormously that only Wilson could have integrated it adequately. In fact, during the quarter century following the second edition, even he had sometimes questioned whether the results and hypotheses were not accumulating faster than he could master, organize, and give expression to them. Yet it is this reviewer's conviction that the first edition was by far the greatest of them all, for in it Wilson was largely leading the way, especially for the English-speaking world, rather than hurrying after to give a connected account. After all, however, this is a situation which—unfortunate though it may be—is a fairly typical one for pioneering efforts.

Despite Wilson's caution that led him not to accord all-out acceptance to the main conclusions indicated in his book of 1896, he documented them so well and put them so convincingly that many readers must have been led to place more confidence in them than he himself appeared at times to have done. Undoubtedly his full and cogent arguments, with their abundant backing by results, opened a great new day for American research on the material basis of heredity, and was of great influence in setting it to work along really constructive lines. Thus when Mendelism, and then crossing over and mutation studies, arrived, cytology was ready, and the integrated science of cytogenetics (as it was later termed) made a rapid advent. Moreover, its developments were so much in accord with the lines of thought that had been outlined in the early editions of "The Cell" as to constitute a verification, expansion, and mighty advance, rather than a break, in the trends there laid down, even though very new methods were added. In a similar way today, molecular biology, with its many facets and still more drastically new methods and concepts, is continuing the older cellular biology and its somewhat more recent offshoot, cytogenetics, and pressing them amazingly deeper, but without breaking with their principles, even though this is hardly realized by many of its newcomers.

Of course it cannot be claimed that Wilson was the originator of most of the theories he advocated in "The Cell" or elsewhere, nor was he even the one who gathered most of the evidence for them. He had the humility to be eclectic, but with rare exceptions he chose to favor just those elements of conflicting views that have survived and pointed forward, and he wove them together into a matchless fabric. Thus, looking backwards, we can say that the combination of principles that he put together was the most nearly correct one of its time. This being the case, the United Siates—backward though it had been in scientific theory—and through this country at last the world as well, was set on the courses that have opened up the greatest new vistas in the understanding and exploration of the most basic processes of inheritance, development, evolution, and life itself. It is fortunate that Wilson was humble enough to sit as he did "at the feet of the mighty" abroad, and that in consequence he was able to provide the extra impetus needed for the success of this great transplantation of science, in view of the languishing that ensued in this field, not long after the rediscovery of Mendelism, in some of the greatest traditional seats of learning.

It was not only the convincing presentation of scientific facts and inferences in the first and second editions of "The Cell" that had so great an influence in leading subsequent researchers to make the progress that they did. It was in comparable measure Wilson's example and teachings in bringing home to the dozens of his research students who later became professional biologists, and to his many other serious readers, the importance of examining all possibilities, of not scorning to find truth in error and error in truth, of unrestricted appraisal of the pronouncements of the lowliest and the most exalted personages, and especially, of rigorous self-criticism. It was, in addition, his emphasis on the need for both free-roving, penetrating imagination, and the strict measuring of the products of that imagination by facts. He led his students and other readers to feel the importance, on the one hand, of meticulous attention to details and love of them, and, on the other hand, of organizing these details into an ever more meaningful whole. In other words, what carried his followers so far was Wilson's gift of conveying to them not only the material content and conceptions of science but also its spirit. As he was fond of pointing out, this is a creative spirit, and it is also active, though without any comparable disciplining by external reality, in true art.

Hermann J. Muller

THE CELL

IN DEVELOPMENT AND INHERITANCE

COLUMBIA UNIVERSITY BIOLOGICAL SERIES. IV.

THE CELL

IN

DEVELOPMENT AND INHERITANCE

BY

EDMUND B. WILSON, Ph.D.

PROFESSOR OF INVERTEBRATE ZOOLOGY, COLUMBIA UNIVERSITY

" Natura nusquam magis est tota quam in minimis "
PLINY

New York

THE MACMILLAN COMPANY

LONDON: MACMILLAN & CO., Ltd.

1896

All rights reserved

COPYRIGHT, 1896,
BY THE MACMILLAN COMPANY.

To my Friend

THEODOR BOVERI

PREFACE

This volume is the outcome of a course of lectures, delivered at Columbia University in the winter of 1892–93, in which I endeavoured to give to an audience of general university students some account of recent advances in cellular biology, and more especially to trace the steps by which the problems of evolution have been reduced to problems of the cell. It was my first intention to publish these lectures in a simple and general form, in the hope of showing to wider circles how the varied and apparently heterogeneous cell-researches of the past twenty years have grown together in a coherent group, at the heart of which are a few elementary phenomena, and how these phenomena, easily intelligible even to those having no special knowledge of the subject, are related to the problems of development. Such a treatment was facilitated by the appearance, in 1893, of Oscar Hertwig's invaluable book on the cell, which brought together, in a form well designed for the use of special students, many of the more important results of modern cell-research. I am glad to acknowledge my debt to Hertwig's book; but it is proper to state that the present volume was fully sketched in its main outlines at the time the *Zelle und Gewebe* appeared. Its completion was, however, long delayed by investigations which I undertook in order to re-examine the history of the centrosomes in the fertilization of the egg, — a subject which had been thrown into such confusion by Fol's extraordinary account of the "Quadrille of Centres" in echinoderms that it seemed for a time impossible to form any definite conception of the cell in its relation to inheritance. By a fortunate coincidence the same task was independently undertaken, nearly at the same time, by several other investigators. The concordant results of these researches led to a decisive overthrow of Fol's conclusions, and the way was thus cleared for a return to the earlier and juster views founded by Hertwig, Strasburger, and Van Beneden, and so lucidly and forcibly developed by Boveri.

The rapid advance of discovery in the mean time has made it seem desirable to amplify the original plan of the work, in order to render it useful to students as well as to more general readers; and to this end it has been found necessary to go over a considerable part of the ground already so well covered by Hertwig.[1] This book does not, however, in any manner aim to be a treatise on general histology, or to give an exhaustive account of the cell. It has rather been my endeavour to consider, within moderate limits, those features of the cell that seem more important and suggestive to the student of development, and in some measure to trace the steps by which our present knowledge has been acquired. A work thus limited necessarily shows many gaps ; and some of these, especially on the botanical side, are, I fear, but too obvious. On its historical side, too, the subject could be traced only in its main outlines, and to many investigators of whose results I have made use it has been impossible to do full justice.

To the purely speculative side of the subject I do not desire to add more than is necessary to define some of the problems still to be solved ; for I am mindful of Blumenbach's remark that while Drelincourt rejected two hundred and sixty-two " groundless hypotheses " of development, " nothing is more certain than that Drelincourt's own theory formed the two hundred and sixty-third." [2] I have no wish to add another to this list. And yet, even in a field where standpoints are so rapidly shifting and existing views are still so widely opposed, the conclusions of the individual observer may have a certain value if they point the way to further investigation of the facts. In this spirit I have endeavoured to examine some of the more important existing views, to trace them to their sources, and in some measure to give a critical estimate of their present standing, in the hope of finding suggestion for further research.

Every writer on the cell must find himself under a heavy obligation to the works of Van Beneden, Oscar Hertwig, Flemming, Strasburger, and Boveri ; and to the last-named author I have a special sense of gratitude. I am much indebted to my former student, Mr. A. P. Mathews, for calling my attention to the importance of the recent work of physiological chemists in its bearing on the problems of synthetic metabolism. The views developed in Chapter VII. have been considerably influenced by his suggestions, and this subject will be more fully treated by him in a forthcoming work ; but I have endeavoured as far as possible to avoid anticipating his own special conclusions. Among many others to whom I am indebted for kindly suggestion and advice, I must particularly mention my ever helpful friend, Professor Henry F. Osborn, and Professors J. E. Humphrey, T. H. Morgan, and F. S. Lee.

In copying so great a number of figures from the papers of other

[1] Henneguy's *Leçons sur la cellule* is received, too late for further notice, as this volume is going through the press.

[2] Allen Thomson.

investigators, I must make a virtue of necessity. Many of the facts could not possibly have been illustrated by new figures equal in value to those of special workers in the various branches of cytological research, even had the necessary material and time been available. But, apart from this, modern cytology extends over so much debatable ground that no general work of permanent value can be written that does not aim at an objective historical treatment of the subject; and I believe that to this end the results of investigators should as far as practicable be set forth by means of their original figures. Those for which no acknowledgment is made are original or taken from my own earlier papers.

The arrangement of the literature lists is as follows. A general list of all the works referred to in the text is given at the end of the book (p. 343). These are arranged in alphabetical order, and are referred to in the text by name and date, according to Mark's convenient system. In order, however, to indicate to students the more important references and partially to classify them, a short separate list is given at the end of each chapter. The chapter-lists include only a few selections from the general list, comprising especially works of a general character and those in which reviews of the special literature may be found.

E. B. W.

COLUMBIA UNIVERSITY, NEW YORK,
July, 1896.

TABLE OF CONTENTS

———•◦•———

INTRODUCTION

CHAPTER I

GENERAL SKETCH OF THE CELL

CHAPTER II

CELL-DIVISION

xi

CHAPTER IX

THEORIES OF INHERITANCE AND DEVELOPMENT

LIST OF FIGURES

INTRODUCTION

———oo°°oo———

"Jedes Thier erscheint als eine Summe vitaler Einheiten, von denen jede den vollen Charakter des Lebens an sich trägt." VIRCHOW.[1]

DURING the half-century that has elapsed since the enunciation of the cell-theory by Schleiden and Schwann, in 1838–39, it has become ever more clearly apparent that the key to all ultimate biological problems must, in the last analysis, be sought in the cell. It was the cell-theory that first brought the structure of plants and animals under one point of view by revealing their common plan of organization. It was through the cell-theory that Kölliker and Remak opened the way to an understanding of the nature of embryological development, and the law of genetic continuity lying at the basis of inheritance. It was the cell-theory again which, in the hands of Virchow and Max Schultze, inaugurated a new era in the history of physiology and pathology, by showing that all the various functions of the body, in health and in disease, are but the outward expression of cell-activities. And at a still later day it was through the cell-theory that Hertwig, Fol, Van Beneden, and Strasburger solved the long-standing riddle of the fertilization of the egg, and the mechanism of hereditary transmission. No other biological generalization, save only the theory of organic evolution, has brought so many apparently diverse phenomena under a common point of view or has accomplished more for the unification of knowledge. The cell-theory must therefore be placed beside the evolution-theory as one of the foundation stones of modern biology.

And yet the historian of latter-day biology cannot fail to be struck with the fact that these two great generalizations, nearly related as they are, have been developed along widely different lines of research, and have only within a very recent period met upon a common ground. The theory of evolution originally grew out of the study of natural history, and it took definite shape long before the ultimate structure of living bodies was in any degree comprehended. The evolutionists

---

[1] *Cellularpathologie,* p. 12, 1858.

of the Lamarckian period gave little heed to the finer details of internal organization. They were concerned mainly with the more obvious characters of plants and animals — their forms, colours, habits, distribution, their anatomy and embryonic development — and with the systems of classification based upon such characters; and long afterwards it was, in the main, the study of like characters with reference to their historical origin that led Darwin to his splen-

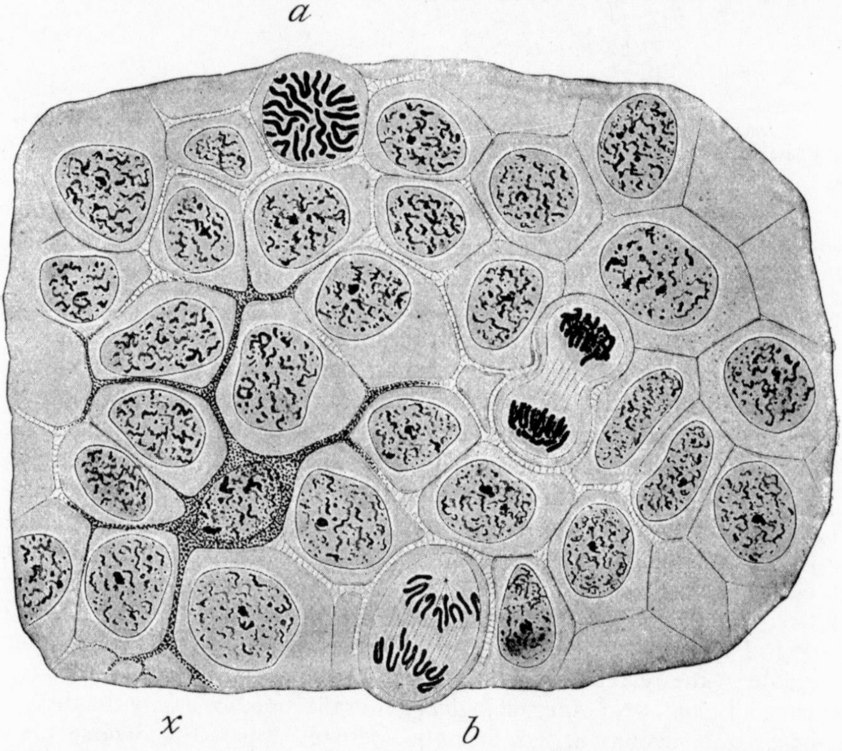

a

x   *b*

Fig. 1.—A portion of the epidermis of a larval salamander (*Amblystoma*) as seen in slightly oblique horizontal section, enlarged 550 diameters. Most of the cells are polygonal in form, contain large nuclei, and are connected by delicate protoplasmic bridges. Above *x* is a branched, dark pigment-cell that has crept up from the deeper layers and lies between the epidermal cells. Three of the latter are undergoing division, the earliest stage (*spireme*) at *a*, a later stage (mitotic figure in the anaphase) at *b*, showing the chromosomes, and a final stage (*telophase*), showing fission of the cell-body, to the right.

did triumphs. The study of microscopical anatomy, on which the cell-theory was based, lay in a different field. It was begun and long carried forward with no thought of its bearing on the origin of living forms; and even at the present day the fundamental problems of organization, with which the cell-theory deals, are far less accessible to historical inquiry than those suggested by the more obvious external characters of plants and animals. Only within a few years, indeed, has the ground been cleared for that close alliance of the evolutionists and the cytologists which forms so striking a feature of contemporary biology. We may best examine the steps by which this alliance has been effected by an outline of the cell-theory, followed by a brief statement of its historical connection with the evolution-theory.

During the past thirty years, the theory of organic descent has been shown, by an overwhelming mass of evidence, to be the only tenable conception of the origin of diverse living forms, however we may conceive the causes of the process. While the study of general zoölogy and botany has systematically set forth the results, and in a measure the method, of organic evolution, the study of microscopical anatomy has shown us the nature of the material on which it has operated, demonstrating that the obvious characters of plants and animals are but varying expressions of a subtle interior organization common to all. In its broader outlines the nature of this organization is now accurately determined; and the "cell-theory," by which it is formulated, is, therefore, no longer of an inferential or hypothetical character, but a generalized statement of observed fact which may be outlined as follows:—

In all the higher forms of life, whether plants or animals, the body may be resolved into a vast host of minute structural units known as *cells*, out of which, directly or indirectly, every part is built (Fig. 1). The substance of the skin, of the brain, of the blood, of the bones or muscles or any other tissue, is not homogeneous, as it appears to the unaided eye. The microscope shows it to be an aggregate composed of innumerable minute bodies, as if it were a colony or congeries of organisms more elementary than itself. These elementary bodies, the *cells*, are essentially minute masses of living matter or *protoplasm*, a substance characterized by Huxley many years ago as the "physical basis of life" and now universally recognized as the immediate substratum of all vital action. Endlessly diversified in the details of their form and structure, cells nevertheless possess a characteristic type of organization common to them all; hence, in a certain sense, they may be regarded as elementary organic units out of which the body is compounded. In the lowest forms of life the entire body consists of but a single cell (Fig. 2). In the higher multicellular forms the body consists of a multitude of such cells associated in one organic whole. Structurally, therefore, the multicellular body is in a certain sense comparable with a colony or aggregation of the lower one-celled forms.[1] From the physiological point of view a like comparison may be drawn. In the one-celled forms all of the

[1] This comparison must be taken with some reservation, as will appear beyond.

vital functions are performed by a single cell; in the higher types they are distributed by a physiological division of labour among different groups of cells specially devoted to the performance of specific functions. The cell is therefore not only a unit of structure, but also a unit of function. "It is the cell to which the consideration of every bodily function sooner or later drives us. In the muscle-cell lies the riddle of the heart-beat, or of muscular contraction; in the gland-cell are the causes of secretion; in the epithelial cell, in the white blood-cell, lies the problem of the absorption of food, and the secrets of the mind are slumbering in the ganglion-cell. . . . If then physiology is not to rest content with the mere extension of our

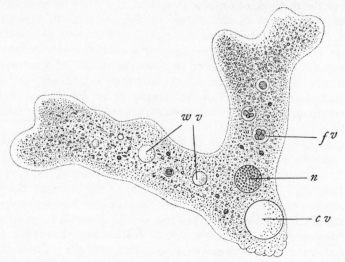

Fig. 2. — *Amœba Proteus*, an animal consisting of a single naked cell, × 280.   (From Sedgwick and Wilson's Biology.)

n. The nucleus; *w.v.* Water-vacuoles; *c.v.* Contractile vacuole; *f.v.* Food-vacuole.

knowledge regarding the more obvious operations of the human body, if it would seek a real explanation of the fundamental phenomena of life, it can only attain its end through the study of *cell-physiology*."[1]

Great as was the impulse which the cell-theory gave to anatomical and physiological investigation, it did not for many years measurably affect the more speculative side of biological inquiry. *The Origin of Species*, published in 1859, scarcely mentions it; nor, if we except the theory of pangenesis, did Darwin attempt at any later period to bring it into any very definite relation to his views. The cell-theory first came in contact with the evolution-theory nearly twenty years

[1] Verworn, *Allgemeine Physiologie*, p. 53, 1895.

later through researches on the early history of the germ-cells and the fertilization of the ovum. Begun in 1873–74 by Auerbach, Fol, and Bütschli, and eagerly followed up by Oscar Hertwig, Van Beneden, Strasburger, and a host of later workers, these investigations raised wholly new questions regarding the mechanism of development and the *rôle* of the cell in hereditary transmission. The identification of the *cell-nucleus* as the vehicle of inheritance, made independently and almost simultaneously in 1884–85 by Oscar Hertwig, Strasburger, Kölliker, and Weismann, must be recognized as the first definite advance [1] towards the internal problems of inheritance through the cell-theory; and the discussions to which it gave rise, in which Weismann has taken the foremost place, must be reckoned as the most interesting and significant of the post-Darwinian period.

These discussions have set forth in strong relief the truth that the general problems of evolution and heredity are indissolubly bound up with those of cell-structure and cell-action. This can best be appreciated from an historical point of view. The views of the early embryologists in regard to inheritance were vitiated by their acceptance of the Greek doctrine of the equivocal or spontaneous generation of life; and even Harvey did not escape this pitfall, near as he came to the modern point of view. "The egg," he says, "is the mid-passage or transition stage between parents and offspring, between those who are, or were, and those who are about to be; it is the hinge or pivot upon which the whole generation of the bird revolves. The egg is the terminus from which all fowls, male and female, have sprung, and to which all their lives tend — it is the result which nature has proposed to herself in their being. And thus it comes that individuals in procreating their like for the sake of their species, endure forever. The egg, I say, is a period or portion of this eternity." [2]

This passage appears at first sight to be a close approximation to the modern doctrine of germinal continuity about which all theories of heredity are revolving. To the modern student the germ is, in Huxley's words, simply a detached living portion of the substance of a pre-existing living body [3] carrying with it a definite structural organization characteristic of the species. Harvey's view is only superficially similar to this; for, as Huxley pointed out, it was obscured by his belief that the germ might arise "spontaneously," or through

---

[1] It must not be forgotten that Haeckel expressed the same view in 1866 — only, however, as a speculation, since the data necessary to an inductive conclusion were not obtained until long afterwards. "The internal nucleus provides for the transmission of hereditary characters, the external plasma on the other hand for accommodation or adaptation to the external world" (*Gen. Morph.*, p. 287–9).

[2] *De Generatione*, 1651; Trans., p. 271.

[3] *Evolution in Biology*, 1878; *Science and Culture*, p. 291.

the influence of a mysterious "*calidum innatum*," out of not-living matter. Whitman, too, in a recent brilliant essay,[1] has shown how far Harvey was from any real grasp of the law of genetic continuity, which is well characterized as the central fact of modern biology. Neither could the great physiologist of the seventeenth century have had the remotest conception of the actual structure of the egg. The cellular structure of living things was not comprehended until nearly two centuries later. The spermatozoön was still undiscovered, and the nature of fertilization was a subject of fantastic and baseless speculation. For a hundred years after Harvey's time embryologists sought in vain to penetrate the mysteries enveloping the beginning of the individual life, and despite their failure the controversial writings of this period form one of the most interesting chapters in the history of biology. By the extreme "evolutionists" or "præformationists" the egg was believed to contain an embryo fully formed in miniature, as the bud contains the flower or the chrysalis the butterfly. Development was to them merely the unfolding of that which already existed; inheritance, the handing down from parent to child of an infinitesimal reproduction of its own body. It was the service of Bonnet to push this conception to its logical consequence, the theory of *emboîtement* or encasement, and thus to demonstrate the absurdity of its grosser forms; for if the egg contains a complete embryo, this must itself contain eggs for the next generation, these other eggs in their turn, and so *ad infinitum*, like an infinite series of boxes, one within another — hence the term "emboîtement." Bonnet himself renounced this doctrine in his later writings, and Caspar Frederich Wolff (1759) led the way in a return to the teachings of Harvey, showing by precise actual observation that the egg does not at first contain any formed embryo whatever; that the structure is wholly different from that of the adult; that development is not a mere process of unfolding, but a progressive process, involving the continual formation, one after another, of new parts, previously nonexistent as such. This is somewhat as Harvey, himself following Aristotle, had conceived it — a process of *epigenesis* as opposed to *evolution*. Later researches established this conclusion as the very foundation of embryological science.

But although the external nature of development was thus determined, the actual structure of the egg and the mechanism of inheritance remained for nearly a century in the dark. It was reserved for Schwann (1839) and his immediate followers to recognize the fact, conclusively demonstrated by all later researches, that *the egg is a cell* having the same essential structure as other cells of the

---

[1] *Evolution and Epigenesis*, Wood's Holl Biological Lectures, 1894.

body. And thus the wonderful truth became manifest that a single cell may contain within its microscopic compass the sum-total of the heritage of the species. This conclusion first reached in the case of the female sex was soon afterwards extended to the male as well. Since the time of Leeuwenhoek (1677) it had been known that the sperm or fertilizing fluid contained innumerable minute bodies endowed in nearly all cases with the power of active movement, and therefore regarded by the early observers as parasitic animalcules or infusoria, a view which gave rise to the name *spermatozoa* (sperm-animals) by which they are still generally known.[1] As long ago as 1786, however, it was shown by Spallanzani that the fertilizing power must lie in the spermatozoa, not in the liquid in which they swim, because the spermatic fluid loses its power when filtered. Two years after the appearance of Schwann's epoch-making work Kölliker demonstrated (1841) that the spermatozoa arise directly from cells in the testis, and hence cannot be regarded as parasites, but are, like the ovum, derived from the parent-body. Not until 1865, however, was the final proof attained by Schweigger-Seidel and La Valette St. George that the spermatozoön contains not only a nucleus, as Kölliker believed, but also cytoplasm. It was thus shown to be, like the egg, a single cell, peculiarly modified in structure, it is true, and of extraordinary minuteness, yet on the whole morphologically equivalent to other cells. A final step was taken ten years later (1875), when Oscar Hertwig established the all-important fact that fertilization of the egg is accomplished by its union with one spermatozoön, and one only. In sexual reproduction, therefore, each sex contributes a single cell of its own body to the formation of the offspring, a fact which beautifully tallies with the conclusion of Darwin and Galton that the sexes play, on the whole, equal, though not identical parts in hereditary transmission. The ultimate problems of sex, fertilization, inheritance, and development were thus shown to be *cell-problems.*

Meanwhile, during the years immediately following the announcement of the cell-theory the attention of investigators was especially focussed upon the question: How do the cells of the body arise? Schwann and Schleiden held that cells might arise in two different ways; viz. either by the division or fission of a pre-existing mother-cell, or by " free cell-formation," new cells arising in the latter case not from pre-existing cells, but by crystallizing, as it were, out of a formative or nutritive substance, termed the "cytoblastema." It was only after many years of painstaking research that "free cell-

---

[1] The discovery of the spermatozoa is generally accredited to Ludwig Hamm, a pupil of Leeuwenhoek (1677), though Hartsoeker afterwards claimed the merit of having seen them as early as 1674 (Dr. Allen Thomson).

formation" was absolutely proved to be a myth, though many of
Schwann's immediate followers threw doubts upon it, and as early
as 1855 Virchow positively maintained the universality of cell-division, contending that every cell is the offspring of a pre-existing
parent-cell, and summing up in the since famous aphorism, "*omnis*

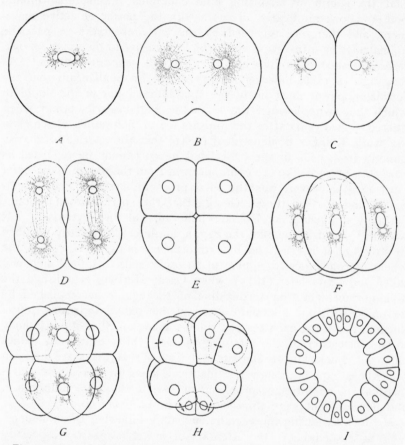

Fig. 3.—Cleavage of the ovum of the sea-urchin *Toxopneustes*, × 330, from life. The successive divisions up to the 16-cell stage (*H*) occupy about two hours. *I* is a section of the embryo
(blastula) of three hours, consisting of approximately 128 cells surrounding a central cavity or
.blastocœl.

cellula e cellula."[1]   At the present day this conclusion rests upon a
foundation so firm that we are justified in regarding it as a universal
law of development.

Now, if the cells of the body always arise by the division of pre-
existing cells, all must be traceable back to the fertilized egg-cell as

[1] *Arch. für Path. Anat.*, VIII., p. 23, 1855.

their common ancestor. Such is, in fact, the case in every plant and animal whose development is accurately known. The first step in development consists in the division of the egg into two parts, each of which is a cell, like the egg itself. The two then divide in turn to form four, eight, sixteen, and so on in more or less regular progression (Fig. 3) until step by step the egg has split up into the multitude of cells which build the body of the embryo, and finally of the adult. This process, known as the *cleavage* or *segmentation* of the egg, was observed long before its meaning was understood. It seems to have been first definitely described in the case of the frog's egg, by Prévost and Dumas (1824), though earlier observers had seen it; but at this time neither the egg nor its descendants were known to be cells, and its true meaning was first clearly perceived by Bergmann, Kölliker, Reichert, von Baer, and Remak, some twenty years later. The interpretation of cleavage as a process of cell-division was followed by the demonstration that cell-division does not begin with cleavage, but *can be traced back into the foregoing generation;* for the egg-cell, as well as the sperm-cell, arises by the division of a cell pre-existing in the parent-body. *It is therefore derived by direct descent from an egg-cell of the foregoing generation, and so on ad infinitum.* Embryologists thus arrived at the conception so vividly set forth by Virchow in 1858[1] of an uninterrupted series of cell-divisions extending backward from existing plants and animals to that remote and unknown period when vital organization assumed its present form. Life is a continuous stream. The death of the individual involves no breach of continuity in the series of cell-divisions by which the life of the race flows onwards. The individual body dies, it is true, but the germ-cells live on, carrying with them, as it were, the traditions of the race from which they have sprung, and handing them on to their descendants.

These facts clearly define the problems of heredity and variation as they confront the investigator of the present day. All theories of evolution take as fundamental postulates the facts of variation and heredity ; for it is by variation that new characters arise and by heredity that they are perpetuated. Darwin recognized two kinds of variation, both of which, being inherited and maintained through the conserving action of natural selection, might give rise to a permanent transformation of species. The first of these includes congenital or inborn variations ; *i.e.* such as appear at birth or are developed "spontaneously," without discoverable connection with the activities of the organism itself or the direct effect of the environment upon it. In a second class of variations are placed the so-called acquired char-

[1] See the quotation from the original edition of the *Cellularpathologie* at the head of Chapter II., p. 45.

acters; *i.e.* changes that arise in the course of the individual life as
the effect of use and disuse, or of food, climate, and the like. The
inheritance of congenital characters is now universally admitted, but
it is otherwise with acquired characters. The inheritance of the
latter, now the most debated question of biology, had been taken for
granted by Lamarck a half-century before Darwin; but he made no
attempt to show how such transmission is possible. Darwin, on the
other hand, squarely faced the physiological requirements of the problem, recognizing that the transmission of acquired characters can
only be possible under the assumption that the germ-cell definitely
reacts to all other cells of the body in such wise as to register the
changes taking place in them. In his ingenious and carefully elaborated theory of pangenesis,[1] Darwin framed a provisional physiological hypothesis of inheritance in accordance with this assumption,
suggesting that the germ-cells are reservoirs of minute germs or
gemmules derived from every part of the body; and on this basis he
endeavoured to explain the transmission both of acquired and of congenital variations, reviewing the facts of variation and inheritance
with wonderful skill, and building up a theory which, although it forms
the most speculative and hypothetical portion of his writings, must
always be reckoned one of his most interesting contributions to science.

The theory of pangenesis has been generally abandoned in spite
of the ingenious attempt to remodel it made by Brooks in 1883.[2] In
the same year the whole aspect of the problem was changed, and a
new period of discussion inaugurated by Weismann, who put forth
a bold challenge of the entire Lamarckian principle.[3] "I do not
propose to treat of the whole problem of heredity, but only of a
certain aspect of it, — the transmission of acquired characters, which
has been hitherto assumed to occur. In taking this course I may say
that it was impossible to avoid going back to the foundation of all
phenomena of heredity, and to determine the substance with which
they must be connected. In my opinion this can only be the substance of the germ-cells; and this substance transfers its hereditary
tendencies from generation to generation, at first unchanged, and
always uninfluenced in any corresponding manner, by that which
happens during the life of the individual which bears it. If these
views be correct, all our ideas upon the transformation of species require thorough modification, for the whole principle of evolution by
means of exercise (use and disuse) as professed by Lamarck, and
accepted in some cases by Darwin, entirely collapses" (*l.c.*, p. 69).

[1] *Variation of Animals and Plants*, Chapter XXVII.
[2] *The Law of Heredity*, Baltimore, 1883.
[3] *Ueber Vererbung*, 1883. See *Essays upon Heredity*, I., by A. Weismann, Clarendon
Press, Oxford, 1889.

It is impossible, he continues, that acquired traits should be transmitted, for it is inconceivable that definite changes in the body, or
" soma," should so affect the protoplasm of the germ-cells, as to cause
corresponding changes to appear in the offspring.   How, he asks, can
the increased dexterity and power in the hand of a trained piano-
player so affect the molecular structure of the germ-cells as to produce
a corresponding development in the hand of the child?   It is a physiological impossibility.   If we turn to the facts, we find, Weismann
affirms, that not one of the asserted cases of transmission of acquired
characters will stand the test of rigid scientific scrutiny.   It is a
reversal of the true point of view to regard inheritance as taking
place from the body of the parent to that of the child.   The child
inherits from the parent *germ-cell*, not from the parent-body, and the
germ-cell owes its characteristics not to the body which bears it, but
to its descent from a pre-existing germ-cell of the same kind.   Thus
the body is, as it were, an offshoot from the germ-cell (Fig. 4).   As

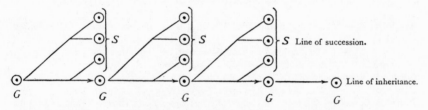

Fig. 4. — Diagram illustrating Weismann's theory of inheritance.
G. The germ-cell, which by division gives rise to the body or soma (*S*) and to new germ-cells
(*G*) which separate from the soma and repeat the process in each successive generation.

far as inheritance is concerned, the body is merely the carrier of the
germ-cells, which are held in trust for coming generations.

Weismann's subsequent theories, built on this foundation, have
given rise to the most eagerly contested controversies of the post-
Darwinian period, and, whether they are to stand or fall, have played
a most important part in the progress of science.   For aside from the
truth or error of his special theories, it has been Weismann's great
service to place the keystone between the work of the evolutionists
and that of the cytologists, and thus to bring the cell-theory and the
evolution-theory into organic connection.   It is from this point of
view that the present volume has been written.   It has been my
endeavour to treat the cell primarily as the organ of inheritance and
development; but, obviously, this aspect of the cell can only be
apprehended through a study of the general phenomena of cell-life.
The order of treatment, which is a convenient rather than a strictly
logical one, is as follows : —

The opening chapter is devoted to a general sketch of cell-structure, and the second to the phenomena of cell-division. The following three chapters deal with the germ-cells, — the third with their structure and mode of origin, the fourth with their union in fertilization, the fifth with the phenomena of maturation by which they are prepared for their union. The sixth chapter contains a critical discussion of cell-organization, completing the morphological analysis of the cell. In the seventh chapter the cell is considered with reference to its more fundamental chemical and physiological properties as a prelude to the examination of development which follows. The succeeding chapter approaches the objective point of the book by considering the cleavage of the ovum and the general laws of cell-division of which it is an expression. The ninth chapter, finally, deals with the elementary operations of development considered as cell-functions and with the theories of inheritance and development based upon them.

SOME GENERAL WORKS ON THE CELL-THEORY

Bergh, R. S. — Vorlesungen über die Zelle und die einfachen Gewebe : *Wiesbaden*, 1894.

Delage, Yves. — La Structure du Protoplasma et les Théories sur l'hérédité et les grands Problèmes de la Biologie Générale : *Paris*, 1895.

Geddes & Thompson. — The Evolution of Sex : *New York*, 1890.

Henneguy, L. F. — Leçons sur la cellule : *Paris*, 1896.

Hertwig, O. — Die Zelle und die Gewebe : *Fischer, Jena*, 1892. Translation, published by *Macmillan, London and New York*, 1895.

Huxley, T. H. — Review of the Cell-theory : *British and Foreign Medico-Chirurgical Review*, XII. 1853.

Minot, C. S. — Human Embryology : *New York*, 1892.

Remak, R. — Untersuchungen über die Entwicklung der Wirbelthiere : *Berlin*, 1850–55.

Schleiden, M. J. — Beiträge zur Phytogenesis : *Müller's Archiv*, 1838. Translation in Sydenham Soc., XII. *London*, 1847.

Schwann, Th. — Mikroscopische Untersuchungen über die Uebereinstimmung in der Structur und dem Wachsthum der Thiere und Pflanzen : *Berlin*, 1839. Translation in Sydenham Soc., XII. *London*, 1847.

Tyson, James. — The Cell-doctrine, 2d ed. *Philadelphia*, 1878.

Virchow, R. — Die Cellularpathologie in ihrer Begründung auf physiologische und pathologische Gewebelehre. *Berlin*, 1858.

Weismann, A. — Essays on Heredity. Translation : First series, *Oxford*, 1891 ; Second series, *Oxford*, 1892.

Id. — The Germ-plasm. *New York*, 1893.

CHAPTER I

GENERAL SKETCH OF THE CELL

" Wir haben gesehen, dass alle Organismen aus wesentlich gleichen Theilen, nämlich aus Zellen zusammengesetzt sind, dass diese Zellen nach wesentlich denselben Gesetzen sich bilden und wachsen, dass also diese Prozesse überall auch durch dieselben Kräfte hervorgebracht werden müssen." SCHWANN.[1]

THE term " cell " is a biological misnomer; for whatever the living cell is, it is not, as the word implies, a hollow chamber surrounded by solid walls. The term is merely an historical survival of a word casually employed by the botanists of the seventeenth century to designate the cells of certain plant-tissues which, when viewed in section, give somewhat the appearance of a honeycomb.[2] The cells of these tissues are, in fact, separated by conspicuous solid walls which were mistaken by Schleiden, unfortunately followed by Schwann in this regard, for their essential part. The living substance contained within the walls, to which Hugo von Mohl gave the name *protoplasm*[3] (1846) was at first overlooked or was regarded as a waste-product, a view based upon the fact that in many important plant-tissues such as cork or wood it may wholly disappear, leaving only the lifeless walls. The researches of Bergmann, Kölliker, Bischoff, Cohn, Max Schultze, and many others, showed, however, that some kinds of cells, for example, the corpuscles of the blood, are naked masses of living protoplasm not surrounded by walls, — a fact which proves that not the wall, but the cell-contents, is the essential part, and must therefore be the seat of life. It was found further that with the possible exception of some of the lowest forms of life, such as the bacteria, the protoplasm invariably contains a definite rounded body, the *nucleus*,[4] which in turn may contain a still

[1] *Untersuchungen*, p. 227, 1839.
[2] The word seems to have been first employed by Robert Hooke, in 1665, to designate the minute cavities observed in cork, a tissue which he described as made up of " little boxes or cells distinct from one another " and separated by solid walls.
[3] The same word had been used by Purkyně some years before (1840) to designate the formative material of young animal embryos.
[4] First described by Robert Brown in 1833.

13

smaller body, the *nucleolus*. Thus the cell came to be defined by
Max Schultze and Leydig as a *mass of protoplasm containing
a nucleus*, a morphological definition which remains sufficiently satisfactory even at the present day. Nothing could be less appropriate
than to call such a body a "cell"; yet the word has become so firmly
established that every effort to replace it by a better has failed, and
it probably must be accepted as part of the established nomenclature
of science.[1]

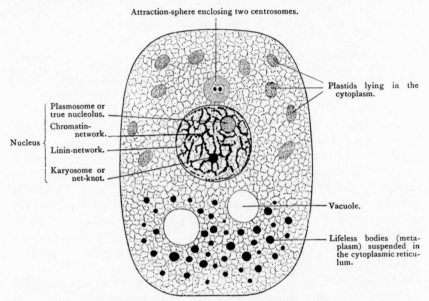

Attraction-sphere enclosing two centrosomes.

Plasmosome or
true nucleolus.

Chromatin-
network.

Nucleus

Linin-network.

Karyosome or
net-knot.

Plastids lying in the
cytoplasm.

Vacuole.

Lifeless bodies (meta-
plasm) suspended in
the cytoplasmic reticu-
lum.

Fig. 5. — Diagram of a cell. Its basis consists of a thread-work (*mitome*, or *reticulum*) composed of minute granules (*microsomes*) and traversing a transparent ground-substance.

A. General Morphology of the Cell

The cell is a rounded mass of protoplasm which in its simplest
form is approximately spherical. This form is, however, seldom
realized save in isolated cells such as the unicellular plants and
animals or the egg-cells of the higher forms. In vastly the greater
number of cases the typical spherical form is modified by unequal
growth and differentiation, by active movements of the cell-substance,
or by the mechanical pressure of surrounding structures. The

[1] Sachs has proposed the convenient word *energid* (*Flora*, '92, p. 57) to designate the
essential living part of the cell, *i.e.* the nucleus with that portion of the active cytoplasm
that falls within its sphere of influence, the two forming an organic unit both in a morphological and in a physiological sense. It is to be regretted that this convenient and appropriate term has not come into general use. (See also *Flora*, '95, p. 405.)

protoplasm which forms its living basis is a viscid, translucent, granular substance, often forming a network or sponge-like structure extending through the cell-body and showing various structural modifications in different regions and under different physiological states of the cell. Besides the living protoplasm the cell almost invariably contains various lifeless bodies suspended in the meshes of the network; examples of these are food-granules, pigment-bodies, drops of oil or water, and excretory matters. These bodies play a purely passive part in the activities of the cell, being either reserve food-matters destined to be absorbed and built up into the living substance, or by-products formed from the protoplasm as waste matters, or in order to play some *rôle* subsidiary to the actions of the protoplasm itself. The lifeless inclusions in the protoplasm have been collectively designated as *metaplasm* (Hanstein) in contradis-

tinction to the living *protoplasm;* but this convenient term is not in general use. Among the lifeless products of the protoplasm must be reckoned also the *cell-wall* or *membrane* by which the cell-body may be surrounded; but it must be remembered that the cell-wall in many cases arises by a direct transformation of the protoplasmic substance, and that it often retains the power of growth by intussusception like living matter.

In all save a few of the lowest and simplest forms, perhaps even in them, the protoplasmic substance is differentiated into two very distinct parts, viz., the *cell-body,* forming the principal mass of the cell, and a smaller body, the *nucleus,* which lies in its interior (Fig. 5). Both structurally and chemically these two parts show differences of so marked and constant a character that they must be regarded as the most important of all protoplasmic differentiations. The

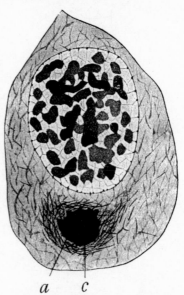

a   c

Fig. 6.—A resting cell (*spermatogonium*) from the testis of the salamander, showing the typical parts. Above, the large nucleus, with scattered masses of chromatin, linin-network and membrane. Around it, the cytoplasmic thread-work. Below, the attraction-sphere (*a*) and centrosome (*c*). [After RAWITZ.]

nuclear substance is therefore often designated as *nucleoplasm* or *karyoplasm;* that of the cell-body as *cytoplasm* (Strasburger). Some of the foremost authorities, however, among them Oscar Hertwig, reject this terminology and use the word "protoplasm" in its historic sense, applying it solely to the cytoplasm or substance of the cell-body.

At a first examination the nucleus appears to be a perfectly distinct body suspended in the cytoplasm. Most of the latest researches point, however, to the conclusion that nucleus and cytoplasm are pervaded by a common structural basis, morphologically continuous

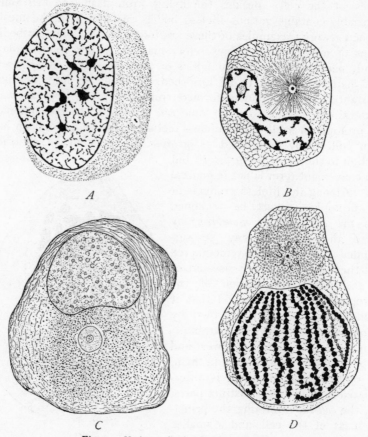

Fig. 7. — Various cells showing the typical parts.

A. From peritoneal epithelium of the salamander-larva. Two centrosomes at the right. Nucleus showing net-knots. [FLEMMING.]

B. Spermatogonium of frog. Attraction-sphere (aster) containing a single centrosome. Nucleus with a single plasmosome. [HERMANN.]

C. Spinal ganglion-cell of frog. Attraction-sphere near the centre, containing a single centrosome with several centrioles. [LENHOSSÉK.]

D. Spermatocyte of *Proteus*. Nucleus in the spireme-stage. Centrosome single; attraction-sphere containing rod-shaped bodies. [HERMANN.]

under certain conditions from one to the other, and that both are to be regarded as specially differentiated areas in that basis.[1] The terms

---

[1] The fact that the nucleus may move actively through the cytoplasm, as occurs during the fertilization of the egg and in some other cases, seems to show that the morphological continuity may at times be interrupted.

"nucleus" and "cell-body" are therefore only topographical expressions, and in a measure the same is true of the terms "karyoplasm" and "cytoplasm." The latter, however, acquire a special significance from the fact that there is on the whole a definite chemical contrast between the nuclear substance and that of the cell-body, the former being characterized by the abundance of a substance rich in phosphorus known as *nuclein*, while the latter contains no true nuclein and is especially rich in proteids and related substances (nucleo-albumins, albumins, globulins, and others), which contain a much lower percentage of phosphorus.

The differentiation of the protoplasmic substance into nucleus and cytoplasm is a fundamental character of the cell, both in a morphological and in a physiological sense; and, as will appear hereafter, there is reason to believe that it is in a measure the expression of a corresponding localization of the operations of constructive and destructive metabolism which lie at the basis of the individual cell-life. A third element, the *centrosome* (Figs. 5–7), present in many if not in all cells, is especially concerned with the process of division and cell-reproduction. Recent research has rendered it probable that in point of morphological persistency the centrosome is comparable with the nucleus; but this conclusion is not yet definitely established.

B. STRUCTURAL BASIS OF PROTOPLASM

As ordinarily seen under moderate powers of the microscope protoplasm shows no definite structural organization. A more precise examination under high powers, especially after treatment with suitable fixing and staining reagents, reveals the fact that both nucleus and cytoplasm possess a complicated structure. Regarding the precise nature of this structure opinion still differs. According to the view most widely held, one of its essential features is the presence of two constituents, one of which, the *ground-substance, cytolymph*, or *enchylema*, is more liquid, while the other, the *spongioplasm* or *reticulum*, is of firmer consistency, and forms a sponge-like network or alveolar structure extending everywhere through the more liquid portion. At the present time it seems probable that the more solid portion is the more active and is perhaps to be identified as the living substance proper, the ground-substance being passive; but the reverse of this view is maintained by Leydig, Schäfer, and some others. The most elaborate and painstaking investigation has moreover failed to determine with absolute certainty even the physical configuration of the network.

Bütschli and a considerable school of followers among both

c

zoölogists and botanists regard protoplasm as essentially a liquid, or rather a mixture of liquids, which forms a foam-like alveolar structure[1] like an emulsion, in which the firmer portion forms the walls of separate chambers, filled with the more liquid substance (Fig. 8). By

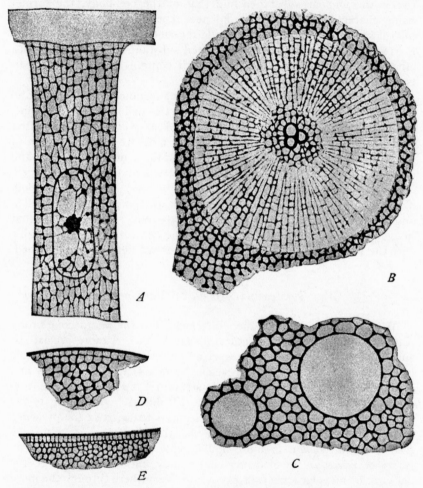

Fig. 8.—Alveolar or foam-structure of protoplasm, according to Bütschli. [BÜTSCHLI.]

A. Epidermal cell of the earthworm. *B*. Aster, attraction-sphere, and centrosome from sea-urchin egg. *C*. Intra-capsular protoplasm of a radiolarian (*Thalassicolla*) with vacuoles. *D*. Peripheral cytoplasm of sea-urchin egg. *E*. Artificial emulsion of olive-oil, sodium chloride, and water.

special local modifications of this structure all the parts of the cell are formed.   Bütschli has shown that artificial emulsions, variously prepared, may show under the microscope a marvellously close resem-

1 *" Wabenstruktur."*

blance to actual protoplasm, and that drops of oil-emulsions suspended in water may even exhibit amœboid changes of form.

Opposed to Bütschli's conception is the view, first clearly set forth by Frommann and Arnold ('65–'67), and now maintained by such authorities as Flemming, Van Beneden, Strasburger, and perhaps the greater number of contemporary investigators, that the more solid portion consists of coherent *threads* which extend through the ground-substance, either separately or connected by branches to form a mesh-work like the fibres of a sponge (Figs. 7, 9).

In the present state of the subject it is difficult, indeed, impossible, to decide which of these opposing views should be accepted ; for the evidence is very strong that each expresses a part of the truth. It is generally admitted that such an alveolar structure as Bütschli describes is characteristic of many unicellular forms, and occurs in many higher forms where the cell-substance is filled with vacuoles or with solid inclusions such as starch-grains or deutoplasm-spheres. In the latter case the structure has been termed "pseudo-alveolar" (Reinke); but it remains to be seen whether there is any real distinction between this and the true alveolar structure described by Bütschli. On the other hand the evidence of true fibrillar or reticular structure in many tissue-cells, especially during cell-division, is very convincing ; and my own observations have led me to regard this structure as the more typical and characteristic. For descriptive purposes I shall accordingly adopt the terms of the fibrillar or reticular hypothesis, designating the more solid portion of protoplasm as the *thread-work* or *reticulum* ("Gerüstwerk," "Fadenwerk" of German writers) in contradistinction to the more liquid *ground-substance*. It should be clearly understood, however, that these terms are used only as a matter of convenience, and are not meant to exclude the possibility that the "fibres" or the "reticulum" may in many cases be open to Bütschli's interpretation.

From a theoretical point of view the finer structure of the network is a question of very great interest and importance. The earlier investigators, such as Virchow and Max Schultze, failed to observe the thread-work, and described protoplasm as consisting of a clear homogeneous basis in which were embedded numerous granules. Even at the present time a similar view is held by a few investigators, more especially among botanists (*e.g.*, Berthold, Schwarz), who regard the thread-work either as an artificial effect produced by reagents, or, if normal, as an inconstant and hence unimportant feature. The best and most careful recent studies on protoplasm have, however, yielded very convincing evidence that, whatever be the precise configuration of the protoplasmic reticulum, it is not only a normal structure, but one of very wide occurrence.

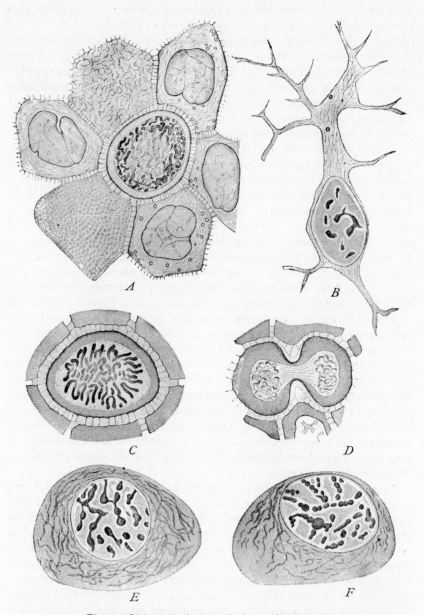

Fig. 9. — Living cells of salamander-larva. [FLEMMING.]

A. Group of epidermal cells at different foci, showing protoplasmic bridges, nuclei, and cytoplasmic fibrillæ; the central cell with nucleus in the spireme-stage. *B.* Connective tissue-cell. *C.* Epidermal cell in early mitosis (segmented spireme) surrounded by protoplasmic bridges. *D.* Dividing-cell. *E. F.* Cartilage-cells with cytoplasmic fibrillæ (the latter somewhat exaggerated in the plate).

These studies have raised interesting problems regarding the significance of the granules described by the early observers. Many of the
granules, especially the larger and more obvious of them, are unquestionably inert bodies, such as reserve food-matters, suspended in the
meshwork. Others are nodes of the network or optical sections of
the threads. But there is some reason to believe that, apart from
these appearances, discrete living particles may form a constant
and essential structural feature of the protoplasmic thread. These
particles, now generally known as *microsomes*,[1] are embedded in the
threads of the network, and are sometimes so closely and regularly set
as irresistibly to suggest the view that they are definite structural elements out of which the thread is built. More than this, their behaviour
is in some cases such as to have led to the hypothesis long since
suggested by Henle ('41) and at a later period developed by Béchamp
and Estor, by Maggi and especially by Altmann, that microsomes are
actually organic units or bioblasts, capable of assimilation, growth, and
division, and hence to be regarded as elementary units of structure
standing between the cell and the ultimate molecules of living matter.
And thus the theory of genetic continuity expressed by Redi in the
aphorism "*omne vivum ex vivo*," reduced by Virchow to "*omnis
cellula e cellula*," finally appears in the writings of Altmann as "*omne
granulum e granulo!*"[2]

Altmann's premature generalization rests upon a very insecure
foundation and has been received with just scepticism. That the cell
consists of more elementary units of organization is nevertheless indicated by *a priori* evidence so cogent as to have driven many of the
foremost leaders of biological thought into the belief that such units
must exist, whether or not the microscope reveals them to view.
Among those who have accepted this conception in one form or
another are numbered such men as Spencer, Darwin, Beale, Haeckel,
Michael Foster, Nägeli, De Vries, Wiesner, Roux, Weismann, Oscar
Hertwig, Verworn, and Whitman. The modern conception of ultra-
cellular units, ranking between the molecule and the cell, was first
definitely suggested by Brücke ('61),[3] only, however, to be rejected
as without the support of facts, though this eminent physiologist
insisted that the cell must possess a more complicated organization
than that revealed by the best microscopes of his time. It was soon
afterwards taken up by Herbert Spencer, and elaborated into the
theory of physiological units by which he endeavoured to explain
the phenomena of regeneration, development, and heredity. Darwin

[1] Hanstein ('82).

[2] *Die Elementarorganismen*, Leipsic, 1894, p. 155.

[3] For a review of speculations in the same direction by Buffon and other early writers see
Yves Delage ('95).

too, in his celebrated hypothesis of pangenesis, adopted a nearly related conception, which as remodelled by De Vries twenty years afterwards ('89) forms the basis of the theories of development maintained by such leaders of biological research as Weismann and Hertwig. The same view appears in a different form in the writings of Nägeli, Wiesner, Foster, Verworn, and many other morphologists and physiologists.[1]

An hypothesis backed by such authority and based on evidence drawn from sources so diverse cannot be lightly rejected. We are compelled by the most stringent evidence to admit that the ultimate basis of living matter is not a single chemical substance, but a mixture of many substances *that are self-perpetuating* without loss of their specific character. The open question is whether these substances are localized in discrete morphological bodies aggregated to form the cell somewhat as cells are aggregated to form tissues and organs, and whether such bodies, if they exist, lie within the reach of the microscope. Altmann's identification of the "granulum" as such a body is undoubtedly premature; it is certain that his description of cell-structures from this point of view is often very inaccurate; it is extremely doubtful how far the granules or microsomes are normal structures, and how far they are artefacts produced by the coagulating effect of the reagents. It is nevertheless certain, as will be shown in Chapter VI., that at least one part of the cell, namely the nucleus, actually consists of self-propagating units of a lower order than itself, and there is some ground for regarding the cyto-microsomes in the same light.

C. THE NUCLEUS

A fragment of a cell deprived of its nucleus may live for a considerable time and manifest the power of co-ordinated movement without perceptible impairment. Such a mass of protoplasm is, however, devoid of the powers of assimilation, growth, and repair, and sooner or later dies. In other words, those functions that involve destructive metabolism may continue for a time in the absence of the nucleus; those that involve constructive metabolism cease with its removal. There is, therefore, strong reason to believe that the nucleus plays an essential part in the constructive metabolism of the

---

[1] The following list includes only some of the various names that have been given to these hypothetical units by modern writers : *Physiological units* (Spencer); *gemmules* (Darwin); *pangens* (De Vries); *plasomes* (Wiesner); *micellæ* (Nägeli); *plastidules* (Haeckel and Elssberg); *inotagmata* (Engelmann); *biophores* (Weismann); *bioblasts* (Beale); *somacules* (Foster); *idioblasts* (Hertwig); *idiosomes* (Whitman); *biogens* (Verworn); *microzymas* (Béchamp and Estor); *gemmæ* (Haacke).

cell, and through this is especially concerned with the formative processes involved in growth and development. For these and many
other reasons, to be discussed hereafter, the nucleus is generally regarded as a controlling centre of cell-activity, and hence a primary
factor in growth, development, and the transmission of specific qualities from cell to cell, and so from one generation to another.

1. *General Structure*

The cell-nucleus passes through two widely different phases, one
of which is characteristic of cells in their ordinary or vegetative condition, while the other only occurs during the complicated changes
involved in cell-division. In the first phase, falsely characterized
as the "resting state," the nucleus usually appears as a rounded
sac-like body surrounded by a distinct membrane and containing a
conspicuous irregular network (Figs. 5, 7, 10). Its form, though
subject to variation, is on the whole singularly constant, and shows
no definite relation to that of the cell in which it lies. Typically
spherical, it may, in certain cases, assume an irregular or amœboid
form, may break up into a group of more or less completely separated lobes (polymorphic nuclei), or may be perforated to form an
irregular ring (Fig. 11, *D*). It is usually very large in gland-cells
and others that show a very active metabolism, and in such cases
its surface is sometimes increased by the formation of complex
branches ramifying through the cell (Fig. 11, *E*). Interesting modifications of the nucleus occur in the unicellular forms. In the
ciliate Infusoria the body contains nuclei of two kinds, viz. a large
macronucleus and one or more smaller *micronuclei*. The first of
these shows a remarkable diversity of structure in different forms,
being often greatly elongated and sometimes showing a moniliform
structure like a string of beads. In *Trachelocerca* and some other
Infusoria, according to Gruber ('84), the nucleus is not a single definite
body, but is represented by minute granules scattered throughout the
cell-substance (Fig. 12); Bütschli describes somewhat similar diffused
nuclei in some of the Flagellates, and in the Bacteria.

In the ordinary forms of nuclei in their resting state the following
structural elements may as a rule be distinguished (Figs. 5, 6, 7, 10, 11):—

a. The *nuclear membrane*, a well-defined delicate wall which gives
the nucleus a sharp contour and differentiates it clearly from the
surrounding cytoplasm.

b. The *nuclear reticulum*. This, the most essential part of the
nucleus, forms an irregular branching network or *reticulum* which
consists of two very different constituents. The first of these, the

nuclear substance *par excellence*, is known as *chromatin* (Flemming) on account of its very marked staining capacity when treated with various dyes. In some cases the chromatin forms a nearly continuous network, but it often appears in the form of more or less detached rounded granules or irregular bodies. The second constituent is a transparent substance, invisible until after treatment by reagents, known as *linin* (Schwarz). This substance, which is probably of the same nature as the cytoplasmic network outside the nucleus, surrounds and supports the chromatin, and thus forms the basis of the nuclear network.

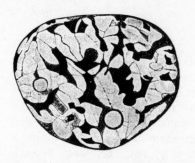

c. The *nucleoli*, one or more larger rounded or irregular bodies, suspended in the network, and staining intensely with many dyes; they may be absent. The bodies known by this name are of at least two different kinds. The first of these, the so-called true nucleoli or *plasmosomes* (Figs. 5, 7, *B*, 10), are of spherical form, and by treatment with differential stains such as hæmatoxylin and eosin are found to consist typically of a central mass staining like the cytoplasm, surrounded by a shell which stains like chromatin. Those of the other form, the "net-knots" (Netzknoten), or *karyosomes*, are either spherical or irregular in form, stain like the chromatin, and

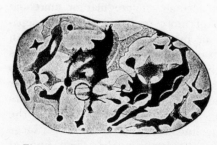

Fig. 10.—Two nuclei from the crypts of Lieberkühn in the salamander. [HEIDENHAIN.] The character of the chromatin-network (*basichromatin*) is accurately shown. The upper nucleus contains three plasmosomes or true nucleoli; the lower, one. A few fine linin-threads (*oxychromatin*) are seen in the upper nucleus running off from the chromatin-masses. The clear spaces are occupied by the ground-substance.

appear to be no more than thickened portions of the chromatic network (Figs. 5, 7, *A*, 10). Besides the nucleoli the nucleus may in exceptional cases contain the centrosome (p. 225), which has undoubtedly been confounded in some instances with a true nucleolus or plasmosome.[1] There is strong evidence that the true nucleoli are

[1] Flemming first called attention to the chemical difference between the true nucleoli and the chromatic reticulum ('82, pp. 138, 163) in animal cells, and Zacharias soon afterwards studied more closely the difference of staining-reaction in plant-cells, showing that the

relatively passive bodies that represent accumulations of reserve-substance or by-products, and play no direct part in the nuclear activity (p. 93).

d. The *ground-substance, nuclear sap,* or *karyolymph,* a clear sub-

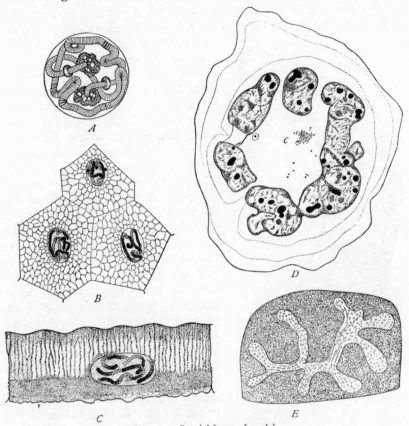

Fig. 11. — Special forms of nuclei.

A. Permanent spireme-nucleus, salivary gland of *Chironomus* larva. Chromatin in a single thread, composed of chromatin-discs (chromomeres), terminating at each end in a true nucleolus or plasmosome. [BALBIANI.]

B. Permanent spireme-nuclei, intestinal epithelium of dipterous larva *Ptychoptera.* [VAN GEHUCHTEN.] *C.* The same, side view.

D. Polymorphic ring-nucleus, giant-cell of bone-marrow of the rabbit; *c,* a group of centrosomes or centrioles. [HEIDENHAIN.]

E. Branching nucleus, spinning-gland of butterfly larva (*Pieris*). [KORSCHELT.]

stance occupying the interspaces of the network and left unstained by many dyes which colour the chromatin intensely. Until recently

former are especially coloured by alkaline carmine solutions, the latter by acid solutions. Still later studies by Zacharias, and especially by Heidenhain, show that the medullary substance (pyrenin) of true nuclei is coloured by acid anilines and other plasma stains, while the chromatin has a special affinity for basic anilines. Cf. p. 242.

the ground-substance has been regarded as a fluid or semi-fluid, but recent researches by Reinke and others have thrown doubt on this view, as described at p. 28.

The configuration of the chromatic network varies greatly in different cases. It is sometimes of a very loose and open character, as in many epithelial cells (Fig. 1); sometimes extremely coarse and irregular, as in leucocytes (Fig. 10); sometimes so compact as to appear nearly or quite homogeneous, as in the nuclei of spermatozoa and in many Protozoa. In some cases the chromatin does not form a network, but appears in the form of a thread closely similar to the spireme-stage of dividing nuclei (cf. p. 47). The most striking case of this kind occurs in the salivary glands of dipterous larvæ (*Chironomus*), where, as described by Balbiani, the chromatin has the form of a single convoluted thread, composed of transverse discs and terminating at each end in a large nucleolus (Fig. 11, *A*). Somewhat similar nuclei (Fig. 11, *B*) occur in various glandular cells of other insects (Van Gehuchten, Gilson), and also in the young ovarian eggs of certain animals (cf. p. 193). In certain gland-cells of the marine isopod *Anilocra* it is arranged in regular rosettes (Vom Rath). Rabl, followed by Van Gehuchten, Heidenhain, and others, has endeavoured to show that the nuclear network shows a distinct polarity, the nucleus having a "pole" towards which the principal chromatin-threads converge, and near which the centrosome lies.[1] In many nuclei, however, no trace of such polarity can be discerned.

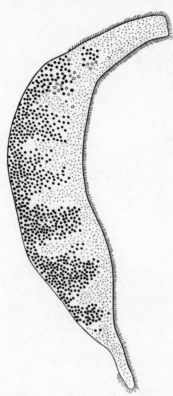

Fig. 12.—An infusorian, *Trachelocerca*, with diffused nucleus consisting of scattered chromatin-granules. [GRUBER.]

The network may undergo great changes both in physical configuration and in staining capacity at different periods in the life of the same cell, and the actual amount of chromatin fluctuates, sometimes to an enormous extent. Embryonic cells are in general

---

[1] Cf. the polarity of the cell, p. 38.

characterized by the large size of the nucleus; and Zacharias has shown in the case of plants that the nuclei of meristem and other embryonic tissues are not only relatively large, but contain a larger percentage of chromatin than in later stages. The relation of these changes to the physiological activity of the nucleus is still imperfectly understood.[1]

A description of the nucleus during division is deferred to the following chapter.

2. *Finer Structure of the Nucleus*

Many recent researches indicate that some at least of the nuclear structures are aggregates of more elementary morphological bodies, though there is still no general agreement regarding their nature and relationships. The most definite evidence in this direction relates to the chromatic network. In the stages preparatory to division this network revolves itself into a definite number of rod-shaped bodies known as *chromosomes* (Fig. 16), which split lengthwise as the cell divides. These bodies arise as aggregations of minute rounded bodies or microsomes to which various names have been given (*chromomeres*, Fol; *ids*, Weismann). They are as a rule most clearly visible and most regularly arranged during cell-division, when the chromatin is arranged in a thread (*spireme*), or in separate *chromosomes* (Figs. 7, *D*, 38, *B*); but in many cases they are distinctly visible in the reticulum of the "resting" nucleus (Fig. 39). It is, however, an open question whether the chromatin-granules of the reticulum are individually identical with those forming the chromosomes or the spireme-thread. The larger masses of the reticulum undoubtedly represent aggregations of such granules, but whether the latter completely fuse or remain always distinct is unknown. Even the chromosomes may appear perfectly homogeneous, and the same is sometimes true of the entire nucleus, as in the spermatozoön. The opinion is nevertheless gaining ground that the chromatin-granules have a persistent identity and are to be regarded as morphological units of which the chromatin is built up.[2]

Heidenhain ('93, '94), whose views have been accepted by Reinke, Waldeyer, and others, has shown that the "achromatic" nuclear network is likewise composed of granules which he distinguishes as *lanthanin-* or *oxychromatin*-granules from the *basichromatin*-granules of the chromatic network. Like the latter, the oxychromatin-granules are suspended in a non-staining clear substance, for which he reserves

[1] See Chapter VII.   [2] Cf. Chapter VI.

the term "linin." Both forms of granules occur in the chromatic network, while the achromatic network contains only oxychromatin. They are sharply differentiated by dyes, the basichromatin being coloured by the basic anilines (methyl green, saffranin, etc.) and other true "nuclear stains"; while the oxychromatin-granules, like many cytoplasmic structures, and like the substance of true nucleoli (pyrenin), are coloured by acid anilines (rubin, eosin, etc.) and other "plasma stains." This distinction, as will appear in Chapter VII., is probably one of great physiological significance.

Still other forms of granules have been distinguished in the nucleus by Reinke ('94) and Schloter ('94). Of these the most important are the "œdematin-granules," which according to the first of these authors form the principal mass of the ground-substance or "nuclear sap" of Hertwig and other authors. These granules are identified by both observers with the "cyanophilous granules," which Altmann regarded as the essential elements of the nucleus. It is at present impossible to give a consistent interpretation of the morphological value and physiological relations of these various forms of granules. The most that can be said is that the basichromatin-granules are probably normal structures; that they play a principal *rôle* in the life of the nucleus; that the oxychromatin-granules are nearly related to them; and that not improbably the one form may be transformed into the other in the manner suggested in Chapter VII.

The nuclear membrane is not yet thoroughly understood, and much discussion has been devoted to the question of its origin and structure. The most probable view is that long since advocated by Klein ('78) and Van Beneden ('83) that the membrane arises as a condensation of the general protoplasmic reticulum, and is part of the same structure as the linin-network and the cyto-reticulum. Like these, it is in some cases "achromatic," but in other cases it shows the same staining reactions as chromatin, or may be double, consisting of an outer achromatic and an inner chromatic layer. According to Reinke, it consists of oxychromatin-granules like those of the linin-network.

3. *Chemistry of the Nucleus*

The chemical nature of the various nuclear elements will be considered in Chapter VII., and a brief statement will here suffice. The following classification of the nuclear substances, proposed by Schwarz in 1887, has been widely accepted, though open to criticism on various grounds.

1. *Chromatin*. The chromatic substance (basichromatin) of the network and of those nucleoli known as net-knots or karyosomes.
2. *Linin*. The achromatic network and the spindle-fibres arising from it.

3. *Paralinin.* The ground-substance.
4. *Pyrenin* or *Parachromatin.* The inner mass of true nucleoli.
5. *Amphipyrenin.* The substance of the nuclear membrane.

Chromatin is probably identical with *nuclein* (p. 240), which is a compound of *nucleic acid* (a complex organic acid, rich in phosphorus) and albumin. In certain cases (nuclei of spermatozoa, and probably also the chromosomes at the time of mitosis), chromatin may be composed of nearly pure nucleic acid. The *linin* is probably composed of "plastin," a substance similar to nuclein, but containing a lower percentage of phosphorus, and either belonging to the nucleo-proteids or approaching them. It is nearly related with the substance of the cyto-reticulum. *Pyrenin* consists of a plastin-substance which stains like linin. *Amphipyrenin* is probably identical with linin, since the nuclear membrane is probably a condensed portion of the general reticulum which forms the boundary between the intra- and extra-nuclear networks. It should be borne in mind, however, that the membrane often has an inner chromatic layer composed of chromatin.

D. The Cytoplasm

It has long been recognized that in the unicellular forms the cytoplasmic substance is often differentiated into two well-marked zones; viz. an inner medullary substance or *endoplasm* in which the nucleus lies, and an outer cortical substance or *exoplasm* (ectoplasm) from which the more differentiated products of the cytoplasm, such as cilia, trichocysts, and membrane, take their origin. Indications of a similar differentiation are often shown in the tissue-cells of higher plants and animals,[1] though it may take the form of a polar differentiation of the cell-substance, or may be wholly wanting. Whether the distinction is of fundamental importance remains to be seen; but it appears to be a general rule that the nucleus is surrounded by protoplasm of relatively slight differentiation, while the more highly differentiated products of cell-activity are laid down in the more peripheral region of the cell, either in the cortical zone or at one end of the cell.[2] This fact is full of meaning, not only because it is an expression of the adaptation of the cell to its external environment, but also because of its bearing on the problems of nutrition.[3] For if, as we shall see reason to conclude in Chapter VII., the nucleus be immediately concerned with synthetic metabolism, we should expect to find the immediate and less differentiated products of its action in its neighbourhood, and on the whole the facts bear out this view.

[1] This fact was first pointed out in the tissue-cells of animals by Kupffer ('75), and its importance has since been urged by Waldeyer, Reinke, and others. The cortical layer is by Kupffer termed *paraplasm*, by Pfeffer *hyaloplasm*, by Pringsheim the *Hautschicht*. The medullary zone is termed by Kupffer, *protoplasm, sensu strictu;* by Strasburger *Körnerplasma*, by Nägeli *polioplasm*.

[2] Cf. p. 38.

[3] See Kupffer ('90), pp. 473-476.

The most pressing of all questions regarding the cytoplasmic structure is whether the sponge-like, fibrillar, or alveolar appearance is a normal condition existing during life. There are many cases, especially among plant-cells, in which the most careful examination has thus far failed to reveal the presence of a reticulum, the cytoplasm appearing, even under the highest powers and after the most

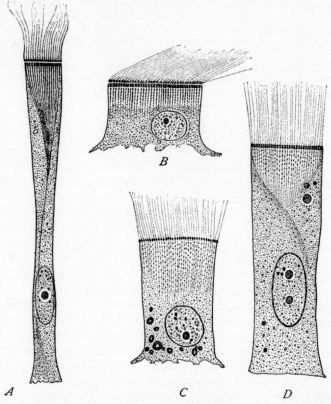

A   C   D

Fig. 13. — Ciliated cells, showing cytoplasmic fibrillæ terminating in a zone of peripheral microsomes to which the cilia are attached. [ENGELMANN.]

A. From intestinal epithelium of *Anodonta.*   *B.* From gill of *Anodonta.*   *C. D.* Intestinal epithelium of *Cyclas.*

careful treatment, merely as a finely granular substance. This and the additional fact that the cytoplasm may show active streaming and flowing movements, has led some authors, especially among botanists, to regard the reticulum as non-essential and as being, when present, a secondary differentiation of the cytoplasmic substance specially developed for the performance of particular functions. It has been shown, moreover, that structureless proteids, such as egg-albumin and other substances, when coagulated by various reagents, often show a structure closely similar to that of protoplasm as observed in microscopical sections. Bütschli has made careful studies of such coagulation-phenomena which show that coagulated or dried albumin, starch-solutions, gelatin, gum arabic, and other substances show a fine aveolar structure scarcely to be distinguished from that which he believes to be the normal and typical structure of protoplasm. Fischer ('94, '95) has made still more extensive tests of solutions of albumin, peptone, and related substances, in various degrees of concentration, fixed and stained by a great variety of the reagents ordinarily used for the demonstration of cell-structures. The result was to produce a marvellously close *simulacrum* of the appearances observed in the cell, reticulated and fibrillar structures being produced that often consist of rows of granules closely similar in every respect to those described by Altmann and other students of the cell. After impregnating pith with peptone-solution and then hardening, sectioning, and staining, the cells may even contain a central nucleus-like mass suspended in a network of anastomosing threads that extend in every direction outward to the walls, and give a remarkable likeness of a normal cell.

These facts show how cautious we must be in judging the appearances seen in preserved cells, and justify in some measure the hesitation with which many existing accounts of cell-structure are received. The evidence is nevertheless overwhelmingly strong, as I believe, that not only the fibrillar and alveolar formations, but also the microsomes observed in cell-structures, are in part normal structures. This evidence is derived partly from a study of the living cell, partly from the regular and characteristic arrangement of the thread-work and microsomes in certain cases. In many Protozoa, for example, a fine alveolar structure may be seen in the living protoplasm ; and Flemming as well as many later observers has clearly seen fibrillar structures in the living cells of cartilage, epithelium connective-tissue, and some other animal cells (Fig. 9). Mikosch, also, has recently described *granular* threads in living plant-cells.

Almost equally conclusive is the beautifully regular arrangement of the fibrillæ in ciliated cells (Fig. 13, Engelmann), in muscle-fibres and nerve fibres, and especially in the mitotic figure of dividing-cells (Figs. 16, 24), where they are likewise more or less clearly visible in life. A very convincing case is afforded by the pancreas-cells of *Necturus*, which Mathews has carefully studied in my laboratory. Here the thread-work consists of long, conspicuous, definite fibrillæ, some of which may under certain conditions be wound up more or less clearly in a spiral mass to form the so-called *Nebenkern*. In all these cases it is impossible to regard the thread-work as an accidental coagulation-product. On the whole, therefore, it is probable that careful treatment by reagents gives at least an approximately true picture of the normal thread-work, though we must always allow for the possible occurrence of artificial products.

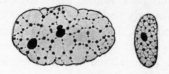

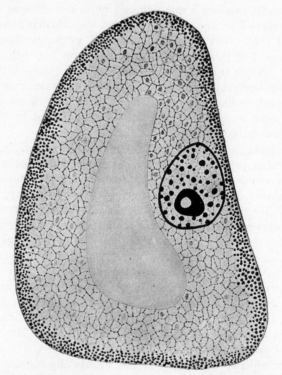

Fig. 14. — Section through a nephridial cell of the leech, *Clepsine* (drawn by Arnold Graf from one of his own preparations).

The centre of the cell is occupied by a large vacuole, filled with a watery liquid. The cytoplasm forms a very regular and distinct reticulum with scattered microsomes which become very large in the peripheral zone. The larger pale bodies, lying in the ground-substance, are excretory granules (*i.e.* metaplasm). The nucleus, at the right, is surrounded by a thick chromatic membrane, is traversed by a very distinct linin-network, contains numerous scattered chromatin-granules, and a single large nucleolus within which is a vacuole. Above are two isolated nuclei showing nucleoli and chromatin-granules suspended on the linin-threads.

One of the most beautiful forms of cyto-reticulum with which I am acquainted has been described by Bolsius and Graf in the ne-

phridial cells of leeches as shown in Fig. 14 (from a preparation by
Dr. Arnold Graf). The reticulum is here of great distinctness and
regularity, and scattered microsomes are found along its threads. It
appears with equal clearness, though in a somewhat different form,

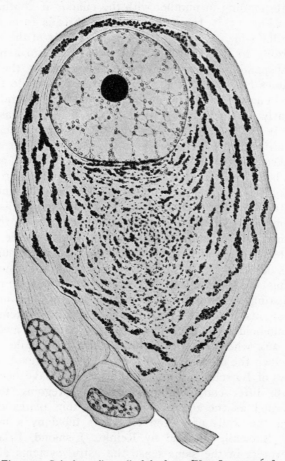

Fig. 15.—Spinal ganglion-cell of the frog. [VON LENHOSSÉK.]

The nucleus contains a single intensely chromatic nucleolus, and a paler linin-network with
rounded chromatin-granules. The cytoplasmic fibrillæ are faintly shown passing out into the
nerve-process below. (They are figured as far more distinct by Flemming.) The dark cytoplasmic masses are the deeply staining "chromophilic granules" (Nissl) of unknown function.
(The centrosome, which lies near the centre of the cell, is shown in Fig. 7, *C.*) At the left, two
connective tissue-cells.

in many eggs, where the meshes are rounded and often contain food-
matters or deutoplasm in the inter-spaces (Figs. 42, 43). In cartilage-
cells and connective tissue-cells, where the threads can be plainly seen
in life, the network is loose and open, and appears to consist of more
or less completely separate threads (Fig. 9). In the cells of colum-

D

nar epithelium, the threads in the peripheral part of the cell often assume a more or less parallel course, passing outwards from the central region, and giving the outer zone of the cell a striated appearance. This is very conspicuously shown in ciliated epithelium, the fibrillæ corresponding in number with the cilia as if continuous with their bases (Fig. 13).[1] In nerve-fibres the threads form closely set parallel fibrillæ which may be traced into the body of the nerve-cell; here, according to most authors, they break up into a network in which are suspended numerous deeply staining masses, the "chromophilic granules" of Nissl (Fig. 15). In the contractile tissues the threads are in most cases very conspicuous and have a parallel course. This is clearly shown in smooth muscle-fibres and also, as Ballowitz has shown, in the tails of spermatozoa. This arrangement is most striking in striped muscle-fibres where the fibrillæ are extremely well marked. According to Retzius, Carnoy, Van Gehuchten, and others, the meshes have here a rectangular form, the principal fibrillæ having a longitudinal course and being connected at regular intervals by transverse threads; but the structure of the muscle-fibre is probably far more complicated than this account would lead one to suppose, and opinion is still divided as to whether the contractile substance is represented by the reticulum proper or by the ground-substance.

Nowhere, however, is the thread-work shown with such beauty as in dividing-cells, where (Figs. 16, 24) the fibrillæ group themselves in two radiating systems or *asters*, which are in some manner the immediate agents of cell-division. Similar radiating systems of fibres occur in amœboid cells, such as leucocytes (Fig. 35) and pigment-cells (Fig. 36), where they probably form a contractile system by means of which the movements of the cell are performed.

The views of Bütschli and his followers, which have been touched on at p. 18, differ considerably from the foregoing, the fibrillæ being regarded as the optical sections of thin plates or lamellæ which form the walls of closed chambers filled by a more liquid substance. Bütschli, followed by Reinke, Eismond, Erlanger, and others, interprets in the same sense the astral systems of dividing-cells which are regarded as a radial configuration of the lamellæ about a central point (Fig. 8, *B*). Strong evidence against this view is, I believe, afforded by the appearance of the spindle and asters in cross-section. In the early stages of the egg of *Nereis*, for example, the astral rays are coarse anastomosing fibres that stain intensely and are therefore very favourable for observation (Fig. 43). That they are actual fibres is, I think, proved by sagittal sections of the asters in which the rays are cut at various angles. The

---

[1] The structure of the ciliated cell, as described by Engelmann, may be beautifully demonstrated in the funnel-cells of the nephridia and sperm-ducts of the earthworm.

cut ends of the branching rays appear in the clearest manner, not as plates but as distinct dots, from which in oblique sections the ray may be traced inwards towards the centrosphere. Drüner, too, figures the spindle in cross-section as consisting of rounded dots, like the end of a bundle of wires, though these are connected by cross-branches (Fig. 22, *F*). Again, the crossing of the rays proceeding from the asters (Fig. 69), and their behaviour in certain phases of cell-division, is difficult to explain under any other than the fibrillar theory.

We must admit, however, that the network varies greatly in

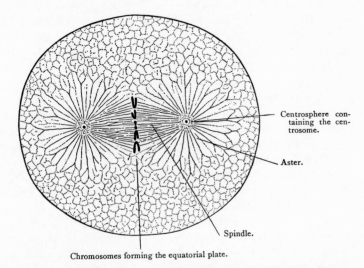

Centrosphere containing the centrosome.

Aster.

Spindle.

Chromosomes forming the equatorial plate.

Fig. 16.—Diagram of the dividing cell, showing the mitotic figure and its relation to the cytoreticulum.

different cells and even in different physiological phases of the same cell; and that it is impossible at present to bring it under any rule of universal application. It is possible, nay probable, that in one and the same cell a portion of the network may form a true alveolar structure such as is described by Bütschli, while other portions may, at the same time, be differentiated into actual fibres. If this be true the fibrillar or alveolar structure is a matter of secondary moment, and the essential features of protoplasmic organization must be sought in a more subtle underlying structure.[1]

[1] See Chapter VI.

E. THE CENTROSOME

No element of the cell has aroused a wider interest of late than the remarkable body known as the *centrosome*, which is now generally regarded as the especial organ of cell-division, and in this sense as the *dynamic centre* of the cell (Van Beneden, Boveri).[1] In its simplest form the centrosome is a body of extreme minuteness, often indeed scarce larger than a microsome, which nevertheless exerts an extraordinary influence on the cytoplasmic network during cell-division and the fertilization of the egg. As a rule it lies outside, though near, the nucleus, in the cyto-reticulum, surrounded by a granular, reticular, or radiating area of the latter known as the *attraction-sphere* or *centrosphere* (Figs. 5, 6, 7).[2] It may, however, lie within the nuclear membrane in the linin-network (Fig. 107). In some cases the centrosome is a single body which divides into two as the cell prepares for division. More commonly, it becomes double during the later phases of cell-division, in anticipation of the succeeding division, the two centrosomes thus formed lying passively within the attraction-sphere during the ordinary life of the cell. They only become active as the cell prepares for the ensuing division, when they diverge from one another, and each becomes the centre of one of the astral systems referred to at p. 49. Each of the daughter-cells receives one of the centrosomes, which meanwhile again divide into two. The centrosome seems, therefore, to be in some cases a permanent cell-organ, like the nucleus, being handed on by division from one cell to another. There are, however, some cells, *e.g.* muscle-cells, most gland-cells, and many unicellular organisms, in which no centrosome has thus far been discovered in the resting-cell; but it is uncertain whether the centrosome is really absent in such cases, for it may be hidden in the nucleus, or too small to be distinguished from other bodies in the cytoplasm. There is, however, good reason to believe that it degenerates and disappears in the mature eggs of many animals, and this may likewise occur in other cells. At present, therefore, we are not able to say whether the centrosome is of equal constancy with the nucleus.[3]

---

[1] The centrosome was discovered by Van Beneden in the cells of Dycyemids ('76), and first carefully described by him in the egg of *Ascaris* seven years later. The name is due to Boveri ('88, 2, p. 68).

[2] Cf. p. 229.

[3] Its nature is more fully discussed at p. 224.

F. OTHER ORGANS

The cell-substance is often differentiated into other more or less definite structures, sometimes of a transitory character, sometimes showing a constancy and morphological persistency comparable with that of the nucleus and centrosome. From a general point of view the most interesting of these are the bodies known as *plastids* or *proto-plasts* (Fig. 5), which, like the nucleus and centrosome, are capable of growth and division, and may thus be handed on from cell to cell. The most important of these are the *chromatophores* or *chromoplasts*, which are especially characteristic of plants, though they occur in some animals as well. These are definite bodies, varying greatly in form and size, which never arise spontaneously, so far as known, but always by the division of pre-existing bodies of the same kind. They possess in some cases a high degree of morphological independence, and may even live for a time after removal from the remaining cell-substance, as in the case of the "yellow cells" of Radiolaria. This has led to the view, advocated by Brandt and others, that the chlorophyll-bodies found in the cells of many Protozoa and a few Metazoa (*Hydra*, *Spongilla*, some Planarians) are in reality distinct Algæ living symbiotically in the cell. This view is probably correct in some cases, *e.g.* in the Radiolaria; but it may well be doubted whether it is of general application. In the plants the chlorophyll-bodies and other chromoplasts are almost certainly to be regarded as differentiations of the cytoplasmic substance. The same is true of the *amyloplasts*, which act as centres for the formation of starch.

The contractile or pulsating vacuoles that occur in most Protozoa and in the swarm-spores of many Algæ are also known in some cases to multiply by division; and the same is true, according to the researches of De Vries, Went, and others, of the non-pulsating vacuoles of plant-cells. These vacuoles have been shown to have, in many cases, distinct walls, and they are regarded by De Vries as a special form of plastid ("tonoplasts") analogous to the chromatophores and other plastids. It is, however, probable that this view is only applicable to certain forms of vacuoles.

The existence of cell-organs which have the power of independent assimilation, growth, and division, is a fact of great theoretical interest in its bearing on the general problem of cell-organization; for it is one of the main reasons that have led De Vries, Wiesner, and many others to regard the entire cell as made up of elementary self-propagating units.

G. THE CELL-MEMBRANE

From a general point of view the cell-membrane or intercellular substance is of relatively minor importance, since it is not of constant occurrence, belongs to the lifeless products of the cell, and hence plays no direct part in the active cell-life. In plant-tissues the membrane is almost invariably present and of firm consistency. Animal tissues are in general characterized by the slight development or absence of cell-walls. Many forms of cells, both among unicellular and multicellular forms, are quite naked, for example *Amœba* and the leucocytes; but in most, if not in all, such cases, the outer limit of the cell-body is formed by a more resistant layer of protoplasm — the "pellicle" of Bütschli — that may be so marked as to simulate a true membrane, for example, in the red blood-corpuscles (Ranvier, Waldeyer) and in various naked animal eggs. Such a "pellicle" differs from a true cell-membrane only in degree; and it is now generally agreed that the membranes of plant-cells, and of many animal-cells, arise by a direct physical and chemical transformation of the peripheral layer of protoplasm. On the other hand, according to Leydig, Waldeyer, and some others, the membrane of certain animal-cells may be formed not by a direct transformation of the protoplasmic substance, but as a secretion poured out by the protoplasm at its surface. Such membranes, characterized as "cuticular," occur mainly or exclusively on the free surfaces of cells (Waldeyer). It remains to be seen, however, how far this distinction can be maintained, and the greatest diversity of opinion still exists regarding the origin of the different forms of cell-membranes in animal-cells.

The chemical composition of the membrane or intercellular substance varies extremely. In plants membrane consists of a basis of *cellulose*, a carbohydrate having the formula $C_6H_{10}O_5$; but this substance is very frequently impregnated with other substances, such as silica, lignin, and a great variety of others. In animals the intercellular substances show a still greater diversity. Many of them are nitrogenous bodies, such as keratin, chitin, elastin, gelatin, and the like; but inorganic deposits, such as silica and carbonate of lime, are common.

H. POLARITY OF THE CELL

In a large number of cases the cell exhibits a definite polarity, its parts being symmetrically grouped with reference to an ideal *organic axis* passing from pole to pole. No definite criterion for the identification of the cell-axis has, however, yet been determined; for the

general conception of cell-polarity has been developed in two different directions, one of which starts from purely morphological considerations, the other from physiological, and a parallelism between
them has not thus far been very clearly made out.

On the one hand, Van Beneden ('83) conceived cell-polarity as a
primary morphological attribute of the cell, the organic axis being
identified as a line drawn through the centre of the nucleus and the
centrosome (Fig. 17, *A*). With this view Rabl's theory ('85) of
nuclear polarity harmonizes, for the chromosome-loops converge towards the centrosome, and the nuclear axis coincides with the cell-axis.
Moreover, it identifies the polarity of the egg, which is so important
a factor in development, with that of the tissue-cells; for the egg-

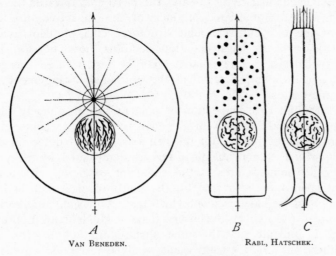

A
Van Beneden.

B   *C*
Rabl, Hatschek.

Fig. 17. — Diagrams of cell-polarity.
A. Morphological polarity of Van Beneden. Axis passing through nucleus and centrosome.
Chromatin-threads converging towards the centrosome. *B. C.* Physiological polarity of Rabl
and Hatschek, *B* in a gland-cell, *C* in a ciliated cell.

centrosome almost invariably appears at or near one pole of the
ovum.

Heidenhain ('94, '95) has recently developed this conception of
polarity in a very elaborate manner, maintaining that all the structures of the cell have a definite relation to the primary axis, and that
this relation is determined by conditions of tension in the astral rays
focussed at the centrosome. On this basis he endeavours to explain
the position and movements of the nucleus, the succession of division-
planes, and many related phenomena. In the present state of the
subject, Heidenhain's theories must be regarded as somewhat trans-
cendental, though they give many suggestions for further investigation.

Hatschek ('88) and Rabl ('89, '92), on the other hand, have advanced a quite different hypothesis based on physiological considerations. By "cell-polarity" these authors mean, not a predetermined morphological arrangement of parts in the cell, but a polar differentiation of the cell-substance arising secondarily through adaptation of the cell to its environment in the tissues, and having no necessary relation to the polarity of Van Beneden. (Fig. 17, *B*, *C*.) This is typically shown in epithelium, which, as Kölliker and Häckel long since pointed out, is to be regarded, both ontogenetically and phylogenetically, as the most primitive form of tissue. The free and basal ends of the cells here differ widely in relation to the food-supply, and show a corresponding structural differentiation. In such cells the nucleus usually lies nearer the basal end, towards the source of food, while differentiated products of the cell-activity are formed either at the free end (cuticular structures, cilia, pigment, zymogen-granules), or at the basal end (muscle-fibres, nerve-fibres). In the non-epithelial tissues the polarity may be lost, though traces of it are often shown as a survival of the epithelial arrangement of the embryonic stages.

But, although this conception of polarity has an entirely different point of departure from Van Beneden's, it leads, in some cases at least, to the same result; for the cell-axis, as thus determined, may coincide with the morphological axis as determined by the position of the centrosome. This is the case, for example, with both the spermatozoön and the ovum; for the morphological axis in both is also the physiological axis about which the cytoplasmic differentiations are grouped. Moreover, the observations of Heidenhain, Lebrun, and Kostanecki indicate that the same is true in epithelium; for, according to these authors, the centrosome is always situated on that side of the nucleus turned towards the free end of the cell. How far this law holds good remains to be seen, and, until the facts have been further investigated, it is impossible to frame a consistent hypothesis of cell-polarity. The facts observed in epithelial cells, are, however, of great significance; for the position of the centrosome, and hence the direction of the axis, is here obviously related to the cell-environment, and it is difficult to avoid the conclusion that the latter must be the determining condition to which the intracellular relations conform. When applied to the germ-cells, this conclusion becomes of high interest; for the polarity of the egg is one of the primary conditions of development, and we have here, as I believe, a clue to its origin.[1]

[1] Cf. pp. 288, 320.

I. The Cell in Relation to the Multicellular Body

In analyzing the structure and functions of the individual cell we are accustomed, as a matter of convenience, to regard it as an independent elementary organism or organic unit. Actually, however, it is such an organism only in the case of the unicellular plants and animals and the germ-cells of the multicellular forms. When we consider the tissue-cells of the latter we must take a somewhat different view. As far as structure and origin are concerned the tissue-cell is unquestionably of the same morphological value as the one-celled plant or animal; and *in this sense* the multicellular body is equivalent to a colony or aggregate of one-celled forms. Physiologically, however, the tissue-cell can only in a limited sense be regarded as an independent unit; for its autonomy is merged in a greater or less degree into the general life of the organism. From this point of view the tissue-cell must in fact be treated as merely a localized area of activity, provided it is true with the complete apparatus of cell-life, and even capable of independent action within certain limits, yet nevertheless a part and not a whole.

There is at present no biological question of greater moment than the means by which the individual cell-activities are co-ordinated, and the organic unity of the body maintained; for upon this question hangs not only the problem of the transmission of acquired characters, and the nature of development, but our conception of life itself. Schwann, the father of the cell-theory, very clearly perceived this; and after an admirably lucid discussion of the facts known to him (1839), drew the conclusion that the life of the organism is essentially a composite; that each cell has its independent life; and that "the whole organism subsists only by means of the reciprocal action of the single elementary parts."[1] This conclusion, afterwards elaborated by Virchow and Häckel to the theory of the "cell-state," took a very strong hold on the minds of biological investigators, and is even now widely accepted. It is, however, becoming more and more clearly apparent that this conception expresses only a part of the truth, and that Schwann went too far in denying the influence of the totality of the organism upon the local activities of the cells. It would of course be absurd to maintain that the whole can consist of more than the sum of its parts. Yet, as far as growth and development are concerned, it has now been clearly demonstrated that only in a limited sense can the cells be regarded as co-operating units. They are rather local centres of a formative power pervading the growing

[1] *Untersuchungen*, p. 191.

mass as a whole,[1] and the physiological autonomy of the individual cell falls into the background. It is true that the cells may acquire a high degree of physiological independence in the later stages of embryological development. The facts to be discussed in the eighth and ninth chapters will, however, show strong reason for the conclusion that this is a secondary result of development through which the cells become, as it were, emancipated in a greater or less degree, from the general control. Broadly viewed, therefore, the life of the multicellular organism is to be conceived as a whole; and the apparently composite character, which it may exhibit, is owing to a secondary distribution of its energies among local centres of action.[2]

In this light the structural relations of tissue-cells becomes a question of great interest; for we have here to seek the means by which the individual cell comes into relation with the totality of the organism, and by which the general equilibrium of the body is maintained. It must be confessed that the results of microscopical research have not thus far given a very certain answer to this question. Though the tissue-cells are often apparently separated from one another by a non-living intercellular substance, which may appear in the form of solid walls, it is by no means certain that their organic continuity is thus actually severed. Many cases are known in which division of the nucleus is not followed by division of the cell-body, so that multinuclear cells or *syncytia* are thus formed, consisting of a continuous mass of protoplasm through which the nuclei are scattered. Heitzmann long since contended ('73), though on insufficient evidence, that division is incomplete in nearly all forms of tissue, and that even when cell-walls are formed they are traversed by strands of protoplasm by means of which the cell-bodies remain in organic continuity. The whole body was thus conceived by him as a syncytium, the cells being no more than nodal points in a general reticulum, and the body forming a continuous protoplasmic mass.

This interesting view, long received with scepticism, has been in a measure sustained by later researches, though it still remains *sub judice*. Tangl, Gardiner, and many later observers have shown that the cell-walls of many plant-tissues are traversed by delicate intercellular bridges, and similar bridges have been conclusively demonstrated by Bizzozero, Retzius, Flemming, Pfitzner, and many others in the case of animal epithelial cells (Figs. 1, 9). The same has been asserted to be the case with the smooth muscle-fibres, with cartilage-cells and connective-tissue cells, and in a few cases with nerve-cells. Paladino and Retzius ('89) have endeavoured to show, further, that the follicle-cells of the ovary are connected by protoplasmic

---

[1] Cf. Chapters VIII., IX.

[2] For a fuller discussion see pp. 293 and 311.

bridges not only with one another, *but also with the ovum*, a conclusion which, if established by further research, will be of the greatest interest.

As far as adult animal-tissues are concerned, it still remains undetermined how far the cells are in direct protoplasmic continuity. It is obvious that no such continuity exists in the case of the corpuscles of blood and lymph and the wandering leucocytes and pigment-cells. In case of the nervous system, which from an *a priori* point of view would seem to be above all others the structure in which protoplasmic continuity is to be expected, the latest researches are rendering it more and more probable that no such continuity exists, and that nerve-impulses are transmitted from cell to cell by contact-action. When, however, we turn to the embryonic stages we find strong reason for the belief that a material continuity between cells must exist. This is certainly the case in the early stages of many arthropods, where the whole embryo is at first an unmistakable syncytium; and Adam Sedgwick has endeavoured to show that in *Peripatus* and even in the vertebrates the entire embryonic body, up to a late stage, is a continuous syncytium. I have pointed out ('93) that even in a total cleavage, such as that of *Amphioxus* or the echinoderms, the results of experiment on the early stages of cleavage are difficult to explain, save under the assumption that there must be a structural continuity from cell to cell that is broken by mechanical displacement of the blastomeres. This conclusion is supported by the recent work of Hammar ('96), whose observations on sea-urchin eggs I can in the main confirm.

As the subject now lies, however, the facts do not, I believe, justify any general statement regarding the occurrence, origin, or physiological meaning of the protoplasmic continuity of cells; and a most important field here lies open for future investigation.

LITERATURE. I[1]

Altmann, R. — Die Elementarorganismen und ihre Beziehungen zu den Zellen, 2d ed. *Leipzig*, 1894.

Van Beneden, E. — (See Lists II., IV.)

Boveri, Th. — (See Lists IV., V.)

Bütschli, O. — Untersuchungen über mikroskopische Schäume und das Protoplasma. *Leipzig* (Engelmann), 1892.

Engelmann, T. W. — Zur Anatomie und Physiologie der Flimmerzellen: *Arch. ges. Phys.*, XXIII. 1880.

von Erlanger, R. — Neuere Ansichten über die Struktur des Protoplasmas: *Zool. Centralbl.*, III. 8, 9. 1896.

[1] See also Introductory list, p. 12.

Flemming, W. — Zellsubstanz, Kern und Zellteilung. *Leipzig*, 1882.

Id. — Zelle : *Merkel und Bonnet's Ergebnisse*, I.–IV. 1891–94. (Admirable reviews and literature-lists.)

Heidenhain, M. — Über Kern und Protoplasma : *Festschr. z. 50-jähr. Doctorjub. von v. Kölliker. Leipzig*, 1893.

Klein, E. — Observations on the Structure of Cells and Nuclei : *Quart. Journ. Mic. Sci.*, XVIII. 1878.

Kölliker, A. — Handbuch der Gewebelehre, 6th ed. *Leipzig*, 1889.

Leydig, Fr. — Zelle und Gewebe. *Bonn*, 1885.

Schäfer, E. A. — General Anatomy or Histology ; in *Quain's Anatomy*, I. 2, 10th ed. *London*, 1891.

Schiefferdecker & Kossel. — Die Gewebe des Menschlichen Körpers. *Braunschweig*, 1891.

Schwarz, Fr. — Die morphologische und chemische Zusammensetzung des Protoplasmas. *Breslau*, 1887.

Strasburger, E. — Zellbildung und Zellteilung, 3d ed. 1880.

Stricker, S. — Handbuch der Lehre von den Geweben. *Leipzig*, 1871.

Thoma, R. — Text-book of General Pathology and Pathological Anatomy : trans. by Alex. Bruce. *London*, 1896.

De Vries, H. — Intracellulare Pangenesis. *Jena*, 1889.

Waldeyer, W. — Die neueren Ansichten über den Bau und das Wesen der Zelle : *Deutsch. Med. Wochenschr.*, Oct., Nov., 1895.

Wiesner, J. — Die Elementarstruktur u. das Wachstum der lebenden Substanz : *Wien, Hölder*. 1892.

Zimmerman, A. — Beiträge zur Morphologie und Physiologie der Pflanzenzelle. *Tübingen*, 1893.

CHAPTER II

CELL–DIVISION

" Wo eine Zelle entsteht, da muss eine Zelle vorausgegangen sein, ebenso wie das Thier nur aus dem Thiere, die Pflanze nur aus der Pflanze entstehen kann. Auf diese Weise ist, wenngleich es einzelne Punkte im Körper gibt, wo der strenge Nachweis noch nicht geliefert ist, doch das Princip gesichert, dass in der ganzen Reihe alles Lebendigen, dies mögen nun ganze Pflanzen oder thierische Organismen oder integrirende Theile derselben sein, ein ewiges Gesetz der *continuirlichen Entwicklung* besteht." VIRCHOW.[1]

THE law of genetic cellular continuity, first clearly stated by Virchow in the above words, has now become one of the primary data of biology. The cell has no other mode of origin than by division of a pre-existing cell. In the multicellular organism all the tissue-cells have arisen by continued division from the original germ-cell, and this in its turn arose by the division of a cell pre-existing in the parent-body. By *cell-division*, accordingly, the hereditary substance is split off from the parent-body ; and by cell-division, again, this substance is handed on by the fertilized egg-cell or oösperm to every part of the body arising from it.[2] Cell-division is, therefore, one of the central facts of development and inheritance.

The first two decades after Schleiden and Schwann (1840–60) were occupied with researches, on the part both of botanists and of zoölogists, which finally demonstrated the universality of this process and showed the authors of the cell-theory to have been in error in asserting the independent origin of cells out of a formative blastema.[3] The mechanism of cell-division was not precisely investigated until long afterwards, but the researches of Remak ('41), Kolliker ('44), and others showed that an essential part of the process is a division of both the nucleus and the cell-body. In 1855 (*l.c.*, pp. 174, 175), and again in 1858, Remak gave as the general result of his researches the following synopsis or scheme of cell-division. Cell-division, he asserted, proceeds from the centre toward the periphery.[4] It begins

[1] *Cellularpathologie*, p. 25, 1858.
[2] Cf. Introduction, p. 9.
[3] For a full historical account of this period, see Remak, *Untersuchungen über die Entwicklung der Wirbelthiere*, 1855, pp. 164–180.
[4] *Untersuchungen*, p. 175.

with the division of the nucleolus, is continued by simple constriction and division of the nucleus, and is completed by division of the cell-body and membrane (Fig. 18). For many years this account was accepted, and no essential advance beyond Remak's scheme was made for nearly twenty years. A number of isolated observations were, however, from time to time made, even at a very early period, which seemed to show that cell-division was by no means so simple an operation as Remak believed. In some cases the nucleus seemed to disappear entirely before cell-division (the germinal vesicle of the ovum, according to Reichert, Von Baer, Robin, etc.); in others to become lobed or star-shaped, as described by Virchow and by Remak himself (Fig. 18, f). It was not until 1873 that the way was opened for a better understanding of the matter. In this year the

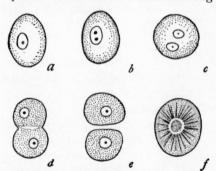

Fig. 18. — Direct division of blood-cells in the embryo chick, illustrating Remak's scheme. [REMAK.]

a–e. Successive stages of division; *f.* Cell dividing by mitosis.

discoveries of Anton Schneider, quickly followed by others in the same direction by Bütschli, Fol, Strasburger, Van Beneden, Flemming, and Hertwig, showed cell-division to be a far more elaborate process than had been supposed, and to involve a complicated transformation of the nucleus to which Schleicher ('78) afterwards gave the name of *Karyokinesis.* It soon appeared, however, that this mode of division was not of universal occurrence ; and that cell-division is of two widely different types, which Van Beneden ('76) distinguished as *fragmentation,* corresponding nearly to the simple process described by Remak, and *division,* involving the more complicated process of karyokinesis. Three years later Flemming ('79) proposed to substitute for these the terms *direct* and *indirect* division, which are still used. Still later ('82) the same author suggested the terms *mitosis* (indirect or karyokinetic division) and *amitosis* (direct or akinetic division), which have rapidly made their way into general use, though the earlier terms are often employed.

Modern research has demonstrated the fact that amitosis or direct division, regarded by Remak and his immediate followers as of universal occurrence, is in reality a rare and exceptional process ; and there is reason to believe, furthermore, that it is especially characteristic of highly specialized cells incapable of long-continued multiplication or such as are in the early stages of degeneration, for instance, in glandular epithelia, in the cells of transitory em-

bryonic envelopes, and in tumours and other pathological formations, where it is of frequent occurrence. Whether this view be
well founded or not, it is certain that in all the higher and in many
of the lower forms of life, indirect division or mitosis is the typical
mode of cell-division. It is by mitotic division that the germ-cells
arise and are prepared for their union during the process of maturation, and by mitotic division the oösperm segments and gives rise
to the tissue-cells. It occurs not only in the highest forms of plants
and animals, but also in such simple forms as the Rhizopods, Flagellates, and Diatoms. We may, therefore, justly regard it as the most
general expression of the "eternal law of continuous development"
on which Virchow insisted.

A. Outline of Indirect Division or Mitosis (Karyokinesis)

The process of mitosis involves three parallel series of changes
which affect the nucleus, the centrosome, and the cytoplasm of the
cell-body respectively. For descriptive purposes it may conveniently
be divided into a series of successive stages or phases, which, however, graduate into one another and are separated by no well-defined
limits. These are: (1) The *Prophases*, or preparatory changes;
(2) the *Metaphase*, which involves the most essential step in the
division of the nucleus; (3) the *Anaphases*, in which the nuclear
material is distributed; (4) the *Telophases*, in which the entire cell
divides and the daughter-cells are formed.

1. *Prophases.* — (*a*) *The Nucleus.* As the cell prepares for division
the most conspicuous fact is a transformation of the nuclear substance, involving both physical and chemical changes. The chromatin resolves itself little by little into a more or less convoluted thread,
known as the *skein* (Knäuel) or *spireme*, and its substance stains far
more intensely than that of the reticulum (Fig. 19). In some
cases there is but a single continuous thread; in others, the thread
is from its first appearance divided into a number of separate pieces
or segments forming a *segmented spireme*. In either case it ultimately breaks transversely into a definite number of distinct bodies,
known as *chromosomes* (Waldeyer, '88), which in most cases have
the form of rods, straight or curved, though they are sometimes
spherical or ovoidal, and in certain cases may be joined together
in the form of rings. The staining power of the chromatin is now
at a maximum. As a rule the nuclear membrane meanwhile fades
away and finally disappears. The chromosomes now lie naked in the
cell, and the ground-substance of the nucleus becomes continuous
with the surrounding cytoplasm (Fig. 19, *D, E, F*).

Every species of plant or animal has a fixed and characteristic num-
ber of chromosomes, which regularly recurs in the division of all of its
cells; and in all forms arising by sexual reproduction the number is

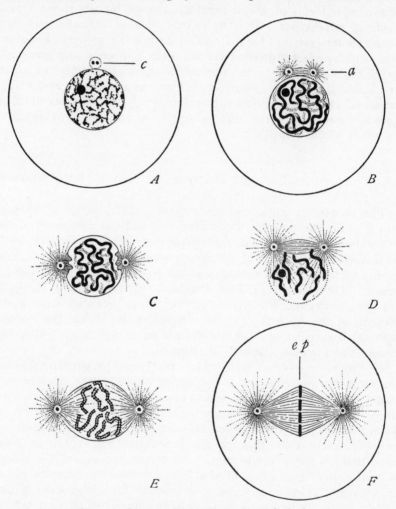

Fig. 19. — Diagrams showing the prophases of mitosis.

    A. Resting-cell with reticular nucleus and true nucleolus; at *c* the attraction-sphere contain-
ing two centrosomes. *B.* Early prophase; the chromatin forming a continuous *spireme*, nucleolus
still present; above, the amphiaster (*a*). *C. D.* Two different types of later prophases; *C.* Disappearance of the primary spindle, divergence of the centrosomes to opposite poles of the nucleus
(examples, many plant-cells, cleavage-stages of many eggs). *D.* Persistence of the primary
spindle (to form in some cases the "central spindle"), fading of the nuclear membrane, ingrowth
of the astral rays, segmentation of the spireme-thread to form the chromosomes (examples, epidermal cells of salamander, formation of the polar bodies). *E.* Later prophase of type *C*; fading
of the nuclear membrane at the poles, formation of a new spindle inside the nucleus; precocious
splitting of the chromosomes (the latter not characteristic of this type alone). *F.* The mitotic
figure established; *e.p.* The equatorial plate of chromosomes. (Cf. Figs. 16, 21, 24.)

even. Thus, in some of the sharks the number is 36; in certain gasteropods it is 32; in the mouse, the salamander, the trout, the lily, 24; in the worm *Sagitta*, 18; in the ox, guinea-pig, and in man the number is said to be 16, and the same number is characteristic of the onion.   In the grasshopper it is 12; in the hepatic *Pallavicinia* and some of the nematodes, 8; and in *Ascaris*, another thread-worm, 4 or 2.   In the crustacean *Artemia* it is 168.[1]   Under certain conditions, it is true, the number of chromosomes may be less than the normal in a given species; but these variations are only apparent exceptions (p. 61).   The even number of chromosomes is a most interesting fact, which, as will appear hereafter (p. 135), is due to the derivation of one-half the number from each of the parents.

The nucleoli differ in their behaviour in different cases. Net-knots, consisting of true chromatin, probably enter into the formation of the spireme-thread.   True nucleoli seem to dissolve and disappear, or in some cases are cast out bodily into the cytoplasm, where they degenerate and have no further function.   Whether they ever contribute to the formation of chromosomes is uncertain.

(*b*) *The Amphiaster*.   Meanwhile, more or less nearly parallel with these changes in the chromatin, a complicated structure known as the *amphiaster* (Fol, '77) makes its appearance in the position formerly occupied by the nucleus (Fig. 19, *B–F*).   This structure consists of a fibrous spindle-shaped body, the *spindle*, at either pole of which is a star or *aster* formed of rays or astral fibres radiating into the surrounding cytoplasm, the whole strongly suggesting the arrangement of iron filings in the field of a horseshoe magnet.   The centre of each aster is occupied by a minute body, known as the *centrosome* (Boveri, '88), which may be surrounded by a spherical mass known as the *centrosphere* (Strasburger, '93).   As the amphiaster forms, the chromosomes group themselves in a plane passing through the equator of the spindle, and thus form what is known as the *equatorial plate*.

The amphiaster arises under the influence of the centrosome of the résting-cell, which divides into two similar halves, an aster being developed around each while a spindle stretches between them (Fig. 19, *A–D*).   In most cases this process begins outside the nucleus, but the subsequent phenomena vary considerably in different forms.   In some forms (tissue-cells of the salamander) the amphiaster at first lies tangentially outside the nucleus, and as the nuclear membrane fades away, some of the astral rays grow into the nucleus from the side, become attached to the chromosomes, and finally pull them into position around the equator of the spindle, which is here called the *central spindle* (Figs. 19, *D*, *F*; 21).   In other cases the original spindle

---

[1] For a more complete list see p. 154.

E

disappears, and the two asters pass to opposite poles of the nucleus (most plant mitoses and in many animal cells). A spindle is now formed from rays that grow into the nucleus from each aster, the nuclear membrane fading away at the poles, though in some cases it may be pushed in by the spindle-fibres for some distance before its

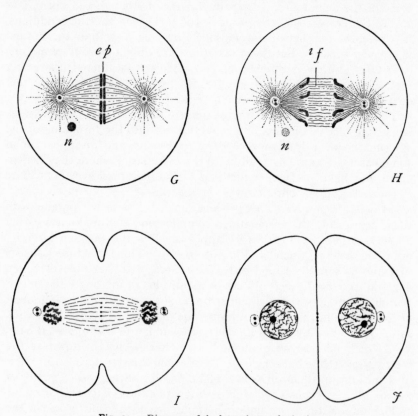

Fig. 20. — Diagrams of the later phases of mitosis.

G. Metaphase; splitting of the chromosomes (*e. p.*); *n*. The cast-off nucleolus. H. Anaphase; the daughter-chromosomes diverging, between them the interzonal fibres (*i. f.*), or central spindle; centrosomes already doubled in anticipation of the ensuing division. I. Late anaphase or telophase, showing division of the cell-body, mid-body at the equator of the spindle and beginning reconstruction of the daughter-nuclei. J. Division completed.

disappearance (Fig. 19, *C, E*). In this case there is apparently no central spindle. In a few exceptional cases, finally, the amphiaster may arise inside the nucleus (p. 225).

The entire structure, resulting from the foregoing changes, is known as the *karyokinetic* or *mitotic figure*. It may be described as consisting of two distinct parts; namely, 1, the *chromatic figure*, formed by the deeply staining chromosomes; and, 2, the *achromatic figure*, consisting of the spindle and asters which, in general, stain but slightly. The fibrous substance of the achromatic figure is generally known as *archoplasm* (Boveri, '88), but this term is not applied to the centrosome within the aster.

2. *Metaphase.* — The *prophases* of mitosis are, on the whole, preparatory in character. The *metaphase*, which follows, forms the initial phase of actual division. Each chromosome splits lengthwise into two exactly similar halves, which afterwards diverge to opposite poles of the spindle, and here each group of daughter-chromosomes finally gives rise to a daughter-nucleus (Fig. 20). In some cases the splitting of the chromosomes cannot be seen until they have grouped themselves in the equatorial plane of the spindle; and it is only in this case that the term "metaphase" can be applied to the mitotic figure as a whole. In a large number of cases, however, the splitting may take place at an earlier period in the spireme stage, or even, in a few cases, in the reticulum of the mother-nucleus (Figs. 38, 39). Such variations do not, however, affect the essential fact that *the chromatic network is converted into a thread*[1] *which, whether continuous or discontinuous, splits throughout its entire length into two exactly equivalent halves.* The splitting of the chromosomes, discovered by Flemming in 1880, is the most significant and fundamental operation of cell-division; for by it, as Roux first pointed out ('83), the entire substance of the chromatic network is precisely halved, and *the daughter-nuclei receive precisely equivalent portions of chromatin from the mother-nucleus.* It is very important to observe that the *nuclear* division always shows this exact equality, whether division of the cell-body be equal or unequal. The minute polar body, for example (p. 131), receives exactly the same amount of chromatin as the egg, though the latter is of gigantic size as compared with the former. On the other hand, the size of the asters varies with that of the daughter-cells (cf. Figs. 43, 71) though not in strict ratio. The fact is one of great significance for the general theory of mitosis, as will appear beyond.

3. *Anaphases.* — After splitting of the chromosomes, the daughter-chromosomes, arranged in two corresponding groups,[2] diverge to opposite poles of the spindle, where they become closely crowded in a mass near the centre of the aster. As they diverge, the two groups of daughter-chromosomes are connected by a bundle of achromatic fibres, stretching across the interval between them, and known as the *interzonal fibres* or *connecting fibres.*[3] In some cases, these differ in a

---

[1] It was this fact that led Flemming to employ the word "mitosis" ($\mu\iota\tau\sigma$, a thread).

[2] This stage is termed by Flemming the *dyaster*, a term which should, however, be abandoned in order to avoid confusion with the earlier word *amphiaster*. The latter convenient and appropriate term clearly has priority.

[3] *Verbindungsfasern* of German authors; *filaments réunissants* of Van Beneden.

marked degree from the other spindle-fibres; and they are believed
by many observers to have an entirely different origin and function.
A view now widely held is that of Hermann, who regards these fibres
as belonging to a *central spindle*, surrounded by a peripheral layer
of *mantle-fibres* to which the chromosomes are attached, and only
exposed to view as the chromosomes separate.[1] They are sometimes
thickened in the equatorial region to form a body known as the *cell-
plate* or *mid-body*, which, in the case of plant-cells, takes part in the
formation of the membrane by which the daughter-cells are separated.

4. *Telophases.* — In the final phases of mitosis, the entire cell
divides in two in a plane passing through the equator of the spindle,
each of the daughter-cells receiving a group of chromosomes, half
of the spindle, and one of the asters with its centrosome.   Meanwhile,
a daughter-nucleus is reconstructed in each cell from the group of
chromosomes it contains.   The nature of this process differs greatly
in different kinds of cells.   Sometimes, as in the epithelial cells of
amphibia, especially studied by Flemming and Rabl, and in many
plant-cells, the daughter-chromosomes become thickened, contorted,
and closely crowded to form a *daughter-spireme*, closely similar to that
of the mother-nucleus (Fig. 23); this becomes surrounded by a membrane, the threads give forth branches, and thus produce a reticular
nucleus.   A somewhat similar set of changes takes place in the segmenting eggs of *Ascaris* (Van Beneden, Boveri).   In other cases, as
in many segmenting ova, each chromosome gives rise to a hollow
vesicle, after which the vesicles fuse together to produce a single
nucleus (Fig. 37).   When first formed, the daughter-nuclei are of
equal size.   If, however, division of the cell-body has been unequal,
the nuclei become, in the end, correspondingly unequal — a fact
which, as Conklin and others have pointed out, proves that the size
of the nucleus is controlled by that of the cytoplasmic mass in which
it lies.

The fate of the achromatic structures varies considerably, and has
been accurately determined in only a few cases.   As a rule, the
spindle-fibres disappear more or less completely, but a portion of their
substance sometimes persists in a modified form.   In dividing plant-
cells, the interzonal fibres become thickened at the equator of the
spindle and form a transverse plate of granules, known as the *cell-
plate* (Fig. 25), which gives rise to the membrane by which the two
daughter-cells are separated.   The remainder of the spindle disappears.   A similar cell-plate occurs in some animal cells; but it is
often greatly reduced, and may form only a minute body known as
the *mid-body* (Zwischenkörper), which lies between the two cells after

[1] Cf. p. 74.

their division (Fig. 23). In other cases, as in the cells of the testis, the remains of the spindle in each cell sometimes gives rise to a more or less definite body known as the *paranucleus* or *Nebenkern* (Fig. 62).

The aster may in some cases entirely disappear, together with the centrosome (as occurs in the mature egg). In a large number of cases, however, the centrosome persists, lying either outside or more rarely inside the nucleus and dividing into two at a very early period. This division is clearly a precocious preparation for the ensuing division of the daughter-cell, and it is a remarkable fact that it occurs as a rule during the early anaphase, before the mother-cell itself has divided. There are, however, some undoubted cases (cf. Figs. 6, 7) in which the centrosome remains undivided during the resting stage and only divides as the process of mitosis begins.

Like the centrosome, the aster or its central portion may persist in a more or less modified form throughout the resting state of the cell, forming a structure generally known as the *attraction-sphere*. This body often shows a true astral structure with radiating fibres (Figs. 7, 35); but it is sometimes reduced to a regular spherical mass which may represent only the centrosphere of the original aster (Fig. 6).

B. Origin of the Mitotic Figure

The chromatic figure (chromosomes) is derived directly from the chromatic network of the resting-nucleus as described above. The derivation of the achromatic figure (spindle and asters) is a far more difficult question, which is still to some extent involved in doubt. By the earlier observers (1873–75) the achromatic figure was supposed to disappear entirely at the close of cell-division, and most of them (Bütschli, Strasburger, Van Beneden, '75) believed it to be reformed at each succeeding division out of the nuclear substance. Later researches (1875–85) gave contradictory and apparently irreconcilable results. Fol ('79) derived the spindle from the nuclear material, the asters from the cytoplasm. Strasburger ('80) asserted that the entire achromatic figure arose from the cytoplasm. Flemming ('82) was in doubt, and regarded the question of nuclear or cytoplasmic origin as one of minor importance, yet on the whole inclined to the opinion that the achromatic figure arose inside the nucleus.[1] In 1887 a new face was put on the whole question through the independent discovery by Van Beneden and Boveri that the centrosome does not disappear at the close of mitosis, but remains as a distinct cell-organ lying beside the nucleus in the cytoplasm. These investigators agreed that the amphiaster is formed under the influence of the centrosome,

[1] *Zellsubstanz*, p. 226.

which leads the way in cell-division by dividing into two similar halves to form the centres of division. "Thus we are justified," said Van Beneden, "in regarding the attraction-sphere with its central

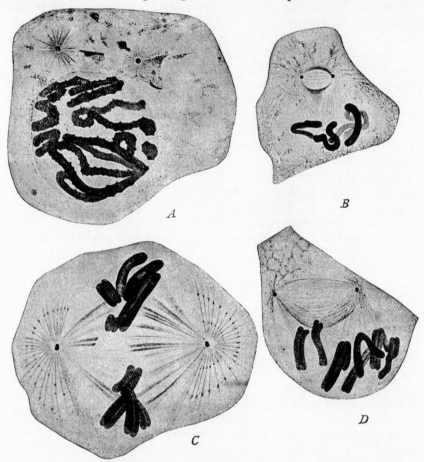

Fig. 21.—The prophases in cells (spermatogonia and spermatocytes) of the salamander. [DRÜNER.]

A. Spermatogonium in the spireme-stage; the chromatin-thread lies in the linin-network, still surrounded by the membrane; above, the two centrosomes, the central spindle not yet formed. B. Later stage (spermatocyte); the nuclear membrane has disappeared, leaving the naked chromosomes; above, the amphiaster, with centrosomes and central spindle; astral rays extending towards the chromosomes. D. Following stage; splitting of the chromosomes, growth of the aster; mantle-fibres and central spindle clearly distinguished. C. The fully formed mitotic figure (metaphase); the chromosomes, fully divided, grouped in the equatorial plate.

corpuscle as forming a permanent organ, not only of the early blastomeres, but of all cells; that it constitutes a cell-organ equal in rank to the nucleus itself; that every central corpuscle is derived from a pre-existing corpuscle, every attraction-sphere from the pre-existing sphere, and that division of the sphere precedes that of the cell-nucleus." [1] Boveri expressed himself in similar terms in the same year ('87, 2, p. 153), and the same general result was reached by Vejdovsky nearly at the same time,[2] though it was less clearly formulated than by either Boveri or Van Beneden.

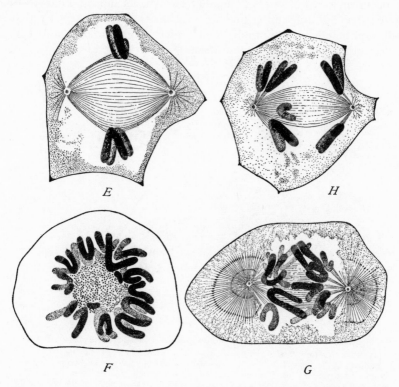

Fig. 22. — Metaphase and anaphases of mitosis in cells (spermatocytes) of the salamander. [DRÜNER.]

E. Metaphase. The continuous central spindle-fibres pass from pole to pole of the spindle. Outside them the thin layer of contractile mantle-fibres attached to the divided chromosomes, of which only two are shown. Centrosomes and asters. *F.* Transverse section through the mitotic figure showing the ring of chromosomes surrounding the central spindle, the cut fibres of the latter appearing as dots. *G.* Anaphase; divergence of the daughter-chromosomes, exposing the central spindle as the interzonal fibres; contractile fibres (principal cones of Van Beneden) clearly shown. *H.* Later anaphase (dyaster of Flemming); the central spindle fully exposed to view; mantle-fibres attached to the chromosomes. Immediately afterwards the cell divides (see Fig. 23).

All these observers agreed, therefore, that the achromatic figure arose outside the nucleus, in the cytoplasm; that the primary impulse to cell-division was given, not by the nucleus, but by the centrosome, and that a new cell-organ had been discovered whose special office

---

[1] '87, p. 279.　　　　　　[2] '88, pp. 151, etc.

was to preside over cell-division. "The centrosome is an independent permanent cell-organ, which, exactly like the chromatic elements, is transmitted by division to the daughter-*cells*. *The centrosome represents the dynamic centre of the cell.*" [1] This view has been widely accepted by later investigators, and the centrosome has been shown to occur in a large number of adult tissue-cells during their resting state; for example in pigment-cells, leucocytes, connective tissue-cells, epithelial and endothelial cells, in certain gland-cells and nerve-cells, in the cells of many plant-tissues, and in some of the unicellular

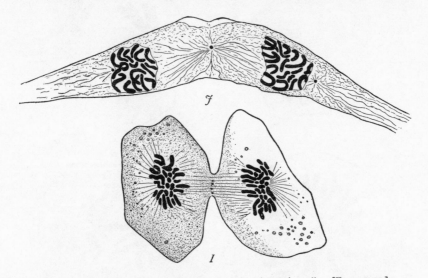

Fig. 23. — Final phases (telophases) of mitosis in salamander cells. [FLEMMING.]

I. Epithelial cell from the lung; chromosomes at the poles of the spindle, the cell-body dividing; granules of the "mid-body" or *Zwischenkörper* at the equator of the disappearing spindle. *J.* Connective-tissue cell (lung) immediately after division; daughter-nuclei reforming, the centrosome just outside of each; mid-body a single granule in the middle of the remains of the spindle.

plants, and animals, such as the Diatoms and Flagellates. That the centrosome gives the primary impulse to cell-division by its own division has, however, been disproved; for there are several accurately determined cases in which the chromatin-elements divide long before the centrosome, and it is now generally agreed that the division of chromatin and centrosome are two parallel events, the causal relation between which still remains undetermined. (Cf. p. 77.)

[1] Boveri, '87, 2, p. 153.

C. Modifications of Mitosis

The evidence steadily accumulates that the essential phenomena of mitosis are of the same general type in all forms of cells, both in plants and in animals. Everywhere, with a single important exception (maturation), the chromatin-thread splits lengthwise throughout its whole extent, and everywhere an achromatic spindle is formed that is in some manner an agent in the transportal of the chromatin-halves to the respective daughter-cells. The exception to this general law, which occurs during the preparation of the germ-cells for their development and constitutes one of the most significant of all cytological phenomena, is considered in Chapter V. We have here only to glance at a number of modifications that affect, not the essential character, but only the details of the typical process.

1. *Varieties of the Mitotic Figure*

All of the mitotic phenomena, and especially those involved in the history of the achromatic figure, are in general most clearly displayed in embryonic cells, and especially in the egg-cell[1] (Fig. 24). In the adult tissue-cells the asters are relatively small, the spindle relatively large and conspicuous. The same is true of plant-cells in general where the very existence of the asters was at first overlooked. Plant-mitoses are characterized by the prominence of the cell-plate (Fig. 25), which is rudimentary or often wanting in animals, a fact correlated no doubt with the greater development of the cell-membrane in plants. With this again is correlated the fact that division of the cell-body in animal-cells generally takes place by constriction in the equatorial plane of the spindle; while in plant-cells the cell is usually cut in two by a cell-wall developed in the substance of the protoplasm and derived in large part from the cell-plate.

The centrosome and centrosphere appear to present great variations that have not yet been thoroughly cleared up and will be more critically discussed beyond.[2] They are known to undergo extensive changes in the cycle of cell-division and to vary greatly in different forms (Fig. 108). In some cases the aster contains at its centre nothing more than a minute deeply staining granule, which doubtless

---

[1] A very remarkable modification of the achromatic figure occurs in the *spiral asters*, discovered by Mark ('81) in the eggs of *Limax*, the astral rays being curved as if the entire aster had been rotated about its centre. The meaning of this phenomenon is unknown.

[2] See p. 224.

represents the centrosome alone.   In other cases the granule is surrounded by a larger body, which in turn lies within the centrosphere
or attraction-sphere.   In still other cases the centre of the aster is
occupied by a large reticular mass, within which no smaller body can
be distinguished (*e.g.* in pigment-cells); this mass is sometimes called
the centrosome, sometimes the centrosphere.   Sometimes, again, the

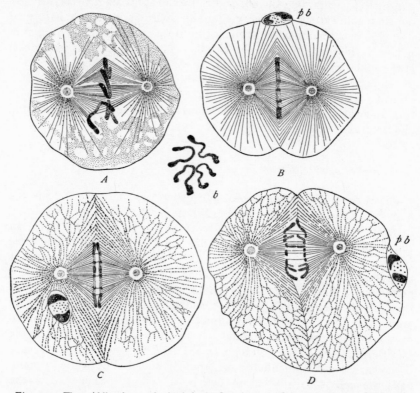

Fig. 24. — The middle phases of mitosis in the first cleavage of the *Ascaris*-egg.   [BOVERI.]
   A. Closing prophase, the equatorial plate forming.   *B.* Metaphase; equatorial plate established and the chromosomes split; *b,* the equatorial plate, viewed *en face,* showing the four chromosomes.   *C.* Early anaphase; divergence of the daughter-chromosomes (polar body at one
side).   *D.* Later anaphase; *p.b.,* second polar body.
   (For preceding stages see Fig. 65; for later stages, Fig. 104.)

spindle-fibres are not focussed at a single point, and the spindle
appears truncated at the ends, its fibres terminating in a transverse
row of granules (maturation-spindles of *Ascaris,* and some plant-cells).
It is not entirely certain, however, that such spindles observed in
preparations represent the normal structure during life.[1]

   [1] Häcker asserts in a recent paper ('94) that the truncated polar spindles are normal,
and that a centrosome lies at each of the four angles; *i.e.* two at either pole.

The variations of the chromatic figure must for the most part be considered in the more special parts of this work. There seems to be doubt that a single continuous spireme-thread may be formed (cf. p. 184), but it is equally certain that the thread may appear from the beginning in a number of distinct segments; *i.e.* as a segmented spireme. The chromosomes, when fully formed, vary greatly in appearance. In many of the tissues of adult plants and animals

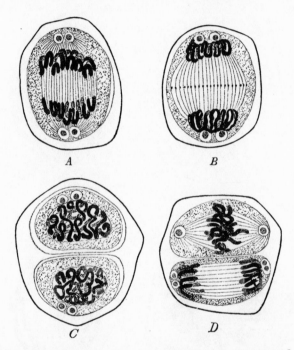

Fig. 25. — Division of pollen-mother-cells in the lily. [GUIGNARD.]

A. Anaphase of the first division, showing the twelve daughter-chromosomes on each side, the interzonal fibres stretching between them, and the centrosomes, already double, at the spindle-poles. *B.* Later stage, showing the cell-plate at the equator of the spindle and the daughter-spiremes (dispireme stage of Flemming). *C.* Division completed; double centrosomes in the resting cell. *D.* Ensuing division in progress; the upper cell at the close of the prophases, the chromosomes and centrosomes still undivided; lower cell in the late anaphase, cell-plate not yet formed.

they are rod-shaped and are often bent in the middle like a **V** (Figs. 21, 33). They often have this form, too, in embryonic cells, as in the segmentation-stages of the egg in *Ascaris* (Fig. 24) and other forms. The rods may, however, be short and straight (segmenting eggs of echinoderms, etc.), and may be reduced to spheres, as in the maturation stages of the germ-cells.

2. *Heterotypical Mitosis*

Under this name Flemming ('87) first described a peculiar modification of the division of the chromosomes that has since been shown to be of very great importance in the early history of the germ-cells,

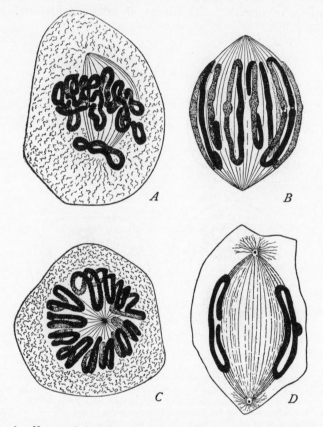

Fig. 26. — Heterotypical mitosis in spermatocytes of the salamander. [FLEMMING.]

A. Prophase, chromosomes in the form of scattered rings, each of which represents two daughter-chromosomes joined end to end. *B.* The rings ranged about the equator of the spindle and dividing; the swellings indicate the ends of the chromosomes. *C.* The same viewed from the spindle-pole. *D.* Diagram (Hermann) showing the central spindle, asters and centrosomes, and the contractile mantle-fibres attached to the rings (one of the latter dividing).

though it is not confined to them. In this form the chromosomes split at an early period, but the halves remain united by their ends. Each double chromosome then opens out to form a closed ring (Fig. 26), which by its mode of origin is shown to represent two daughter-chromosomes, each forming half of the ring, united by their ends. The ring finally breaks in two to form two U-shaped chromosomes which diverge to opposite poles of the spindle as usual. As will be shown in Chapter V., the divisions by which the germ-cells are matured are in many cases of this type; but the primary rings here represent not two but four chromosomes, into which they afterwards break up.

3. *Bivalent and Plurivalent Chromosomes*

The last paragraph leads to the consideration of certain variations in the number of the chromosomes. Boveri discovered that the species *Ascaris megalocephala* comprises two varieties which differ in no visible respect save in the number of chromosomes, the germ-nuclei of one form ("variety bivalens" of Hertwig) having two chromosomes, while in the other form ("variety univalens") there is but one. Brauer discovered a similar fact in the phyllopod *Artemia*, the number of somatic chromosomes being 168 in some individuals, in others only 84 (p. 205).

It will appear hereafter that in some cases the primordial germ-cells show only half the usual number of chromosomes, and in *Cyclops*, the same is true, according to Häcker, of all the cells of the early cleavage-stages.

In all cases where the number of chromosomes is apparently reduced ("pseudo-reduction" of Rückert) it is highly probable that each chromatin-rod represents not one but two or more chromosomes united together, and Häcker has accordingly proposed the terms "bivalent" and "plurivalent" for such chromatin-rods.[1] The truth of this view, which originated with vom Rath, is, I think, conclusively shown by the case of *Artemia* described at p. 203, and by many facts in the maturation of the germ-cells hereafter considered. In *Ascaris* we may regard the chromosomes of Hertwig's "variety univalens" as really bivalent or double; *i.e.* equivalent to two such chromosomes as appear in "variety bivalens." These latter, however, are probably in their turn plurivalent, *i.e.* represent a number of units of a lower order united together; for, as described at p. 111, each of these normally breaks up in the somatic cells into a large number of shorter chromosomes closely similar to those of the related species *Ascaris lumbricoides*, where the normal number is 24.

---

[1] The words "bivalent" and "univalent" have been used in precisely the opposite sense by Hertwig in the case of *Ascaris*, the former term being applied to that variety having *two* chromosomes in the germ-cells, the latter to the variety with one. These terms certainly have priority, but were applied only to a specific case. Häcker's use of the words, which is strictly in accordance with their ·etymology, is too valuable for general descriptive purposes to be rejected.

Häcker has called attention to the striking fact that plurivalent mitosis is very often of the heterotypical form, as is very common in the maturation mitoses of many animals (Chapter V.), and often occurs in the early cleavages of *Ascaris;* but it is doubtful whether this is a universal rule.

4. *Mitosis in the Unicellular Plants and Animals*

The process of mitosis in the one-celled plants and animals has a peculiar interest, for it is here that we must look for indications of

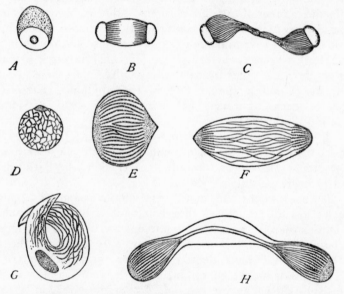

Fig. 27. — Mitotic division in Infusoria. [R. HERTWIG.]

A–C. Macronucleus of *Spirochona*, showing pole-plates. *D–H.* Successive stages in the division of the micronucleus of *Paramœcium*. D. The earliest stage, showing reticulum. *G.* Following stage ("sickle-form") with nucleolus. *E.* Chromosomes and pole-plates. *F.* Late anaphase. *H.* Final phase.

its historical origin. But although traces of mitotic division were seen in the Infusoria by Balbiani ('58–'61), Stein ('59), and others long before it was known in the higher forms, it is still imperfectly understood on account of the practical difficulties of observation. Within a few years, however, our knowledge in this field has rapidly advanced, and we have already good ground for some important conclusions.

Mitotic division has now been observed in many of the main divisions of Protozoa and unicellular plants; but in the present state of the subject it must be left an open question whether it occurs in all.

The essential features of the process appear to be here of the same nature as in the higher types, but show a series of minor modifications that indicate the origin of mitotic division from a simpler type. Four of these modifications are of especial importance, viz. : —

(1) The centrosome or its equivalent lies as a rule inside the nucleus, thus reversing the rule in higher forms.

(2) The nuclear membrane as a rule remains intact and does not disappear at any stage.

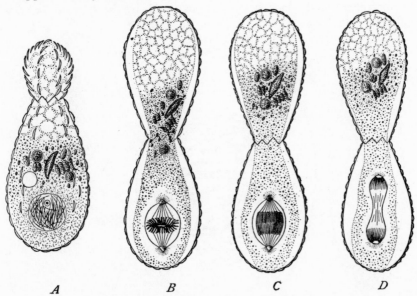

A B C D

Fig. 28. — Mitosis in the rhizopod, *Euglypha.* [SCHEWIAKOFF.]

In this form the body is surrounded by a firm shell which prevents direct constriction of the cell-body. The latter therefore divides by a process of budding from the opening of the shell (the initial phase shown at *A*) ; the nucleus meanwhile divides, and one of the daughter-nuclei afterwards wanders out into the bud.

A. Early prophase; nucleus near lower end containing a nucleolus and numerous chromosomes. *B.* Equatorial plate and spindle formed inside the nucleus; pole-bodies or pole-plates (*i.e.* attraction-spheres or centrosomes) at the spindle-poles. *C.* Metaphase. *D.* Late anaphase, spindle dividing; after division of the spindle the outer nucleus wanders out into the bud.

(3) The asters attain but a slight development, and in some cases appear to be entirely absent (Infusoria).

(4) The arrangement of the chromatin-granules to form chromosomes appears to be of secondary importance as compared with higher forms, and the essential feature in nuclear division appears to be the fission of the individual granules.

The basis of our knowledge in this field was laid by Richard Hertwig through his studies on an infusorian, *Spirochona* ('77), and a rhizopod, *Actinosphærium* ('84). In both these forms a typical spindle and equatorial plate are formed *inside the nuclear membrane* by a transformation of the nuclear substance. In *Spirochona* (Fig. 27, *A–C*) a hemispherical "end-plate" or "pole-plate" is situated at either pole of the spindle, and Hertwig's observations indicated, though they did not prove, that these plates arose by the division of a large "nucleolus." Pole-plates of a somewhat different form were also described in *Actinosphærium*, and somewhat later by Schewiakoff ('88) in *Euglypha* (Fig. 28). Their origin through division of the "nucleolus" has since been demonstrated by Keuten in *Euglena*

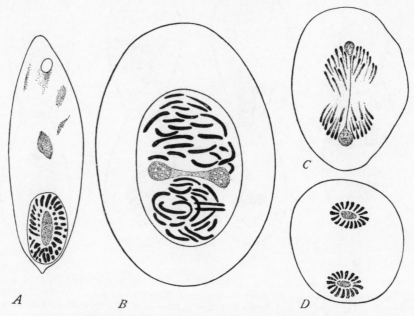

Fig. 29. — Mitosis in the Flagellate *Euglena*. [KEUTEN.]

A. Preparing for division; the nucleus contains a "nucleolus" or nucleolo-centrosome surrounded by a group of chromosomes. *B.* Division of the "nucleolus" to form an intra-nuclear spindle. *C.* Later stage. *D.* The nuclear division completed.

(Fig. 29) and Schaudinn in *Amœba*. There can therefore be little doubt that the "nucleolus" in these forms represents an intra-nuclear centrosome, and that the pole-plates are the daughter-centrosomes or attraction-spheres. Richard Hertwig's latest work ('95) indicates that a similar process occurs in the micronuclei of *Paramœcium*, which at first contain a large "nucleolus" and afterwards a conspicuous pole-plate at either end of the spindle (Fig. 27, *D–H*). The origin of the pole-plates was not, however, positively determined.

These facts indicate, as Richard and Oscar Hertwig have concluded, that the centrosome, in its most primitive form, is an intra-nuclear structure, which may have arisen through a condensation or differentiation of the "achromatic" constituents. *Noctiluca*, the diatoms, and *Actinosphærium* seem to represent transitions to the higher types. In the latter form Brauer discovered a distinct centrosome lying in the late anaphase *outside* the nuclear membrane at the centre of a small but distinct aster and soon dividing into two, precisely as in higher forms (Fig. 31, *I*, *J*). This centrosome, how-

ever, as Brauer infers, lies within the nucleus during the resting state and the earlier stages of division, and only migrates out into the cytoplasm during the late anaphase, afterward returning to the nucleus and lying in the "poleplate." In the diatoms Bütschli discovered an extra-nuclear centrosome and attraction-sphere, and Lauterborn has traced the formation of a central spindle from it. This spindle, at first extra-nuclear, is asserted to pass subsequently into the interior of the nucleus.

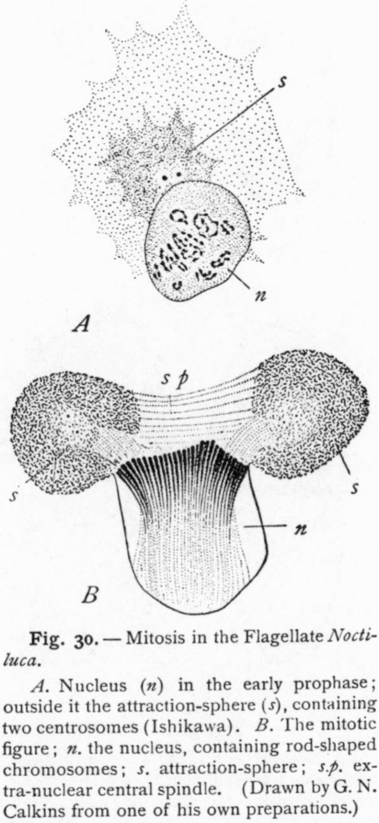

Noctiluca, finally, appears to have attained the condition characteristic of the higher forms. Here, as Ishikawa has shown, the cell contains a typical extra-nuclear centrosome and attraction-sphere lying in the cytoplasm, precisely as in *Ascaris* (Fig. 30). By division of centrosome and sphere a typical central spindle is formed, about which the nucleus wraps itself, and mitosis proceeds much as in the higher types, except that the nuclear membrane does not disappear.[1]

Fig. 30. — Mitosis in the Flagellate *Noctiluca*.

A. Nucleus (*n*) in the early prophase; outside it the attraction-sphere (*s*), containing two centrosomes (Ishikawa). *B*. The mitotic figure; *n*. the nucleus, containing rod-shaped chromosomes; *s*. attraction-sphere; *s.p.* extra-nuclear central spindle. (Drawn by G. N. Calkins from one of his own preparations.)

Regarding the history of the chromatin the most thorough observations have been made by Schewiakoff in *Euglypha* and Brauer in *Actinosphærium*. In the former case a segmented spireme arises from the resting reticulum, and long, rod-shaped chromosomes are formed, which are stated to split lengthwise as in the usual forms of mitosis. The nuclear membrane persists throughout, and the entire mitotic

[1] All of the essential features in this process, as described by Ishikawa, have been confirmed by Calkins in the Columbia laboratory.

F

figure, except the minute asters, is formed inside it (Fig. 28). In *Actinosphærium*, on the other hand, there is no true spireme stage, and no rod-shaped chromosomes are at first formed. The reticulum breaks up into a large number of granules which give rise to an equatorial plate, divide by fission, and are distributed to the daughter-nuclei.

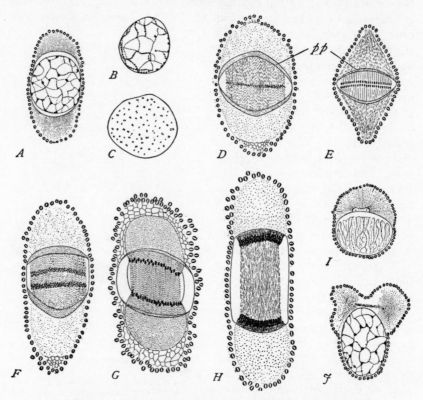

Fig. 31. — Mitosis in the rhizopod *Actinosphærium.* [BRAUER.]

A. Nucleus and surrounding structures in the early prophase; above and below the reticular nucleus lie the semilunar " pole-plates," and outside these the cytoplasmic masses in which the asters afterward develop. *B.* Later stage of the nucleus. *D.* Mitotic figure in the metaphase, showing equatorial plate, intra-nuclear spindle, and pole-plates (*p.p.*). *C.* Equatorial plate, viewed *en face*, consisting of double chromatin-granules. *E.* Early anaphase. *F. G.* Later ana-phases. *H.* Final anaphase. *I.* Telophase; daughter-nucleus forming, chromatin in loop-shaped threads; outside the nuclear membrane the centrosome, already divided, and the aster. *J.* Later stage; the daughter-nucleus established; divergence of the centrosomes. Beyond this point the centrosomes have not been followed.

Only in the late anaphase (telophase) do these granules arrange them-selves in threads (Fig. 31, *I*), *and this process is apparently no more than a forerunner of the reticular stage.* This case is a very convincing argument in favour of the view that the formation and splitting of chro-mosomes is secondary to the division of the ultimate chromatin-granules.

(Cf. pp. 78 and 221.) Richard Hertwig's studies on Infusoria and those of Lauterborn on Flagellates indicate that here also no longitudinal splitting of the chromatin-threads occurs and that the division must be referred to the individual chromatin-granules. Ishikawa describes a peculiar longitudinal splitting of chromosomes in *Noctiluca*, but Calkins' studies indicate that the latter observer has probably misinterpreted certain stages and that the division probably takes place in a somewhat different manner. A typical spireme and chromosome-formation has also been described by Lauterborn in the Diatoms ('93).

In none of the foregoing cases does the nuclear membrane disappear. In the gregarines, however, the observations of Wolters ('91) and Clarke ('95) indicate that the membrane does not persist, and that a perfectly typical mitotic figure is formed.

To sum up: The facts at present known indicate that the unicellular forms exhibit forms of mitosis that are in some respects transitional from the typical mitosis of higher forms to a simpler type. The asters may be reduced (Rhizopods) or wanting (Infusoria); the spindle is typically formed inside the nucleus, either by division of an intra-nuclear "nucleolo-centrosome" (*Euglena, Amœba*), or possibly by rearrangement of the chromatic substance without a differentiated centrosome (? micronuclei of Infusoria). In every case the essential fact in the history of the chromatin is a division of the chromatin-granules; but this may be preceded by their arrangement in threads or chromosomes (*Euglypha*, Diatoms) or may not (*Actinosphærium*). *These facts point towards the conclusion that centrosome, spindle, and chromosomes are all secondary differentiations of the primitive nuclear structure, and indicate that the asters and attraction-spheres may be historically a later acquisition developed in the cytoplasm after the differentiation of the centrosome.*

5. *Pathological Mitoses*

Under certain circumstances the delicate mechanism of cell-division may become deranged, and so give rise to various forms of pathological mitoses. Such a miscarriage may be artificially produced, as Hertwig, Galeotti, and others have shown, by treating the dividing-cells with poisons and other chemical substances (quinine, chloral, nicotine, potassic iodide, etc.). Pathological mitoses may, however, occur without discoverable external cause; and it is a very interesting fact, as Klebs, Hansemann, and Galeotti have especially pointed out, that they are of frequent occurrence in abnormal growths such as cancers and tumours.

The abnormal forms of mitoses are arranged by Hansemann in two general groups, as follows: (1) *asymmetrical mitoses*, in which the chromosomes are unequally distributed to the daughter-cells, and (2) *multipolar mitoses*, in which the number of centrosomes is more than two, and more than one spindle is formed. Under the first group are included not only the cases of unequal distribution of the daughter-chromosomes, but also those in which chromosomes fail to be drawn into the equatorial plate and hence are lost in the cytoplasm.

Klebs first pointed out the occurrence of asymmetrical mitoses in carcinoma cells, where they have been carefully studied by Hanse-

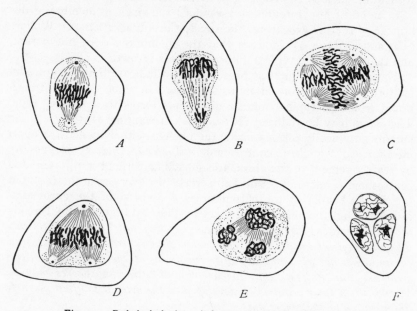

Fig. 32. — Pathological mitoses in human cancer-cells. [GALEOTTI.]

A. Asymmetrical mitosis with unequal centrosomes. *B.* Later stage, showing unequal distribution of the chromosomes. *C.* Quadripolar mitosis. *D.* Tripolar mitosis. *E.* Later stage. *F.* Tri-nucleate cell resulting.

mann and Galeotti. The inequality is here often extremely marked, so that one of the daughter-cells may receive more than twice as much chromatin as the other (Fig. 32). Hansemann, whose conclusions are accepted by Galeotti, believes that this asymmetry of mitosis gives an explanation of the familiar fact that in cancer-cells many of the nuclei are especially rich in chromatin (hyper-chromatic cells), while others are abnormally poor (hypochromatic cells). Lustig and Galeotti ('93) showed that the unequal distribution of chromatin is correlated with and probably caused by a corresponding inequality in the centrosomes which causes an asymmetrical development of the amphiaster. A very interesting discovery made by Galeotti ('93) is that asymmetrical mitoses, exactly like those seen in carcinoma, may be artificially produced in the epithelial cells of salamanders (Fig. 33) by treatment with dilute solutions of various drugs (antipyrin, cocaine, quinine).

Normal multipolar mitoses, though rare, sometimes occur, as in the division of the pollen mother-cells and the endosperm-cells of flowering plants (Strasburger); but such mitotic figures arise through the union of two or more bipolar amphiasters in a syncytium and are due to a rapid succession of the nuclear divisions unaccompanied by fission of the cell-substance. These are not to be confounded with pathological mitoses arising by premature or abnormal division of the centrosome. If one centrosome divide, while the other does not, triasters are produced, from which may arise three cells or a tri-

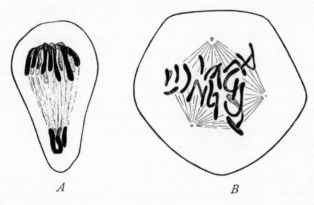

A   *B*

Fig. 33. — Pathological mitoses in epidermal cells of salamander caused by poisons. [GALEOTTI.]

A. Asymmetrical mitosis after treatment with 0.05% antipyrin solution. *B.* Tripolar mitosis after treatment with 0.5% potassic iodide solution.

nucleated cell. If both centrosomes divide tetrasters or polyasters are formed. Here again the same result has been artificially attained by chemical stimulus (cf. Schottländer, '88). Multipolar mitoses are also common in regenerating tissues after irritative stimulus (Ströbe); but it is uncertain whether such mitoses lead to the formation of normal tissue.[1]

The frequency of abnormal mitoses in pathological growths is a most suggestive fact, but it is still wholly undetermined whether the abnormal mode of cell-division is the cause of the disease or the reverse. The latter seems the more probable alternative, since normal mitosis is certainly the rule in abnormal growths; and Galeotti's

[1] The remarkable polyasters formed in polyspermic fertilization of the egg are described at p. 147.

experiments suggest that the pathological mitoses in such growths may be caused by the presence of deleterious chemical products in the diseased tissue, and perhaps point the way to their medical treatment.

D. The Mechanism of Mitosis

We now pass to a consideration of the forces at work in mitotic division, which leads us into one of the most debatable fields of cytological inquiry.

1. *Function of the Amphiaster*

All observers agree that the amphiaster is in some manner an expression of the forces by which cell-division is caused, and many · accept, in one form or another, the view first clearly stated by Fol,[1] that the asters represent in some manner centres of attractive forces focussed in the centrosome or dynamic centre of the cell. Regarding the nature of these forces, there is, however, so wide a divergence of opinion as to compel the admission that we have thus far accomplished little more than to clear the ground for a precise investigation of the subject; and the mechanism of mitosis still lies before us as one of the most fascinating problems of cytology.

(*a*) *The Theory of Fibrillar Contractility.* — The view that has taken the strongest hold on recent research is the hypothesis of *fibrillar contractility*. First suggested by Klein in 1878, this hypothesis was independently put forward by Van Beneden in 1883, and fully outlined by him four years later in the following words : "In our opinion, all the internal movements that accompany cell-division have their immediate cause in the contractility of the protoplasmic fibrillæ and their arrangement in a kind of radial muscular system, composed of antagonizing groups" (*i.e.* the asters with their rays). "In this system the central corpuscle (centrosome) plays the part of an organ of insertion. It is the first of all the various organs of the cells to divide, and its division leads to the grouping of the contractile elements in two systems, each having its own centre. The presence of these two systems brings about cell-division, and actively determines the paths of the secondary chromatic asters" (*i.e.* the daughter-groups of chromosomes) "in opposite directions. An important part of the phenomena of (karyo-) kinesis has its efficient cause, not in the nucleus, but in the protoplasmic body of the cell."[2] This beautiful hypothesis was based on very convincing

[1] '73, p. 473.   [2] '87, p. 280.

evidence derived from the study of the *Ascaris* egg, and it was here that Van Beneden first demonstrated the fact, already suspected by Flemming, that the daughter-chromosomes move apart to the poles of the spindle, and give rise to the two respective daughter-nuclei.[1]

Van Beneden describes the astral rays, both in *Ascaris* and in tunicates, as differentiated into several groups (Fig. 34). One set, forming the "principal cone," are attached to the chromosomes and form one-half of the spindle, and, by the contractions of these fibres, the chromosomes are passively dragged apart. An opposite group, forming the "antipodal cone," extend from the centrosome to the cell-periphery, the base of the cone forming the "polar circle." These rays, opposing the action of the principal cones, not only hold the centrosomes in place, but, by their contractions, drag them apart, and thus cause an actual divergence of the centres. The remaining astral rays are attached to the cell-periphery and are limited by a sub-equatorial circle. Later observations indicate, however, that this arrangement of the astral rays is not of general occurrence, and that the rays often do not reach the periphery, but lose themselves in the general reticulum.

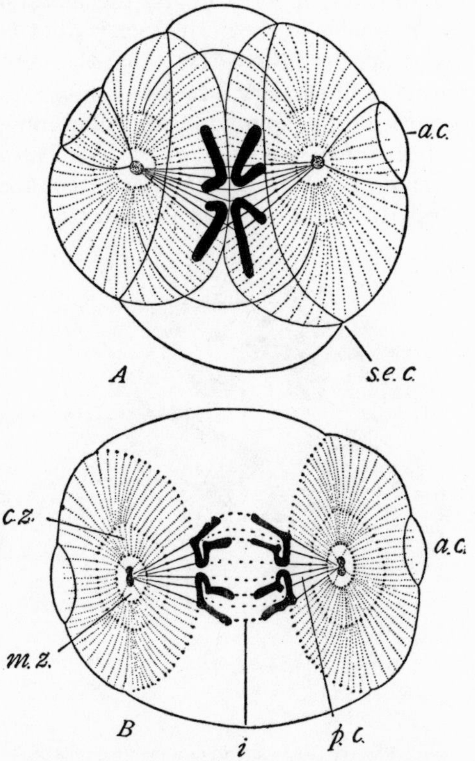

Fig. 34.—Slightly schematic figures of dividing eggs of *Ascaris*, illustrating Van Beneden's theory of mitosis. [VAN BENEDEN and JULIN.]

A. Early anaphase; each chromosome has divided into two. *B*. Later anaphase during divergence of the daughter-chromosomes. *a.c.* Antipodal cone of astral rays; *c.z.* cortical zone of the attraction-sphere; *i.* interzonal fibres stretching between the daughter-chromosomes; *m.z.* medullary zone of the attraction-sphere; *p.c.* principal cone, forming one-half of the contractile spindle (the action of these fibres is reinforced by that of the antipodal cone); *s.e.c.* sub-equatorial circle, to which the astral rays are attached.

Van Beneden's general hypothesis was accepted in the following year by Boveri ('88, 2), who contributed many important additional

[1] '83, p. 544.

facts in its support, though neither his observations nor those of later investigators have sustained Van Beneden's account of the grouping of the astral rays.   Boveri showed in the clearest manner that, during the fertilization of *Ascaris*, the astral rays become attached to the chromosomes of the germ-nuclei; that each comes into connection with rays from both the asters; that the chromosomes, at first irregularly scattered in the egg, are drawn into a position of equilibrium in the equator of the spindle by the shortening of these rays (Figs. 65, 104); and that *the rays thicken as they shorten.*   He showed that as the chromosome splits, each half is connected only with rays (spindle-fibres) from the aster on its own side; and he followed, step by step,

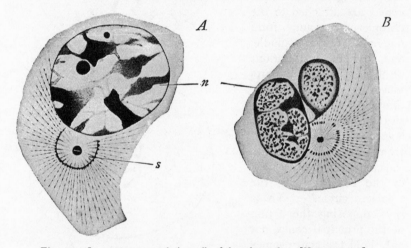

Fig. 35.—Leucocytes or wandering-cells of the salamander.   [HEIDENHAIN.]

A. Cell with a single nucleus containing a very coarse network of chromatin and two nucleoli (plasmosomes); *s.* permanent aster, its centre occupied by a double centrosome surrounded by an attraction-sphere. *B.* Similar cell, with double nucleus; the smaller dark masses in the latter are oxychromatin-granules (linin), the larger masses are basichromatin (chromatin proper).

the shortening and thickening of these rays as the daughter-chromosomes diverge.   In all these operations the behaviour of the rays is precisely like that of muscle-fibres ; and it is difficult to study Boveri's beautiful figures and clear descriptions without sharing his conviction that " of the contractility of the fibrillæ there can be no doubt." [1]

Very convincing evidence in the same direction is afforded by pigment-cells and leucocytes or wandering-cells, in both of which there is a very large permanent aster (attraction-sphere) even in the resting-cell.   The structure of the aster in the leucocyte, where it was first discovered by Flemming in 1891, has been studied very

[1] '88, 2, p. 99.

carefully by Heidenhain in the salamander. The astral rays here
extend throughout nearly the whole cell (Fig. 35), and are believed
by Heidenhain to represent the contractile elements by means of
which the cell changes its form and creeps about. A similar conclusion was reached by Solger ('91) and Zimmerman ('93, 2) in the
case of pigment-cells (chromatophores) in fishes. These cells have,
in an extraordinary degree, the power of changing their form, and of

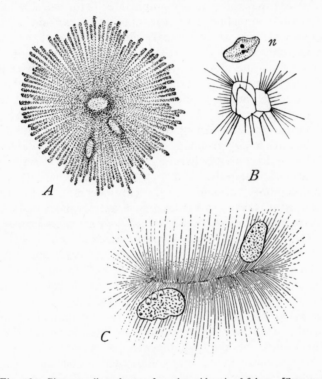

Fig. 36. — Pigment-cells and asters from the epidermis of fishes. [ZIMMERMAN.]

A. Entire pigment-cell, from *Blennius.* The central clear space is the central mass of the aster
from which radiate the pigment-granules; two nuclei below. *B.* Nucleus (*n*) and aster after ex-
traction of the pigment, showing reticulated central mass. *C.* Two nuclei and aster with rod-
shaped central mass, from *Sargus.*

actively creeping about. Solger and Zimmerman have shown that
the pigment-cell contains an enormous aster, whose rays extend in
every direction through the pigment-mass, and it is almost impossible to doubt that the aster is a contractile apparatus, like a radial
muscular system, by means of which the active changes of form are
produced (Fig. 36).

But although these observations seem to place the theory of fibrillar
contractility upon a firm basis, it has since undergone various modifi-

cations and limitations, which show that the matter is by no means so simple as it first appeared. The most important of these modifications are due to Hermann ('91) and Drüner ('95), who have relied mainly on the study of mitosis in various cells of the salamander, well known as extremely favourable objects for study. These observers have demonstrated that in this case the spindle-fibres are of two kinds which, apparently, differ both in origin and in mode of action. Hermann showed that the primary amphiaster is formed outside the nucleus, without connection with the chromosomes, and that the original spindle persists as a "central spindle" (Figs. 21, 22), which he regards as composed of *non-contractile* fibres, and merely forming a support on which the movements of the chromosomes take place. The contractile elements are formed by certain of the astral rays which grow into the nucleus, and become attached to the chromosomes, as Boveri described. *By the contraction of these latter fibres* the chromosomes are now dragged towards the spindle, and around its equator they are finally grouped to form the equatorial plate. The fully formed spindle consists, therefore, of two elements ; namely, (*a*) the original "central spindle," and (*b*) a surrounding mantle of contractile "mantle-fibres" attached to the chromosomes, and originally derived from astral rays. In the anaphase, as Hermann believes, *the daughter-chromosomes are dragged apart solely by the contractile mantle-fibres, the central spindle-fibres being non-contractile and serving as a support or substratum along which the chromosomes move.* As the chromosomes diverge, the central spindle comes into view as the interzonal fibres (Fig. 22, *G, H*). Strasburger ('95) is now inclined to accept a similar view of mitosis in the cells of plants.

Drüner ('95) in his beautiful studies on the mechanism of mitosis has advanced a step beyond Hermann, maintaining that the progressive divergence of the spindle-poles is caused by an active growth or elongation of the central spindle which goes on throughout the whole period from the earliest prophases until the close of the anaphases. This view is supported by the fact that the central spindle-fibres are always contorted during the metaphases, as if pushing against a resistance ; and, as Richard Hertwig points out ('95), it harmonizes with the facts observed in the mitoses of infusorian nuclei. The same view is adopted by Braus and by Reinke. Flemming ('95) is still inclined, however, to the view that the divergence of the centres may be in part caused by the traction of the antipodal fibres, as maintained by Van Beneden and Boveri.

Heidenhain, finally, while accepting the contractility-hypothesis, ascribes only a subordinate *rôle* to an active physiological contractility of the fibres. The main factor in mitosis is ascribed to elastic tension of the astral rays which are attached at one end to the centrosome, at the other to the cell-periphery. By turgor of the cell the rays are passively stretched, thus causing divergence of the spindle-poles and of the daughter-chromosomes to which the spindle-fibres are attached. An active contraction of the fibres is only invoked to explain the closing phases of mitosis.

(b) *Other Theories.* — Watase's ingenious theory of mitosis ('93) is exactly the opposite of Van Beneden's, assuming that the spindle-fibres are not pulling but pushing agents, the daughter-chromosomes being forced apart by continually lengthening fibres which grow out from the centres and dovetail in the region of the interzonal fibres. Each daughter-chromosome is therefore connected with fibres from the aster, not of its own, but of the opposite side. This view is, I believe, irreconcilable with the movements of chromosomes observed in multiple asters, and also with those that occur during the fertilization of the egg, where the chromosomes are plainly drawn towards the astral centres and not pushed away from them.

Bütschli, Carnoy, Platner, and others have sought an explanation in a totally different direction from any of the foregoing, regarding the formation of the amphiaster as due essentially to streaming or osmotic movements of the fluid constituents of the protoplasm, and the movements of the chromosomes as being in a measure mechanically caused by the same agency. Oscar Hertwig adopts a somewhat vague dynamical view, regarding the formation of the mitotic figure as due to an interaction between nucleus and cytoplasm, which he compares to that taking place in a magnetic field between a magnet and a mass of iron filings: " The interaction between nucleus and protoplasm in the cell finds its visible expression in the formation of the polar centres and astral figures; the result of the interaction is that the nucleus always seeks the middle of its sphere of action." [1] He gives, however, no hint of his view regarding the nature of the action or the causes of the chromosomal movements. Ziegler ('95) accepts a somewhat similar view; and he has shown that surprisingly close *simulacra* of the mitotic figure in many of its different phases may be produced by placing bent wires (representing the chromosomes) in the field of a horseshoe magnet strewn with iron filings.

My own studies on the eggs of echinoderms ('95, 2) and annelids have convinced me that no adequate hypothesis of the mitotic mechanism has yet been advanced. In these, as in many other forms, the spindle-fibres show no differentiation into central spindle and peri-

[1] *Zelle und Gewebe*, p. 172.

pheral mable-fibres; and the chromosomes extend entirely through
the substance of the spindle in its equatorial plane.   If there be supporting, as opposed to contractile, fibres, they must be intermingled
with the latter; and both forms must have the same origin.   The

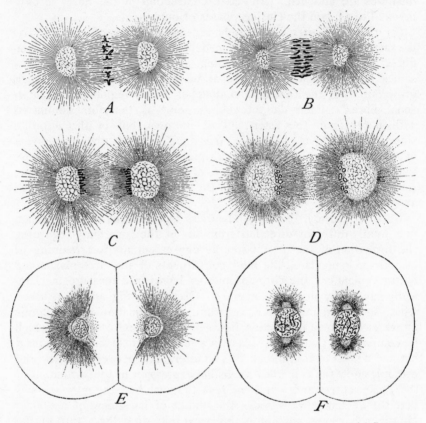

Fig. 37. — The later stages of mitosis in the egg of the sea-urchin *Toxopneustes* (*A–D*, × 1000;
E–F, × 500).

A. Metaphase; daughter-chromosomes drawing apart but still united at one end.   *B*. Daughter-chromosomes separating.   *C*. Late anaphase; daughter-chromosomes lying at the spindle-
poles.   *D*. Final anaphase; daughter-chromosomes converted into vesicles.   *E*. Immediately
after division, the asters undivided; the spindle has disappeared.   *F*. Resting 2-cell stage, the
asters divided into two in anticipation of the next division.

In Figs. *A* to *D*, the centrosphere appears as a large reticulated mass from which the rays proceed.   It is probable that a minute centrosome, or pair of centrosomes, lies near the centre of the
centrosphere, but this is not shown.

daughter-chromosomes appear to move towards the poles *through
the substance* of the spindle, and do not travel along its periphery as
described by Hermann and Drüner in amphibia and by Strasburger
('93, 2) in the plants.   No shortening or thickening of the rays can

be observed, and the chromosomes proceed to the extreme limit of the spindle-poles and appear actually to pass *into the interior* of the huge reticulated centrosphere. I cannot see how this behaviour of the chromosomes is to be explained as the result solely of a contraction of fibres stretching between them and the centrosphere. It is certain, moreover, that another factor is at work. Throughout the anaphases, the centrosphere steadily grows until, at the close, it attains an enormous size (Fig. 37), and its substance differs chemically from that of the rays, for after double staining with Congo red (an acid aniline) and hæmatoxylin it becomes bright red while the rays are blue. It seems probable, therefore, that the movements of the chromosomes are affected by definite chemical changes occurring in the centrosphere, as Bütschli[1] and Strasburger[2] have maintained; and it is possible that the substance of the spindle-fibres may be actually taken up into the centrosphere, and the chromosomes thus drawn towards it. Strasburger has made the interesting suggestion, which seems well worthy of consideration, that the movements of the chromosomes may be of a chemotactic character. In any case, I believe that no satisfactory hypothesis can be framed that does not reckon with the chemical and physical changes going on in the centrosphere, and take into account also the probability of a dynamic action radiating from it into the surrounding structures. Van Beneden's hypothesis is probably, in principle, correct; but, as Boveri himself admits in his latest paper ('95), it seems certain that other factors are involved besides the contractility of the achromatic fibres, and the mechanism of mitosis still awaits adequate physiological analysis.

2. *Division of the Chromosomes*

In developing his theory of fibrillar contractility Van Beneden expressed the view — only, however, as a possibility — that the splitting of the chromosomes might be passively caused by the contractions of the two sets of opposing spindle-fibres to which each is attached.[3] Later observations have demonstrated that this suggestion cannot be sustained; for in many cases the chromatin-thread splits before division of the centrosome and the formation of the achromatic figure, — sometimes during the spireme-stage, or even in the reticulum, while the nuclear membrane is still intact. Boveri showed this to be the case in *Ascaris*, and a similar fact has been observed by many observers since, both in plants and in animals.

The splitting of the chromosomes is therefore, in Boveri's words,

[1] '92, pp. 158, 159.   [2] '93, 2.   [3] '87, p. 279.

"*an independent vital manifestation, an act of reproduction on the part of the chromosomes.*" [1]

All of the recent researches in this field point to the conclusion that this act of division must be referred to the fission of the chromatin-granules or chromomeres of which the chromatin-thread is built. These granules were first clearly described by Balbiani ('76) in the chromatin-network of epithelial cells in the insect-ovary, and he found that the spireme-thread arose by the linear arrangement of these granules in a single row like a chain of bacteria.[2] Six years later Pfitzner ('72) added the interesting discovery, that during the mitosis of various tissue-cells of the salamander, the granules of the spireme-thread *divide by fission and thus determine the*

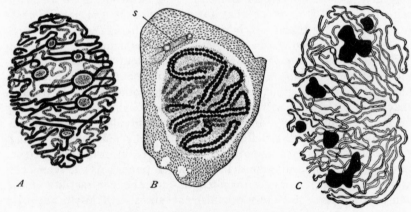

Fig. 38. — Nuclei in the spireme-stage.

A. From the endosperm of the lily, showing true nucleoli. [FLEMMING.]
B. Spermatocyte of salamander. Segmented double spireme-thread composed of chromomeres and completely split. Two centrosomes and central spindle at *s.* [HERMANN.]
C. Spireme-thread completely split, with six nucleoli. Endosperm of *Fritillaria.* [FLEMMING.]

longitudinal splitting of the entire chromosome. This discovery was confirmed by Flemming in the following year ('82, p. 219), and a similar result has been reached by many other observers (Fig. 38). The division of the chromatin-granules may take place at a very early period. Flemming observed as long ago as 1881 that the chromatin-thread might split in the spireme-stage (epithelial cells of the salamander), and this has since been shown to occur in many other cases; for instance, by Guignard in the mother-cells of the pollen in the lily ('91). Brauer's recent work on the spermatogenesis of *Ascaris* shows that the fission of the chromatin-granules here takes place even before the spireme-stage, when the chromatin is still in the form of a

---

[1] '88, p. 113.   [2] See '81, p. 638.

reticulum, and long before the division of the centrosome (Fig. 39). He therefore concludes: "With Boveri I regard the splitting as an independent reproductive act of the chromatin. The reconstruction of the nucleus, and in particular the breaking up of the chromosomes after division into small granules and their uniform distribution through the nuclear cavity, is, in the first place, for the purpose of

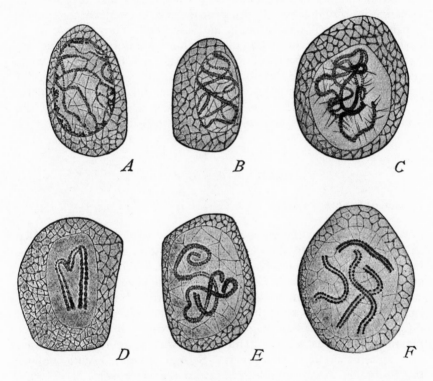

Fig. 39. — Formation of chromosomes and early splitting of the chromatin-granules in sperma-togonia of *Ascaris megalocephala*, var. *bivalens*. [BRAUER.]

A. Very early prophase; granules of the nuclear reticulum already divided. *B*. Spireme; the continuous chromatin-thread split throughout. *C*. Later spireme. *D*. Shortening of the thread. *E*. Spireme-thread divided into two parts. *F*. Spireme-thread segmented into four split chromosomes.

allowing a uniform growth to take place; and in the second place, after the granules have grown to their normal size, *to admit of their precisely equal quantitative and qualitative division*. I hold that all the succeeding phenomena, such as the grouping of the granules in threads, their union to form larger granules, the division of the thread into segments and finally into chromosomes, are of secondary importance; all these are only for the purpose of bringing about in

the simplest and most certain manner, the transmission of the daughter-granules (Spalthälften) to the daughter-cells." [1]   " In my opinion
the chromosomes are not independent individuals, but only groups of
numberless minute chromatin-granules, which alone have the value
of individuals." [2].

These observations certainly lend strong support to the view that
the chromatin is to be regarded as a morphological aggregate — as
a congeries or colony of self-propagating elementary organisms
capable of assimilation, growth, and division.   They prove, moreover, that mitosis involves two distinct though closely related factors,
one of which is the fission of the chromatic nuclear substance, while
the other is the distribution of that substance to the daughter-cells.
In the first of these it is the chromatin that takes the active part;
in the second it would seem that the main *rôle* is played by the
archoplasm, or in the last analysis, the centrosome.

E.   DIRECT OR AMITOTIC DIVISION

1. *General Sketch*

We turn now to the rarer and simpler mode of division known
as amitosis; but as Flemming has well said, it is a somewhat trying
task to give an account of a subject of which the final outcome is
so unsatisfactory as this; for in spite of extensive investigation, we
still have no very definite conclusion in regard either to the mechanism of amitosis or its biological meaning.   Amitosis, or direct division,
differs in two essential respects from mitosis.   First, the nucleus
remains in the resting state (reticulum), and there is no formation
of a spireme or of chromosomes.   Second, division occurs without
the formation of an amphiaster; hence the centrosome is not concerned with the nuclear division, which takes place by a simple
constriction.   The nuclear substance, accordingly, undergoes a division of its total *mass*, but not of its individual elements or chromatin-
granules (Fig. 40).

Before the discovery of mitosis, nuclear division was generally
assumed to take place in accordance with Remak's scheme (p. 45).
The rapid extension of our knowledge of mitotic division between
the years 1875 and 1885 showed, however, that such a mode of
division was, to say the least, of rare occurrence, and led to doubts
as to whether it ever actually took place as a normal process.   As
soon, however, as attention was especially directed to the subject,

---

[1] '93, pp. 203, 204.   [2] *l.c.*, p. 205.

many cases of amitotic division were accurately determined, though very few of them conformed precisely to Remak's scheme. One such case is that described by Carnoy in the follicle-cells of the egg in the mole-cricket, where division begins in the fission of the nucleolus, followed by that of the nucleus. Similar cases have

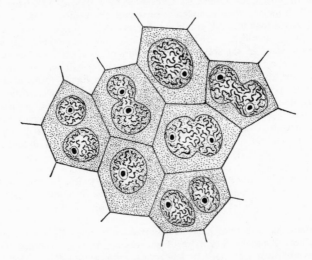

Fig. 40. — Group of cells with amitotically dividing nuclei; ovarian follicular epithelium of the cockroach. [WHEELER.]

been since described, by Hoyer ('90) in the intestinal epithelium of the nematode *Rhabdonema*, by Korschelt in the intestine of the annelid *Ophryotrocha*, and in a few other cases. In many cases, however, no preliminary fission of the nucleolus occurs; and Remak's scheme must, therefore, be regarded as one of the rarest forms of cell-division (!).

2. *Centrosome and Attraction-Sphere in Amitosis*

The behaviour of the centrosome in amitosis forms an interesting question on account of its bearing on the mechanics of cell-division. Flemming observed ('91) that the nucleus of leucocytes might in some cases divide directly without the formation of an amphiaster, the attraction-sphere remaining undivided meanwhile. Heidenhain showed in the following year, however, that in some cases leucocytes containing two nuclei (doubtless formed by amitotic division) might also contain two asters connected by a spindle. Both Heidenhain and Flemming drew from this the conclusion that direct division of the *nucleus* is in this case independent of the centrosome, but that the latter might be concerned in the division of the cell-body, though no such process was observed. A little later, however, Meves published remarkable observations that seem to indicate a functional activity of the attraction-sphere during amitotic nuclear division in the "sperma-

G

togonia" of the salamander.[1] Krause and Flemming observed that in the autumn many of these cells show peculiarly-lobed and irregular nuclei (the "polymorphic nuclei" of Bellonci). These were, and still are by some writers, regarded as degenerating nuclei. Meves, however, asserts — and the accuracy of his observations is in the main vouched for by Flemming — that in the ensuing spring these nuclei become uniformly rounded, and may then divide amitotically. In the autumn the attraction-sphere is represented by a diffused and irregular granular mass, which more or less completely surrounds the nucleus. In the spring, as the nuclei become rounded, the granular substance draws together to form a definite rounded sphere, in which a distinct centrosome may sometimes be made out. Division takes place in the following extraordinary manner: The nucleus assumes a dumb-bell shape, while the attraction-sphere becomes drawn out into a band which surrounds the central part of the nucleus, and finally forms a closed ring, encircling the nucleus. After this the nucleus divides into two, while the ring-shaped attraction-sphere ("archoplasm") is again condensed into a sphere. The appearances suggest that the ring-shaped sphere actually compresses the nucleus, and cuts it through. In a later paper ('94), Meves shows that the diffused "archoplasm" of the autumn-stage arises by the breaking down of a definite spherical attraction-sphere, which is reformed again in the spring in the manner described, and in this condition the cells may divide *either mitotically or amitotically*. He adds the interesting observation, since confirmed by Rawitz ('94), that in the spermatocytes of the salamander, the attraction-spheres of adjoining cells are often connected by intercellular bridges, but the meaning of this has not yet been determined.

It is certain that the remarkable transformation of the sphere into a ring during amitosis is not of universal, or even of general, occurrence, as shown by the later studies of vom Rath ('95, 3). In leucocytes, for example, the sphere persists in its typical form, and contains a centrosome, during every stage of the division; but it is an interesting fact that during all these stages the sphere lies on the concave side of the nucleus in the bay which finally cuts through the entire nucleus. Again, in the liver-cells of the isopod *Porcellio*, the nucleus divides, not by constriction, as in the leucocyte, but by the appearance of a nuclear plate, in the formation of which the attraction-sphere is apparently not concerned.[2] The relations of the centrosome and archoplasm in amitosis are, therefore, still in doubt; but, on the whole, the evidence goes to show that they take no essential part in the process.

3. *Biological Significance of Amitosis*

A survey of the known cases of amitosis brings out the following significant facts. It is of extreme rarity, if indeed it ever occurs in embryonic cells or such as are in the course of rapid and continued multiplication. It is frequent in pathological growths and in cells such as those of the vertebrate decidua, of the embryonic envelopes of insects, or the yolk-nuclei (periblast, etc.), *which are on the way towards degeneration*. In many cases, moreover, direct nuclear division is not followed by fission of the cell-body, so that multinuclear

[1] '91, p. 628.
[2] Such a mode of amitotic division was first described by Sabatier in the crustacea ('89), and a similar mode has been observed by Carnoy and Van der Stricht.

cells and polymorphic nuclei are thus often formed. These and many similar facts led Flemming in 1891 to express the opinion that so far as the higher plants and animals are concerned amitosis is "a process which does not lead to a new production and multiplication of cells, but wherever it occurs represents either a degeneration or an aberration, or perhaps in many cases (as in the formation of multi-nucleated cells by fragmentation) is tributary to metabolism through the increase of nuclear surface."[1] In this direction Flemming sought an explanation of the fact that leucocytes may divide either mitotically or amitotically (t. Peremeschko, Löwit, Arnold, Flemming). In the normal lymph-glands, where new leucocytes are continually regenerated, mitosis is the prevalent mode. Elsewhere (wandering-cells) both processes occur. "Like the cells of other tissues the leucocytes find their normal physiological origin (Neubildung) in mitosis; only those so produced have the power to live on and repro-duce their kind through the same process."[1] Those that divide ami-totically are on the road to ruin. Amitosis in the higher forms is thus conceived as a purely secondary process, not a survival of a primitive process of direct division from the Protozoa, as Strasburger ('82) and Waldeyer ('88) had conceived it.

This hypothesis has been carried still further by Ziegler and vom Rath ('91). In a paper on the origin of the blood in fishes, Ziegler ('87) showed that the periblast-nuclei in the eggs of fishes divide amitotically, and he was thus led like Flemming to the view that amitosis is connected with a high specialization of the cell and may be a forerunner of degeneration. In a second paper ('91), published shortly after Flemming's, he points out the fact that amitotically dividing nuclei are usually of large size and that the cells are in many cases distinguished by a specially intense secretory or assimi-lative activity. Thus, Rüge ('90) showed that the absorption of degenerate eggs in the amphibia is effected by means of leuco-cytes which creep into the egg-substance. The nuclei of these cells become enlarged, divide amitotically, and then frequently degenerate. Other observers (Korschelt, Carnoy) have noted the large size and amitotic division of the nuclei in the ovarian follicle-cells and nutritive-cells surrounding the ovum in insects and crusta-cea. Chun found in the entodermic cells of the radial canals of Siphonophores huge cells filled with nests of nuclei amitotically produced, and suggested ('90) that the multiplication of nuclei was for the purpose of increasing the nuclear surface as an aid to metabolic interchanges between nucleus and cytoplasm. Amitotic division leading to the formation of multinuclear cells is especially

[1] '91, 2, p. 291.

common in gland-cells. Thus, Klein has described such divisions in the mucous skin-glands of Amphibia, and more recently vom Rath has carefully described it in the huge gland-cells (probably salivary) of the isopod *Anilocra* ('95). Many other cases are known. Dogiel ('90) has observed exceedingly significant facts in this field that place the relations between mitosis and amitosis in a clear light. It is a well-known fact that in stratified epithelium, new cells are continually formed in the deeper layers to replace those cast off from the superficial layers. Dogiel finds in the lining of the bladder of the mouse that the nuclei of the superficial cells, which secrete the mucus covering the surface, regularly divide amitotically, giving rise to huge multinuclear cells, which finally degenerate and are cast off. The new cells that take their place are formed in the deeper layers by mitosis alone. Especially significant, again, is the case of the ciliate Infusoria, which possess two kinds of nuclei in the same cell, a macronucleus and a micronucleus. The former is known to be intimately concerned with the processes of metabolism (cf. p. 165). During conjugation the macronucleus degenerates and disappears and a new one is formed from the micronucleus or one of its descendants. The macronucleus is therefore essentially metabolic, the micronucleus generative in function. In view of this contrast it is a significant fact that while both nuclei divide during the ordinary process of fission the mitotic phenomena are as a rule less clearly marked in the macronucleus than in the micronucleus, and in some cases the former appears to divide directly while the latter always goes through a process of mitosis. In view of all these facts and others of like import Ziegler, like Flemming, concludes that amitosis is of a secondary character, and that when it occurs the series of divisions is approaching an end.

This conclusion received a very important support in the work of vom Rath on amitosis in the testis ('93). On the basis of a comparative study of amitosis in the testis-cells of vertebrates, mollusks, and arthropods he concludes that amitosis never occurs in the sperm-producing cells (spermatogonia, etc.), but only in the supporting cells (Randzellen, Stützzellen). The former multiply through mitosis alone. The two kinds of cells have, it is true, a common origin in cells which divide mitotically. When, however, they have once become differentiated, they remain absolutely distinct; amitosis never takes place in the series which finally results in the formation of spermatozoa, and the amitotically dividing "supporting-cells" sooner or later perish. Vom Rath thus reached the remarkable conclusion that "when once a cell has undergone amitotic division it has received its death-warrant; it may indeed continue for a time to divide by amitosis, but inevitably perishes in the end." ('91, p. 331.)

Whether this conclusion can be accepted without modification remains to be seen. Flemming himself regards it as too extreme, and is inclined to accept Meves' conclusion that amitosis may occur in the sperm-producing cells of the testis. The same conclusion is reached by Preusse in the case of insect-ovaries. There can be no doubt, however, that Flemming's hypothesis in a general way represents the truth, and that in the vast majority of cases amitosis is a secondary process which does not fall in the generative series of cell-divisions.

F. SUMMARY AND CONCLUSION

Three distinct elements are involved in the typical mode of cell-division by mitosis; namely, the centrosome, the chromosome, and the cell-body. Of these, the centrosome may be considered the organ of division *par excellence;* for as a rule it leads the way in division, and under its influence, in some unknown manner, is organized the astral system which is the immediate instrument of division. This system appears in the form of two asters, each containing one of the daughter-centrosomes and connected by a spindle to form an *amphiaster.* It arises as a differentiation or morphological rearrangement of the general cell-reticulum, the asters being formed from the extra-nuclear reticulum, the spindle sometimes from the linin-network sometimes from the cyto-reticulum, sometimes from both.

The chromosomes, always of the same number in a given species (with only apparent exceptions), arise by the transformation of the chromatin-reticulum into a thread which breaks into segments and splits lengthwise throughout its whole extent. The two halves are thereupon transported in opposite directions along the spindle to its respective poles and there enter into the formation of the two corresponding daughter-nuclei. The spireme-thread, and hence the chromosome, is formed as a single series of chromatin-granules or chromomeres which, by their fission, cause the splitting of the thread. Every individual chromatin-granule therefore contributes its quota to each of the daughter-nuclei.

The mechanism of mitosis is imperfectly understood. There is good reason to believe that the fission of the chromatin-granules, and hence the splitting of the thread, is not caused by division of the centrosome, but only accompanies it as a parallel phenomenon. The divergence of the daughter-chromosomes, on the other hand, is in some manner determined by the spindle-fibres developed under the influence of the centrosomes. There are cogent reasons for the view that some at least of these fibres are contractile elements which, like muscle-fibres, drag the daughter-chromosomes asunder; while other spindle-fibres act as supporting and guiding elements, and probably by their elongation push the spindle-poles apart. The contractility hypothesis is, however, difficult to apply in certain cases, and is probably an incomplete explanation which awaits further investigation. The functions of the astral rays are involved in even greater doubt, being regarded by some investigators as contractile elements like those of the spindle, by others as rigid supporting fibres like those of the central spindle. In either case one of their functions is probably to hold the kinetic centre in a fixed position while the chromosomes are pulled apart. Whether they play any part in division of the cell-body is unknown; but it must be remembered that the size of the aster is directly related to that of the resulting cell (p. 51) — a fact which indicates a very intimate relation between the aster and the dividing cell-body. On the other hand, in amitosis the cell-body may divide in the absence of asters.

These facts show that mitosis is due to the co-ordinate play of an extremely complex system of forces which are as yet scarcely comprehended. Its purpose is, however, as obvious as its physiological explanation is difficult. *It is the end of mitosis to divide every part of the chromatin of the mother-cell equally between the daughter-nuclei.* All the other operations are tributary to this. We may therefore regard the mitotic figure as essentially an apparatus for the distribution of the hereditary substance, and in this sense as the especial instrument of inheritance.

LITERATURE. II

Auerbach, L. — Organologische Studien. *Breslau*, 1874.
Van Beneden, E. — Recherches sur la maturation de l'œuf, la fécondation et la division cellulaire : *Arch. de Biol.*, IV. 1883.
Van Beneden & Neyt. — Nouvelles recherches sur la fécondation et la division mitosique chez l'Ascaride mégalocephale : *Bull. Acad. roy. de Belgique*, 1887. III. 14, No. 8.
Boveri, Th. — Zellenstudien : I. *Jena. Zeitschr.*, XXI. 1887; II. *Ibid.* XXII. 1888; III. *Ibid.* XXIV. 1890.
Brauer, A. — Über die Encystirung von Actinosphaerium Eichhorni : *Zeitschr. Wiss. Zoöl.*, LVIII. 2. 1894.
Drüner, L. — Studien über den Mechanismus der Zelltheilung. *Jena. Zeitschr.*, XXIX., II. 1894.
Erlanger, R. von. — Die neuesten Ansichten über die Zelltheilung und ihre Mechanik : *Zoöl. Centralb.*, III. 2. 1896.
Flemming, W., '92. — Entwicklung und Stand der Kenntnisse über Amitose : *Merkel und Bonnet's Ergebnisse*, II. 1892.
Id. — Zelle. (See introductory list. Also general list.)

Fol, H. — (See List IV.)

Heidenhain, M. — Cytomechanische Studien : *Arch. f. Entwickmech.*, I. 4. 1895.

Hermann, F. — Beitrag zur Lehre von der Entstehung der karyokinetischen Spindel : *Arch. Mik. Anat.*, XXXVII. 1891.

Hertwig, R. — Über Centrosoma und Centralspindel : *Sitz.-Ber. Ges. Morph. und Phys. München*, 1895, Heft I.

Mark, E. L. — (See List IV.)

Reinke, F. —Zellstudien : I. *Arch. Mik. Anat.*, XLIII. 1894 ; II. *Ibid.* XLIV. 1894.

Strasburger, E. — Karyokinetische Probleme : *Jahrb. f. Wiss. Botan.* XXVIII. 1895.

Waldeyer, W. — Über Karyokinese und ihre Beziehungen zu den Befruchtungsvorgängen : *Arch. Mik. Anat.*, XXXII. 1888. *Q.J.M.S.*, XXX. 1889–90.

CHAPTER III

THE GERM–CELLS

"Not all the progeny of the primary impregnated germ-cells are required for the formation of the body in all animals; certain of the derivative germ-cells may remain unchanged and become included in that body which has been composed of their metamorphosed and diversely combined or confluent brethren; so included, any derivative germ-cell may commence and repeat the same processes of growth by inhibition and of propagation by spontaneous fission as those to which itself owed its origin; followed by metamorphoses and combinations of the germ-masses so produced, which concur to the development of another individual."   RICHARD OWEN.[1]

"Es theilt sich demgemäss das befruchtete Ei in das Zellenmaterial des Individuums und in die Zellen für die Erhaltung der Art."   M. NUSSBAUM.[2]

THE germ from which every living form arises is a single cell, derived by the division of a parent-cell of the preceding generation. In the unicellular plants and animals this fact appears in its simplest form as the fission of the entire parent-body to form two new and separate individuals like itself. In all the multicellular types the cells of the body sooner or later become differentiated into two groups which as a matter of practical convenience may be sharply distinguished from one another. These are, to use Weismann's terms: (1) the *somatic cells*, which are differentiated into various tissues by which the functions of individual life are performed and which collectively form the "body," and (2) the *germ-cells*, which are of minor significance for the individual life and are destined to give rise to new individuals by detachment from the body. It must, however, be borne in mind that the distinction between germ-cells and somatic cells is not absolute, as some naturalists have maintained, but only relative. The cells of both groups have a common origin in the parent germ-cell; both arise through mitotic cell-division during the cleavage of the ovum or in the later stages of development; both have essentially the same structure and both *may* have the same power of development, for there are many cases in which a small fragment of the body consisting of only a few somatic cells, perhaps only of one, may give

---

[1] *Parthenogenesis*, p. 3, 1849.
[2] *Arch. Mik. Anat.* XVIII. p. 112, 1880.

rise by regeneration to a complete body. The distinction between somatic and germ-cells is an expression of the physiological division of labour; and while it is no doubt the most fundamental and important differentiation in the multicellular body, it is nevertheless to be regarded as differing only in degree, not in kind, from the distinctions between the various kinds of somatic cells.

In the lowest multicellular forms, such as *Volvox* (Fig. 41), the differentiation appears in a very clear form. Here the body consists of a hollow sphere the walls of which consist of two kinds of cells. The very numerous smaller cells are devoted to the functions of nutri-

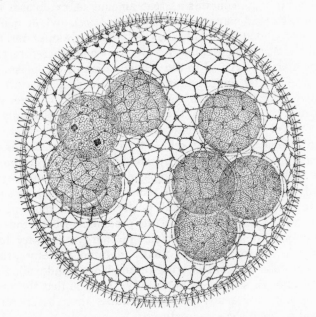

Fig. 41.— *Volvox*, showing the small ciliated somatic cells and eight large germ-cells (drawn from life by J. H. Emerton).

tion and locomotion, and sooner or later die. Eight or more larger cells are set aside as germ-cells, each of which by progressive fission may form a new individual like the parent. In this case the germ-cells are simply scattered about among the somatic cells, and no special sexual organs exist. In all the higher types the germ-cells are more or less definitely aggregated in groups, supported and nourished by somatic cells specially set apart for that purpose and forming distinct sexual organs, the *ovaries* and *spermaries* or their equivalents. Within these organs the germ-cells are carried, protected, and nourished; and here they undergo various differentiations to prepare them for their future functions.

In the earlier stages of embryological development the progenitors of the germ-cells are exactly alike in the two sexes and are indistinguishable from the surrounding somatic cells. As development proceeds, they are first differentiated from the somatic cells and then diverge very widely in the two sexes, undergoing remarkable transformations of structure to fit them for their specific functions. The structural difference thus brought about between the germ-cells is, however, only the result of physiological division of labour. The female germ-cell, or ovum, supplies most of the material for the body of the embryo and stores the food by which it is nourished. It is therefore very large, contains a great amount of cytoplasm more or less laden with food-matter (*yolk* or *deutoplasm*), and in many cases becomes surrounded by membranes or other envelopes for the protection of the developing embryo. On the whole, therefore, the early life of the ovum is devoted to the accumulation of cytoplasm and the storage of potential energy, and its nutritive processes are largely constructive or anabolic. On the other hand, the male germ-cell or spermatozoön contributes to the mass of the embryo only a very small amount of substance, comprising as a rule only a single nucleus and a centrosome. It is thus relieved from the drudgery of making and storing food and providing protection for the embryo, and is provided with only sufficient cytoplasm to form a locomotor apparatus, usually in the form of one or more cilia, by which it seeks the ovum. It is therefore very small, performs active movements, and its metabolism is characterized by the predominance of the destructive or katabolic processes by which the energy necessary for these movements is set free.[1] When finally matured, therefore, the ovum and spermatozoön have no external resemblance; and while Schwann recognized, though somewhat doubtfully, the fact that the ovum is a cell, it was not until many years afterwards that the spermatozoön was proved to be of the same nature.

A. The Ovum

The animal egg (Figs. 42, 43 *A*) is a huge spheroidal cell, sometimes naked, but more commonly surrounded by one or more membranes which may be perforated by a minute opening, the *micropyle*, through which the spermatozoön enters (Fig. 45). It contains an enormous nucleus known as the *germinal vesicle*, within which is a very conspic-

---

[1] The metabolic contrast between the germ-cells has been fully discussed in a most suggestive manner by Geddes and Thompson in their work on the *Evolution of Sex;* and these authors regard this contrast as but a particular manifestation of a metabolic contrast characteristic of the sexes in general.

uous nucleolus known to the earlier observers as the *germinal spot*. In many eggs the latter is single, but in other forms many nucleoli are present, and they are sometimes of more than one kind, as in tissue-cells.[1] In its very early stages the ovum contains a centrosome, but this afterwards disappears from view, and as a rule cannot be discovered until the final stages of maturation (at or near the time of fertilization). It is then found to lie just outside the germinal vesicle on the side nearest the egg-periphery where the polar bodies are subsequently formed After extrusion of the polar bodies (p. 131) the egg-centrosome as a rule degenerates and disappears. The egg thus loses the power of division which is afterwards restored during fertilization through the introduction of a new centrosome by the spermatozoön. In parthenogenetic eggs, on the other hand, the egg-centrosome persists, and the egg

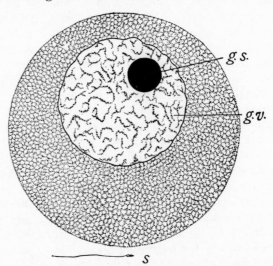

Fig. 42. — Ovarian egg of the sea-urchin *Toxopneustes* (× 750).

g.v. Nucleus or germinal vesicle, containing an irregular discontinuous network of chromatin; *g.s.* nucleolus or germinal spot, intensely stained with hæmatoxylin. The naked cell-body consists of a very regular network, the threads of which appear as irregular rows of minute granules or microsomes. Below, at *s*, is an entire spermatozoön shown at the same enlargement (both middle-piece and flagellum are slightly exaggerated in size).

accordingly retains the power of division without fertilization. The disappearance of the egg-centrosome would, therefore, seem to be in some manner a provision to necessitate fertilization and thus to guard against parthenogenesis.

The egg-cytoplasm almost always contains a certain amount of nutritive matter, the *yolk* or *deutoplasm*, in the form of solid spheres or other bodies suspended in the meshes of the reticulum and varying greatly in different cases in respect to amount, distribution, form, and chemical composition.

---

[1] Häcker ('95, p. 249) has called attention to the fact that the nucleolus is as a rule single in small eggs containing relatively little deutoplasm (cœlenterates, echinoderms, many annelids, and some copepods), while it is multiple in large eggs heavily laden with deutoplasm (lower vertebrates, insects, many crustacea).

1. *The Nucleus*

The nucleus or germinal vesicle occupies at first a central or nearly central position, though it shows in some cases a distinct eccentricity even in its earliest stages. As the growth of the egg proceeds, the eccentricity often becomes more marked, and the nucleus may thus come to lie very near the periphery. In some cases, however, the peripheral movement of the germinal vesicle occurs only a very short time before the final stages of maturation, which may coincide with the time of fertilization. Its form is typically that of a spherical sac, surrounded by a very distinct membrane (Fig. 42); but during the growth of the egg it may become irregular or even amœboid (Fig. 58), and, as Korschelt has shown in the case of insect-eggs, may move through the cytoplasm towards the source of food. Its structure is on the whole that of a typical cell-nucleus, but is subject to very great variation, not only in different animals, but also in different stages of ovarian growth. Sometimes, as in the echinoderm ovum, the chromatin forms a beautiful and regular reticulum consisting of numerous chromatin-granules suspended in a network of linin (Fig. 42). In other cases, no true reticular stage exists, the nucleus containing throughout the whole period of its growth the separate daughter-chromosomes of the preceding division (copepods, selachians, amphibia),[1] and these chromosomes may undergo the most extraordinary changes of form, bulk, and staining-reaction during the growth of the egg.[2] It is a very interesting and important fact that during the growth and maturation of the ovum a large part of the chromatin of the germinal vesicle may be lost, either by passing out bodily into the cytoplasm, by conversion into supernumerary or accessory nucleoli which finally degenerate, or by being cast out and degenerating at the time the polar bodies are formed (p. 177).

The nucleolus of the egg-cell is here, as elsewhere, a variable quantity and is still imperfectly understood. The nucleoli are of two different kinds, either or both of which may be present. One of these, the so-called *principal nucleolus*, is a rounded, usually single body, staining intensely with the same dyes that colour the chromatin, and often containing one or more vacuoles. This is typically shown in the echinoderm egg, in the eggs of many annelids, mollusks, and cœlenterates, in some crustacea, in mammals, and in some other cases. From its staining-reaction this type of nucleolus appears to correspond in a chemical sense not with the "true nucleoli" of tissue-cells, but with the net-knots or karyosomes, such as the nucleoli of nerve-cells and of many gland-cells and epithelial cells. The

[1] p. 193.   [2] p. 245.

second form comprises the so-called "accessory nucleoli," which stain less intensely, are often numerous, and perhaps correspond with the true nucleoli of tissue-cells. As growth proceeds, they usually increase in size and number, and may finally become very numerous, in which case they often occupy a peripheral position in the germinal vesicle. This is typically shown in amphibia and selachians, where there are a large number of nucleoli, which are at first scattered irregularly through the germinal vesicle but at a certain period migrate towards the periphery. In some of the mollusks and crustacea both forms coexist; but even closely related species may differ in this regard. Thus, in *Cyclops brevicornis*, according to Häcker, the very young ovum contains a single intensely chromatic nucleolus; at a later period a number of paler accessory nucleoli appear; and still later the principal nucleolus disappears, leaving only the accessory ones. In *C. strenuus*, on the other hand, there is throughout but a single nucleolus. In some of the mollusks and annelids the "germinal spot" is double, consisting of a deeply staining principal nucleolus and a paler accessory nucleolus lying beside it, as in *Cyclas* and in *Nereis* (Fig. 43).

The physiological meaning of the nucleoli is still involved in doubt. Many cases are, however, certainly known in which the nucleolus plays no part in the later development of the nucleus, being cast out or degenerating *in situ* at the time the polar bodies are formed. It is, for example, cast out bodily in the medusa *Æquorea* (Häcker) and in various annelids and echinoderms, afterwards lying for some time as a "metanucleus" in the egg-cytoplasm before degenerating. In many cases — for example in amphibia, in selachians, in many crustacea, annelids, and echinoderms — the chromosomes are formed in the germinal vesicle independently of the nucleoli (Fig. 96), which degenerate *in situ* when the membrane of the germinal vesicle disappears. The evidence is, therefore, very strong that the nucleoli do not contribute to the formation of the chromosomes, and that their substance represents passive material which is of no further direct use. There is, furthermore, strong evidence that the nucleoli of both kinds are directly or indirectly derived from the chromatin. Hence we can hardly doubt the conclusion of Häcker, that the nucleoli of the germ-cells are accumulations of by-products of the nuclear action, derived from the chromatin either by direct transformation of its substance, or as chemical cleavage-products or secretions.[1] It will be shown in

[1] Häcker regards the principal nucleolus as a more highly differentiated modification of the accessory nucleolus, and regards it as a pulsating excretory organ comparable with the contractile vacuoles of Protozoa.

Chapter V. that in some cases a large part of the chromatic reticulum is cast out, and degenerates at the time the polar bodies are formed. It would seem that the nucleoli may likewise represent a portion of the unused chromatin, more closely aggregated and more or less modified in a chemical sense.

2. *The Cytoplasm*

The egg-cytoplasm varies greatly in appearance with the variations of the deutoplasm. In such eggs as those of the echinoderm (Fig. 42), which have little or no deutoplasm, the cytoplasm forms a regular reticulum, which is perhaps to be interpreted as an alveolar structure. Its meshes consist of closely set intensely staining granules or microsomes embedded in a clearer ground-substance. The latter, which fills the spaces of the network, is apparently homogeneous, and contrasts sharply with the microsomes in staining capacity. In eggs containing yolk the deutoplasm-spheres or granules are laid down between the meshes of the network; and if they are very abundant the latter may be very greatly reduced, the cytoplasm assuming a pseudo-alveolar structure (Fig. 43), much as in plant-cells laden with reserve starch. In many cases a peripheral layer of the ovum, known as the cortical or peri-vitelline layer, is free from deutoplasm-spheres, though it is continuous with the protoplasmic network in which the latter lie (Fig. 43). Upon fertilization, or sometimes before, this layer may disappear by a peripheral movement of the yolk, as appears to be the case in *Nereis*. In other cases the peri-vitelline substance rapidly flows towards the point at which the spermatozoön enters, where a protoplasmic germinal disc is then formed; for example, in many fish-eggs.

The character of the yolk varies so widely that it can here be considered only in very general terms. The deutoplasm-bodies are commonly spherical, but often show a more or less distinctly rhomboidal or crystalloid form as in amphibia and many fishes, and in such cases they may sometimes be split up into parallel lamellæ known as *yolk-plates*. Their chemical composition varies widely, judging by the staining-reactions; but we have very little definite knowledge on this subject, and have to rely mainly on the results of analysis of the total yolk, which in the hen's egg is thus shown to consist largely of proteids, nucleo-albumins, and a variety of related substances which are often associated with fatty substances and small quantities of carbohydrates (glucose, etc.). In some cases the deutoplasm-spheres stain intensely with nuclear dyes, such as hæmatoxylin; *e.g.* in many worms and mollusks; in other cases they show a greater affinity for plasma-stains, as in many fishes and amphibia and in the annelid

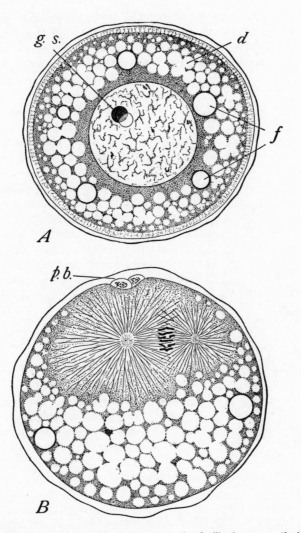

Fig. 43. — Eggs of the annelid *Nereis*, before and after fertilization, × 400 (for intermediate stages see Fig. 71).

A. Before fertilization. The large germinal vesicle occupies a nearly central position. It contains a network of chromatin in which are seen five small darker bodies; these are the quadruple chromosome-groups, or tetrads, in process of formation (not all of them are shown); these alone persist in later stages, the principal mass of the network being lost; *g.s.* double germinal spot, consisting of a chromatic and an achromatic sphere. This egg is heavily laden with yolk, in the form of clear deutoplasm-spheres (*d*) and fat-drops (*f*), uniformly distributed through the cytoplasm. The peripheral layer of cytoplasm (peri-vitelline layer) is free from deutoplasm. Outside this the membrane. *B*. The egg some time after fertilization and about to divide. The deutoplasm is now concentrated in the lower hemisphere, and the peri-vitelline layer has disappeared. Above are the two polar bodies (*p.b.*). Below them lies the mitotic figure, the chromosomes dividing.

Nereis (Fig. 43). Often associated with the proper deutoplasm-spheres are drops of oil, either scattered through the yolk (Fig. 43) or united to form a single large drop, as in many pelagic fish-eggs.

The deutoplasm is as a rule heavier than the protoplasm; and in

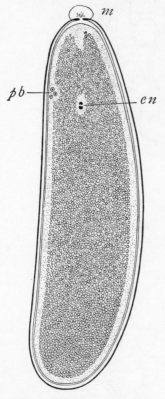

such cases, if the yolk is accumulated in one hemisphere, the egg assumes a constant position with respect to gravity, the egg-axis standing vertically with the animal pole turned upward, as in the frog, the bird, and many other cases. There are, however, many cases in which the egg may lie in any position. When fat-drops are present they usually lie in the vegetative hemisphere, and since they are lighter than the other constituents they usually cause the egg to lie with the animal pole turned downwards, as is the case with some annelids (*Nereis*) and many pelagic fish-eggs.

Fig. 44.—Schematic figure of a median longitudinal section of the egg of a fly (*Musca*), showing axes of the bilateral egg, and the membranes. [From KORSCHELT and HEIDER, after HENKING and BLOCH-MANN.]

e.n. The germ-nuclei uniting; *m.*, micropyle; *p.b.* the polar bodies. The flat side of the egg is the dorsal, the convex side the ventral, and the micropyle is at the anterior end. The deutoplasm (small circles) lies in the centre surrounded by a peripheral or peri-vitelline layer of protoplasm. The outer heavy line is the chorion, the inner lighter line the vitelline membrane, both being perforated by the micropyle, from which exudes a mass of jelly-like substance.

3. *The Egg-envelopes*

The egg-envelopes fall under three categories. These are:—

(*a*) The *vitelline membrane*, secreted by the ovum itself.

(*b*) The *chorion*, formed outside the ovum by the activity of the maternal follicle-cells.

(*c*) *Accessory envelopes*, secreted by the walls of the oviduct or other maternal structures after the ovum has left the ovary.

Only the first of these properly belongs to the ovum, the second and third being purely maternal products. There are some eggs, such as those of certain cœlenterates (*e.g.* *Renilla*), that are naked throughout their whole development. In many others, of which the sea-urchin is a type, the fresh-laid egg is naked but forms a vitelline membrane almost instantaneously after the spermatozoön touches it.[1]   In other forms (insects, birds) the vitelline membrane may be present before fertilization, and in such cases the egg is often surrounded by a chorion as well.   The latter is usually very thick and firm and may have a shell-like consistency, its surface sometimes showing various peculiar markings, prominences, or sculptured patterns characteristic of the species (insects).[2]

The accessory envelopes are too varied to be more than touched upon here.   They include not only the products of the oviduct or uterus, such as the albumin, shell-membrane, and shell of birds and reptiles, the gelatinous mass investing amphibian ova, the capsules of molluscan ova and the like, but also nutritive fluids and capsules secreted by the external surface of the body, as in leeches and earthworms.

When the egg is surrounded by a membrane before fertilization it is often perforated by one or more openings known as *micropyles*, through which the spermatozoa make their entrance (Figs. 44, 45).   Where there is but one micropyle, it is usually situated very near the upper or anterior pole (fishes, many insects), but it may be at the opposite pole (some insects and mollusks), or even on the side (insects).   In many insects there is a group of half a dozen or more micropyles near the upper pole of the egg, and perhaps correlated with this is the fact that several spermatozoa enter the egg, though only one is concerned with the actual process of fertilization.

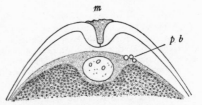

Fig. 45. — Upper pole of the egg of *Argonauta*. [Ussow.]

The egg is surrounded by a very thick membrane, perforated at *m* by the funnel-shaped micropyle; below the latter lies the egg-nucleus in the peri-vitelline layer of protoplasm; *p.b.* the polar bodies.

The plant ovum, which is usually known as the *oösphere* (Figs. 46, 80), shows the same general features as that of animals, being a relatively large, quiescent, rounded cell containing a large nucleus. It never, however, attains the dimensions or the complexity of structure shown in many animal eggs, since it always remains attached to the maternal structures, by which it is provided with food and invested with protective envelopes.   It is therefore naked, as a rule, and is not heavily laden with reserve food-matters such as the deutoplasm of animal ova.   A vitelline membrane is, however, often formed soon after fertilization, as in echinoderms.   The most interesting feature

[1] That the vitelline membrane does not pre-exist seems to be established by the fact that egg-fragments likewise surround themselves with a membrane when fertilized.   (Hertwig).

[2] In some cases, according to Wheeler, the insect-egg has only a chorion, the vitelline membrane being absent.

H

of the plant-ovum is the fact that it often contains plastids (leuco-plasts or chromatophores) which, by their division, give rise to those of the embryonic cells. These sometimes have the form of typical chromatophores containing pyrenoids, as in *Volvox* and many other algæ (Fig. 46). In the higher forms (archegoniate plants), according to the researches of Schmitz and Schimper, the egg contains numerous minute colourless "leucoplasts," which afterwards develop into green chromatophores or into the starch-building amylo-plasts. This is a point of great theoretical interest; for the researches of Schmitz, Schimper, and others have rendered it highly probable

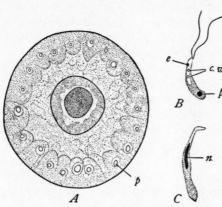

Fig. 46.—Germ-cells of *Volvox*. [OVERTON.]

A. Ovum (oösphere) containing a large central nucleus and a peripheral layer of chromatophores; *p.* pyrenoid. *B.* Spermatozoid; *c.v.* contractile vacuoles; *e.* "eye-spot" (chromoplastid); *p.* pyrenoid. *C.* Spermatozoid stained to show the nucleus (*n*).

that these plastids are persistent morphological bodies that arise only by the division of pre-existing bodies of the same kind, and hence may be traced continuously from one generation to another through the germ-cells. In the lower plants (algæ) they may occur in both germ-cells; in the higher forms they are found in the female alone and in such cases the plastids of the embryonic body are of purely maternal origin.

B. The Spermatozoön

Although spermatozoa were among the first of animal cells observed by the microscope, their real nature was not determined for more than two hundred years after their discovery. Our modern knowledge of the subject may be dated from the year 1841, when Kölliker proved that they were not parasitic animalcules, as the early observers supposed, but the products of cells pre-existing in the parent body. Kölliker, however, did not identify them as cells, but believed them to be of purely nuclear origin. We owe to Schweigger-Seidel and La Valette St. George the proof, simultaneously brought forward by these authors in 1865,[1] that the spermatozoön is a complete cell, consisting of nucleus and cytoplasm, and hence of the same

[1] *Arch. Mik. Anat.*, I., '65.

morphological nature as the ovum.   It is of extraordinary minuteness, being in many cases less than $\frac{1}{100000}$ the bulk of the ovum.[1]   Its precise study is therefore difficult, and it is not surprising that our knowledge of its structure and origin is still far from complete.

1. *Flagellate Spermatozoa*

In its more usual form the animal spermatozoön resembles a minute, elongated tadpole, which swims very actively about by the

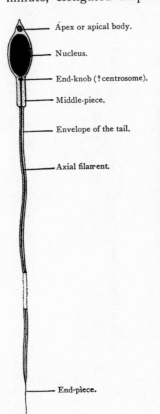

Apex or apical body.

Nucleus.

End-knob (? centrosome).

Middle-piece.

Envelope of the tail.

Axial filament.

End-piece.

Fig. 47. — Diagram of the flagellate spermatozoön.

vibrations of a long, slender tail morphologically comparable with a single cilium or flagellum.   Such a spermatozoön consists typically of four parts, as shown in Fig. 47 : —

1. The *nucleus*, which forms the main portion of the " head," and consists of a very dense and usually homogeneous mass of chromatin staining with great intensity with the so-called "nuclear dyes" (*e.g.* hæmatoxylin or the basic anilines such as methyl-green).   It is surrounded by a very thin cytoplasmic envelope.

2. A minute *apex*, or apical body, as a rule of cytoplasmic origin, though apparently derived in some cases from the nucleus.   This lies at the front end of the head, and in some cases terminates in a sharp spur by means of which the spermatozoön bores its way into the ovum.

3. The *middle-piece*, or connecting piece, a larger cytoplasmic body lying behind the head and giving attachment to the tail. This body shows the same staining-reaction as the tip, having an especial affinity for " plasma-stains " (acid fuchsin, etc.).

4. The *tail*, or *flagellum*, in part, at least, a cytoplasmic product developed from or in connection with the " archoplasm " (attraction-sphere or " Nebenkern ") of the mother-cell.   It consists of a fibrillated *axial filament* surrounded by an *envelope* which sometimes shows a fibrillar structure, sometimes winds spirally about the axial filament, and is in certain cases differ-

[1] In the sea-urchin, *Toxopneustes*, I estimate its bulk as being between $\frac{1}{400000}$ and $\frac{1}{500000}$ the volume of the ovum.   The inequality is in many cases very much greater.

entiated into a fin-like undulating membrane. The axial filament
may be traced through the middle-piece up to the head, at the base of
which it terminates in a minute body, single or double, known as
the *end-knob*, and not improbably representing the centrosome.

There is still some doubt regarding the nature and functions of
these various parts. The nucleus is proved both by its origin and
by its history during fertilization to be exactly equivalent to the
nucleus of the mature egg. The middle-piece and the tail represent

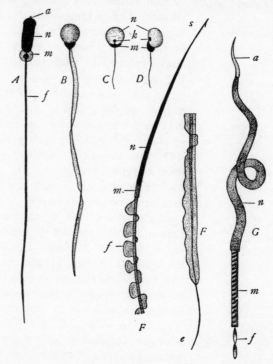

Fig. 48. — Spermatozoa of fishes and amphibia.   [BALLOWITZ.]

A. Sturgeon. *B.* Pike. *C. D. Leuciscus.* *E. Triton* (anterior part). *F. Triton* (posterior
part of flagellum). *G. Raja* (anterior part). *a.* apical body; *e.* end-piece; *f.* flagellum; *k.* end-
knob (? centrosome) ; *m.* middle-piece; *n.* nucleus; *s.* apical spur.

the principal mass of the cytoplasm of the sperm-cell, and the middle-piece is probably to be regarded as merely the thickened basal
portion of the flagellum.

The principal uncertainty relates to the position of the centrosome. It is certain that in most cases the centrosome or attraction-
sphere lies in the *middle-piece;* for from it the centrosome arises
during the fertilization of the egg, in every accurately known case.
In a few cases, moreover, the middle-piece has been traced back to

the attraction-sphere of the mother-cell, from which the spermatozoön is formed in the testis. On the other hand, a few observers
have maintained, apparently on good evidence, that the centrosome
lies, not in the middle-piece, but at the apex (p. 123).

Reviewing these facts from a physiological point of view, we may
arrange the parts of the spermatozoön under two categories as
follows: —

1. The *essential structures* which play a direct part in fertilization.
   These are: —
   (*a*) The *nucleus*, which contains the chromatin and is to be
   regarded as the vehicle of inheritance.
   (*b*) The *centrosome*, certainly contained in the middle-piece as
   a rule, though perhaps lying in the tip in some cases.
   This is the fertilizing element *par excellence*, in Boveri's
   sense, since when introduced into the egg it causes the
   development of the amphiaster by which the egg divides.

2. The *accessory structures*, which play no direct part in fertilization,
   viz. : —
   (*a*) The *apex* or *spur*, by which the spermatozoön attaches itself
   to the egg or bores its way into it.
   (*b*) The *tail*, a locomotor organ which carries the nucleus and
   centrosome, and, as it were, deposits them in the egg at
   the time of fertilization. There can be little doubt that
   the substance of the flagellum is contractile, and that its
   movements are of the same nature as those of ordinary
   cilia. Ballowitz's discovery of its fibrillated structure is
   therefore of great interest, as indicating its structural as
   well as physiological similarity to a muscle-fibre. Moreover, as will appear beyond, it is nearly certain that the
   contractile fibrillæ are derived from the attraction-sphere
   of the mother-cell, and therefore arise in the same manner
   as the archoplasm-fibres of the mitotic figure — a conclusion of especial interest in its relation to Van Beneden's
   theory of mitosis (p. 70).

Tailed spermatozoa conforming more or less nearly to the type
just described are with few exceptions found throughout the Metazoa
from the cœlenterates up to man; but they show a most surprising
diversity in form and structure in different groups of animals, and
the homologies between the different forms have not yet been fully
determined. The simpler forms, for example those of echinoderms
and some of the fishes (Figs. 48 and 74), conform very nearly to the
foregoing description. Every part of the spermatozoön may, how-

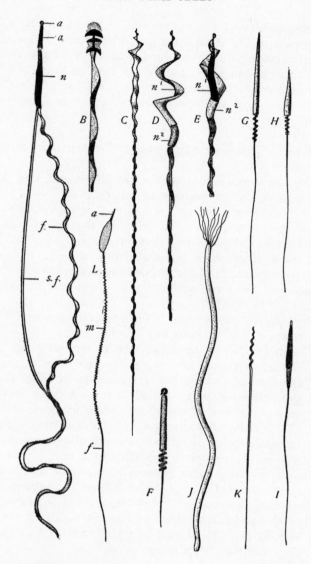

Fig. 49.—Spermatozoa of various animals. [*A–I, L,* from BALLOWITZ; *J, K,* from VON BRUNN.]

A. (At the left). Beetle (*Copris*), partly macerated to show structure of flagellum; it consists of a supporting fibre (*s.f.*) and a fin-like envelope (*f.*); *n.* nucleus; *a. a.* apical body divided into two parts (the posterior of these is perhaps a part of the nucleus). *B.* Insect (*Calathus*), with barbed head and fin-membrane. *C.* Bird (*Phyllopneuste*). *D.* Bird (*Muscicapa*), showing spiral structure; nucleus divided into two parts (n^1, n^2); no distinct middle-piece. *E.* Bulfinch; spiral membrane of head. *F.* Gull (*Larus*) with spiral middle-piece and apical knob. *G. H*, Giant spermatozoön and ordinary form of *Tadorna*. *I.* Ordinary form of the same stained, showing apex, nucleus, middle-piece and flagellum. *J.* "Vermiform spermatozoön" and, *K.* ordinary spermatozoön of the snail *Paludina*. *L.* Snake (*Coluber*), showing apical body (*a*), nucleus, greatly elongated middle-piece (*m*), and flagellum (*f*).

ever, vary more or less widely from it (Figs. 48–50). The head
(nucleus) may be spherical, lance-shaped, rod-shaped, spirally twisted,
hook-shaped, hood-shaped, or drawn out into a long filament; and
it is often divided into an anterior and a posterior piece of different
staining capacity, as is the case with many birds and mammals.
The apex sometimes appears to be wanting — *e.g.* in some fishes
(Fig. 48). When present, it is sometimes a minute rounded knob,
sometimes a sharp stylet, and in some cases terminates in a sharp
barbed spur by which the spermatozoön appears to penetrate the
ovum (*Triton*). In the mammals it seems to be represented by a
cap-like structure, the so-called "head-cap," which in some forms
covers the anterior end of the nucleus. It is sometimes divided into
two distinct parts, a longer posterior piece and a knob-like anterior
piece (insects, according to Ballowitz).

The middle-piece or connecting-piece shows a like diversity
(Figs. 48–50). In many cases it is sharply differentiated from
the flagellum, being sometimes nearly spherical, sometimes flattened
like a cap against the nucleus, and sometimes forming a short
cylinder of the same diameter as the nucleus, and hardly distinguishable from the latter until after staining (newt, earthworm).
In other cases it is very long (reptiles, some mammals), and is
scarcely distinguishable from the flagellum. In still others (birds,
some mammals) it passes insensibly into the flagellum, and no
sharply marked limit between them can be seen. In many of the
mammals the long connecting-piece is separated from the head by
a narrow "neck" in which the end-knobs lie, as described below.

Internally, the middle-piece consists of an axial filament and an
envelope, both of which are continuous with those of the flagellum.
In some cases the envelope shows a distinctly spiral structure, like
that of the tail-envelope; but this is not always visible. The most
interesting part of the middle-piece is the "end-knob" in which the
axial filament terminates, at the base of the nucleus. In some cases
this appears to be single. More commonly it consists of two minute
bodies lying side by side (Fig. 50, *B*, *D*). This body is the only
structure in the middle-piece having the appearance of a centrosome;
and Hermann conjectures that this is probably its real nature.

The flagellum or tail is merely a locomotor organ which plays
no part in fertilization. It is, however, the most complex part of
the spermatozoön, and shows a very great diversity in structure.
Its most characteristic feature is the *axial filament*, which, as Ballowitz has shown, is composed of a large number of parallel fibrillæ,
like a muscle-fibre. This is surrounded by a cytoplasmic envelope,
which sometimes shows a striated or spiral structure, and in which,
or in connection with which, may be developed secondary or acces-

sory filaments and other structures. At the tip the axial filament may lose its envelope and thus give rise to the so-called "end-piece" (Retzius). In *Triton*, for example (Fig. 48, *F*), the envelope of the axial filament ("principal filament") gives attachment to a remarkable fin-like membrane, having a frilled or undulating free margin along which is developed a "marginal filament." Towards the tip of the tail, the fin, and finally the entire envelope, disappears, leaving only the axial filament to form the end-piece. After maceration the envelope shows a conspicuous cross-striation, which perhaps indicates a spiral structure such as occurs in the mammals. The marginal filament, on the other hand, breaks up into numerous parallel fibrillæ, while the axial filament remains unaltered (Ballowitz).

A fin-membrane has also been observed in some insects and fishes, and has been asserted to occur in mammals (man included). Later observers have, however, failed to find the fin in mammals, and their observations indicate that the axial filament is merely surrounded by an envelope which sometimes shows traces of the same spiral arrangement as that which is so conspicuous in the connecting-piece. In the skate the tail has two filaments, both composed of parallel fibrillæ, connected by a membrane and spirally twisted about each other; a somewhat

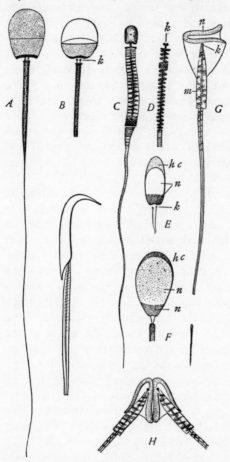

Fig. 50.—Spermatozoa of mammals. (*A–F* from BALLOWITZ.)

A. Badger (living). *B.* The same after staining. *C.* Bat (*Vesperugo*). *D.* The same, flagellum and middle-piece or connecting-piece, showing end-knobs. *E.* Head of the spermatozoön of the bat (*Rhinolophus*) showing details. *F.* Head of spermatozoön of the pig. *G.* Opossum (after staining). *H.* Double spermatozoa from the *vas deferens* of the opossum. *I.* Rat.

h.c. head-cap (apex) ; *k.* end-knob (? centrosome); *m.* middle-piece; *n.* nucleus (in *B, E, F* consisting of two different parts).

similar structure occurs in the toad. In some beetles there is a fin-membrane attached to a stiff axial "supporting fibre" (Fig. 49, *A*). The membrane itself is here composed of four parallel fibres which differ entirely from the supporting fibre in staining capacity and in the fact that each of them may be further resolved into a large number of more elementary fibrillæ.

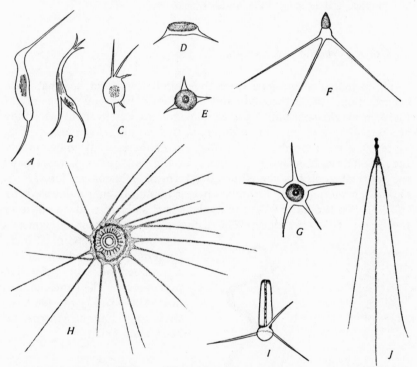

Fig. 51. — Unusual forms of spermatozoa.

A. B. C. Living amœboid spermatozoa of the crustacean *Polyphemus.* [ZACHARIAS.]
D. E. Spermatozoa of crab, *Dromia. F.* Of *Ethusa, G.* of *Maja, H.* of *Inachus,* [GROBBEN.]
I. Spermatozoön of lobster, *Homarus.* [HERRICK.]
J. Spermatozoön of crab, *Porcellana.* [GROBBEN.]

Many interesting details have necessarily been passed over in the foregoing account. One of these is the occurrence, in some birds, amphibia (frog), and mollusks, of two kinds of spermatozoa in the same animal. In the birds and amphibia the spermatozoa are of two sizes, but of the same form, the larger being known as "giant spermatozoa" (Fig. 49, *G, H*). In the gasteropod *Paludina* the two kinds differ entirely in structure, the smaller form being of the usual type and not unlike those of birds, while the larger, or "vermiform," spermatozoa have a worm-like shape and bear a tuft of cilia at one end, somewhat like the spermatozoids of plants (Fig. 49, *J, K*). In this case only the smaller spermatozoa are functional (von Brunn).

No less remarkable is the conjugation of spermatozoa in pairs (Fig. 50, *H*), which takes place in the *vas deferens* in the opossum (Selenka) and in some insects (Ballowitz, Auerbach). Ballowitz's researches ('95) on the double spermatozoa of beetles (*Dytiscidæ*) prove that the union is not primary, but is the result of an actual conjugation of previously separate spermatozoa. Not merely two, but three or more spermatozoa may thus unite to form a " spermatozeugma," which swims like a single spermatozoön. Whether the spermatozoa of such a group separate before fertilization is unknown; but Ballowitz has found the groups, after copulation, in the female receptaculum, and he believes that they may enter the egg in this form. The physiological meaning of the process is unknown.

2. *Other Forms of Spermatozoa*

The principal deviations from the flagellate type of spermatozoön occur among the arthropods and nematodes (Fig. 51). In many of these forms the spermatozoa have no flagellum, and in some cases they are actively amœboid; for example, in the daphnid *Polyphemus* (Fig. 51, *A, B, C*) as described by Leydig and Zacharias. More commonly they are motionless like the ovum. In the chilognathous myriapods the spermatozoön has sometimes the form of a bi-convex lens (*Polydesmus*), sometimes the form of a hat or helmet having a double brim (*Julus*). In the latter case the nucleus is a solid disc at the base of the hat. In many decapod Crustacea the spermatozoön consists of a cylindrical or conical body from one end of which radiate a number of stiff spine-like processes. The nucleus lies near the base. In none of these cases has the centrosome been identified.

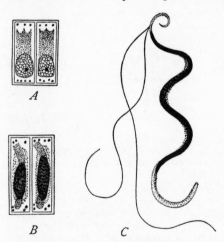

Fig. 52,—Spermatozoids of *Chara*. [BELAJEFF.] *A*. Mother-cells with reticular nuclei. *B*. Later stage, with spermatozoids forming. *C*. Mature spermatozoid (the elongate nucleus black).

3. *Paternal Germ-cells of Plants*

In the flowering plants the male germ-cell is represented by a " generative nucleus," together with two centrosomes and a small amount of cytoplasm, lying at the tip of the pollen-tube (Fig. 80, *A*). On the other hand, in a large number of the lower plants (Pteridophytes, Muscineæ, and many others), the male germ-cell is a minute actively swimming cell, known as the *spermatozoid*, which is closely analogous to the spermatozoön. The spermatozoids are in general less highly differentiated than spermatozoa, and often show a distinct resemblance to the asexual swarmers or zoöspores so common in the lower plants (Figs. 52, 53). They differ in two respects from animal spermatozoa; first in possessing not one but two or several flagella; second, in the fact that these are attached as a rule not to the end of the cell, but on the side. In the lower forms plastids are present in the form of chromatophores, one of which may be differentiated into a red "eye-spot,' as in *Volvox* and *Fucus* (Figs. 41, 53, *A*), and they may even contain contractile vacuoles (*Volvox*); but both these structures are wanting in the higher forms. These consist only of a nucleus with a very small amount of cytoplasm, and have typically a spiral form. In *Chara*, where their structure and development have recently been carefully studied by Belajeff, the spermatozoids have an elongated spiral form with two long flagella attached near the pointed end which is

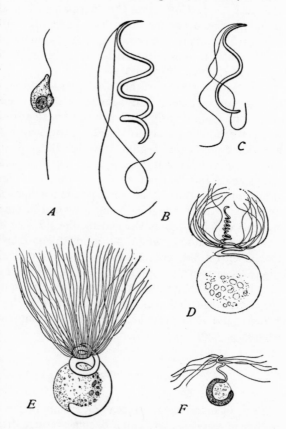

Fig. 53.—Spermatozoids of plants. [*A, B, C, E*, after GUIGNARD; *D, F*, after STRASBURGER.]

A. Of an alga (*Fucus*); a red chromatophore at the right of the nucleus. *B.* Liverwort (*Pellia*). *C.* Moss (*Sphagnum*). *D. Marsilia. E.* Fern (*Angiopteris*). *F.* Fern, *Phegopteris* (the nucleus dark).

directed forwards in swimming (Fig. 52). The main body of the spermatozoid is occupied by a dense, apparently homogeneous nucleus surrounded by a very delicate layer of cytoplasm. Behind the nucleus lies a granular mass of cytoplasm, forming one end of the cell, while in front is a slender cytoplasmic tip to which the flagella are attached. Nearly similar spermatozoids occur in the liverworts and mosses. In the ferns and other pteridophytes a somewhat different type occurs (Fig. 53). Here the spermatozoid is twisted into a conical spiral and bears numerous cilia attached along the upper turns of the spire. The nucleus occupies the lower turns, and attached to them is a large spheroidal cytoplasmic mass, which may, however, be cast off when the spermatozoid is set free or at the time it enters the archegonium. This, according to Strasburger, probably corresponds to the basal cytoplasmic mass of *Chara*. The upper portion of the spire to which the cilia are attached is composed of cytoplasm alone, as in *Chara*.

The homologies, or rather analogies, between the respective parts of the spermatozoid and spermatozoön are not yet very definitely established, since the history of the spermatozoid in fertilization has not yet been accurately followed. Strasburger ('92) believes that the anterior cytoplasmic region, to which the cilia are attached, consists of "kinoplasm" (archoplasm), and hence corresponds with the middle-piece of the spermatozoön. If this view be correct, there is, on the whole, a rather close correspondence between spermatozoid and spermatozoön, the flagella being attached in both cases to that end of the cell which contains the centrosome or kinetic centre, the nucleus lying in the middle, while the opposite end consists of cytoplasm (*i.e.* the apex of the spermatozoön, the cytoplasmic vesicle of pteridophytes, the basal cytoplasm of *Chara*, etc.). The attachment of the flagella in both cases to the archoplasmic region is a significant fact, for Strasburger believes that they arise from the "kinoplasm" (archoplasm), and it is probable that the spermatozoön tail has a similar origin (p. 126).

C. Origin and Growth of the Germ-cells

Both ova and spermatozoa take their origin from cells known as primordial germ-cells, which become clearly distinguishable from the somatic cells at an early period of development, and are at first exactly alike in the two sexes. What determines their subsequent sexual differentiation is unknown save in a few special cases. From such data as we possess, there is very strong reason to believe that, with a few exceptions, the primordial germ-cells are sexually indifferent, *i.e.* neither male nor female, and that their transformation into ova or spermatozoa is not due to an inherent predisposition, but is a reaction to external stimulus. The nature of the stimulus appears to vary in different cases. Thus Maupas's experiments seem to show conclusively that, in rotifers, the differentiation may depend on temperature, a high temperature tending to produce males, a low temperature, females; while those of Mrs. Treat on lepidoptera and of Yung on amphibia seem to leave no doubt that the differentiation here depends on the character of the nutrition, highly-fed individuals producing a great preponderance of females, while those that are underfed give rise to a preponderance of males. These and a multitude of related observations by many botanists and zoölogists render it certain that sex as such is not inherited. What is inherited is, in Düsing's words, only the particular manner in which one or the other sex comes to development. The *determination* of sex is not by inheritance, but by the combined effect of external conditions.[1] In some of the rotifers, however, sex is predetermined from the begin-

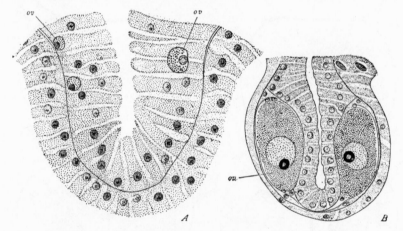

Fig. 54. — Germ-cells in the hydro-medusa, *Hydractinia*. [BUNTING.]
A. Section through young medusa-bud, with very young ova (*ov.*) lying in the entoderm,
B. Mature gonophore, showing two ova lying between ectoderm and entoderm.

ning, the eggs being of two sizes, of which the larger produce females; the smaller, males.

In the greater number of cases, the primordial germ-cells arise in a germinal epithelium which, in the cœlenterates (Fig. 54), may be a part of either the ectoderm or entoderm, and, in the higher types, is a modified region of the peritoneal epithelium lining the body-cavity. In such cases the primordial germ-cells may be scarcely distinguishable at first from the somatic cells of the epithelium. But in other cases the germ-cells may be traced much farther back in the development, and they or their progenitors may sometimes be identified in the gastrula or blastula stage, or even in the early cleavage-stages. Thus in the worm *Sagitta*, Hertwig has traced the germ-cells back to

---

[1] See Düsing, '84; Geddes, *Sex*, in *Encyclopedia Britannica;* Geddes and Thompson, *The Evolution of Sex;* Watase, *On the Phenomena of Sex-differentiation*, '92.

two primordial germ-cells lying at the apex of the archenteron.   In
some of the insects they appear still earlier as the products of a large
"pole-cell" lying at one end of the segmenting ovum, which divides

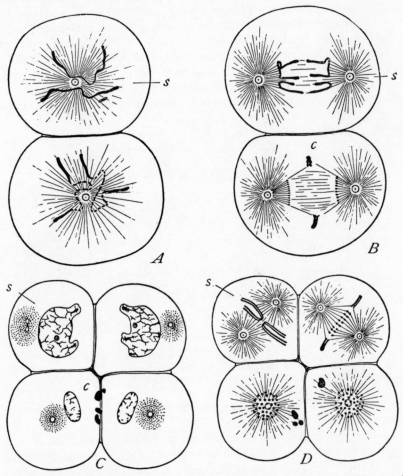

Fig. 55. — Origin of the primordial germ-cells and casting out of chromatin in the somatic
cells of *Ascaris*.   [BOVERI.]

   A. Two-cell stage dividing; *s.* stem-cell, from which arise the germ-cells.   *B*. The same from
the side, later in the second cleavage, showing the two types of mitosis and the casting out of
chromatin (*c*) in the somatic cell.   *C*. Resulting 4-cell stage; the eliminated chromatin at *c*.
D. The third cleavage, repeating the foregoing process in the two upper cells.

into two and finally gives rise to two symmetrical groups of germ-
cells.   Haecker has recently traced very carefully the origin of the
primordial germ-cells in *Cyclops* from a "stem-cell" (Fig. 56) clearly
distinguishable from surrounding cells in the early blastula stage, not

only by its size, but also by its large nuclei rich in chromatin, and by its peculiar mode of mitosis, as described beyond.

The most beautiful and remarkable known case of early differentiation of the germ-cells is that of *Ascaris*, where Boveri was able to trace them back continuously through all the cleavage-stages to the two-cell stage!   Moreover, from the outset the progenitor of the germ-cells *differs from the somatic cells not only in the greater size and richness of chromatin of its nuclei, but also in its mode of mitosis;* for in all those blastomeres destined to produce somatic cells a portion of the chromatin is cast out into the cytoplasm, where it degenerates, and *only in the germ-cells is the sum total of the chromatin retained.*   In *Ascaris megalocephala univalens* the process is as follows (Fig. 55): Each of the first two cells receives two elongated chromosomes.   As the ovum prepares for the second cleavage, the two chromosomes reappear in each, but differ in their behaviour (Fig. 55, *A*, *B*).   In one of them, which is destined to produce only somatic cells, the thickened ends of each chromosome are cast off into the cytoplasm and degenerate.   Only the thinner central part is retained and distributed to the daughter-cells, breaking up meanwhile into a large number of segments which split lengthwise in the usual manner.   In the other cell, which may be called the *stem-cell* (Fig. 55, *s*), all the chromatin is preserved and the chromosomes do not segment into smaller pieces.   The results are plainly apparent in the 4-cell stage, the two somatic nuclei, which contain the reduced amount of chromatin, being small and pale, while those of the two stem-cells are far larger and richer in chromatin (Fig. 55, *C*).   At the ensuing division (Fig. 55, *D*) the numerous, minute segments reappear in the two somatic cells, divide, and are distributed like ordinary chromosomes; and the same is true of all their descendants thenceforward.   The other two cells (containing the large nuclei) exactly repeat the history of the two-cell stage, the two long chromosomes reappearing in each of them, becoming segmented and casting off their ends in one, but remaining intact in the other, which gives rise to two cells with large nuclei as before.   This process is repeated five times (Boveri), or six (Zur Strassen), after which the chromatin-elimination ceases, and the two stem-cells or primordial germ-cells thenceforward give rise only to other germ-cells and the entire chromatin is preserved.   Through this remarkable process it comes to pass that in this animal *only the germ-cells receive the sum total of the egg-chromatin handed down from the parent.   All of the somatic cells contain only a portion of the original germ-substance.*
" The original nuclear constitution of the fertilized egg is transmitted, as if by a law of primogeniture, only to one daughter-cell, and by this again to one, and so on; while in the other daughter-cells, the

chromatin in part degenerates, in part is transformed, so that all of the descendants of these side-branches receive small reduced nuclei." [1]

It would be difficult to overestimate the importance of this discovery; for although it stands at present an almost isolated case, yet it gives us, as I believe, the key to a true theory of differentiation development,[2] and may in the end prove the means of explaining many phenomena that are now among the unsolved riddles of the cell.

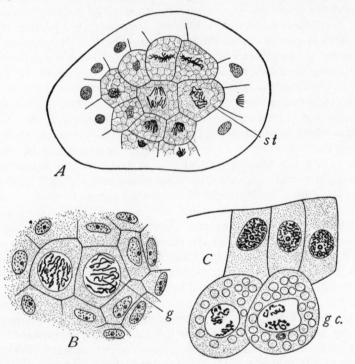

Fig. 56. — Primordial germ-cells in *Cyclops*. [HÄCKER.]

A. Young embryo, showing stem-cell (*st*). *B.* The stem-cell has divided into two, giving rise to the primordial germ-cell (*g*). *C.* Later stage, in section; the primordial germ-cell has migrated into the interior and divided into two; two groups of chromosomes in each.

Häcker ('95) has shown that the nuclear changes in the stem-cells and primordial eggs of *Cyclops* show some analogy to those of *Ascaris*, though no casting out of chromatin occurs. The nuclei are very large and rich in chromatin as compared with the somatic cells, and the number of chromosomes, though not precisely determined, is less than in the somatic cells (Fig. 56). Vom Rath, working in the same direction, has found that in the salamander also the number of chromosomes in the early progenitors of the germ-cells

---

[1] Boveri, '91, p. 437.   [2] Cf. p. 321.

is one-half that characteristic of the somatic cells.[1] In both these cases, the chromosomes are doubtless bivalent, representing two chromosomes joined together. In *Ascaris*, in like manner, each of the two chromosomes of the stem-cell or primordial germ-cells is probably plurivalent, and represents a combination of several units of a lower order which separate during the segmentation of the thread when the somatic mitosis occurs.

D. Growth and Differentiation of the Germ-cells

1. *The Ovum*

(a) *Growth and Nutrition.* — Aside from the transformations of the nucleus, which are considered elsewhere, the story of the ovarian history of the egg is largely a record of the changes involved in nutrition and the storage of material. As the primordial germ-cells enlarge to form the mother-cells of the eggs, they almost invariably become intimately associated with neighbouring cells which not only support and protect them, but also serve as a means for the elaboration of food for the growing egg-cell. One of the simplest arrangements is that occurring in cœlenterates, where the egg lies loose either in one of the general layers or in a mass of germinal tissue, and may crawl actively about among the surrounding cells like an *Amœba*.[2] More commonly, a definite association is established between the egg and the surrounding cells. In one of the most frequent arrangements the ovarian cells form a regular layer or *follicle* about the ovum (Figs. 58, 60), and there is very strong reason to believe that the follicle-cells are immediately concerned with the conveyance of nutriment to the ovum. A number of observers have maintained that the follicle-cells may actually migrate into the interior of the egg, and this seems to be definitely established in the case of the tunicates.[3] Such cases are, in any case, extremely rare; and, as a rule, the material elaborated by the nutritive cells is passed into the egg in solution. Very curious and suggestive conditions occur among the annelids and insects. In the annelids, the nutritive cells often do not form a follicle, but in some forms each egg is accompanied by a single nurse-cell, attached to its side, with which it floats free in the body-cavity. In *Ophryotrocha*, where it has been carefully described by Korschelt, the nurse-cell is at first much larger

---

[1] Cf. p. 194, Chapter V.

[2] It has been asserted that the eggs in such cases feed on the other cells by ingulfing them bodily, Amœba-fashion. This is probably an error.

[3] See Floderus, '95.

I

than the egg itself, and contains a large, irregular nucleus, rich in chromatin (Fig. 57). The egg-cell rapidly grows, apparently at the expense of the nurse-cell, which becomes reduced to a mere rudiment attached to one side of the egg and finally disappears. There can hardly be a doubt, as Korschelt maintains, that the nurse-cell is in some manner connected with the elaboration of food for the growing egg-cell; and the intensely chromatic character of the nucleus is well worthy of note in this connection.

Somewhat similar nurse-cells occur in the insects, where they have been carefully described by Korschelt. The eggs here lie in a series in the ovarian "egg-tubes" alternating with nutritive cells vari-

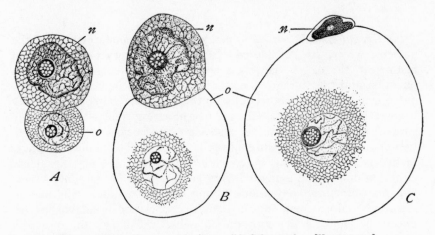

Fig. 57. — Egg and nurse-cell in the annelid, *Ophryotrocha*. [KORSCHELT.]
A. Young stage, the nurse-cell (*n*), larger than the egg (*o*). *B.* Growth of the ovum. *C.* Late stage, the nurse-cell degenerating.

ously arranged in different cases. In the butterfly *Vanessa*, each egg is surrounded by a regular follicular layer of cells, a few of which at one end are differentiated into nurse-cells. These cells are very large and have huge amœboid nuclei, rich in chromatin (Fig. 58, *A*). In the ear-wig, *Forficula*, the arrangement is still more remarkable, and recalls that occurring in *Ophryotrocha*. Here each egg lies in the egg-tube just below a very large nurse-cell, which, when fully developed, has an enormous branching nucleus as shown in Fig. 115. In these two cases, again, the nurse-cell is characterized by the extraordinary development of its nucleus — a fact which points to an intimate relation between the nucleus and the metabolic activity of the cell.[1]

In all these cases it is doubtful whether the nurse-cells are sister-

[1] See p. 254.

cells of the egg which have sacrificed their own development for the sake of their companions, or whether they have had a distinct origin from a very early period. That the former alternative is possible is shown by the fact that such a sacrifice occurs in some animals after the eggs have been laid. Thus in the earthworm, *Lumbricus terrestris*, several eggs are laid, but only one develops into an embryo, and the latter devours the undeveloped eggs. A similar process occurs in the marine gasteropods, where the eggs thus sacrificed may undergo certain stages of development before their dissolution.[1]

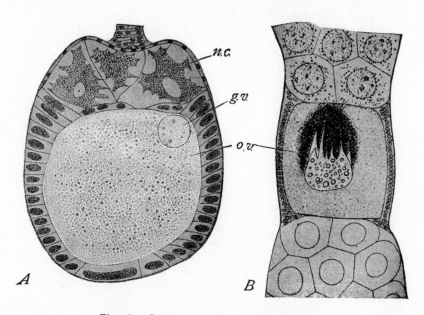

Fig. 58. — Ovarian eggs of insects. [KORSCHELT.]

A. Egg of the butterfly, *Vanessa*, surrounded by its follicle; above, three nurse-cells (*n.c.*) with branching nuclei; *g.v.* germinal vesicle. *B.* Egg of water-beetle, *Dytiscus*, living; the egg (*o.v.*) lies between two groups of nutritive cells; the germinal vesicle sends amœboid processes into the dark mass of food-granules.

(*b*) *Differentiation of the Cytoplasm and Deposit of Deutoplasm.* — In the very young ovum the cytoplasm is small in amount and free from deutoplasm. As the egg enlarges, the cytoplasm increases enormously, a process which involves both the growth of the protoplasm and the formation of passive deutoplasm-bodies suspended in the protoplasmic network. During the growth-period a peculiar body known as the *yolk-nucleus* appears in the cytoplasm of many ova, and this is probably concerned in some manner with the growth

[1] See McMurrich, '86.

of the cytoplasm and the formation of the yolk.   Both its origin and its physiological *rôle* are, however, still involved in doubt.

The deutoplasm first appears, while the eggs are still very small, in the form of granules which seem to have at first no constant position with reference to the egg-nucleus, even in the same species.

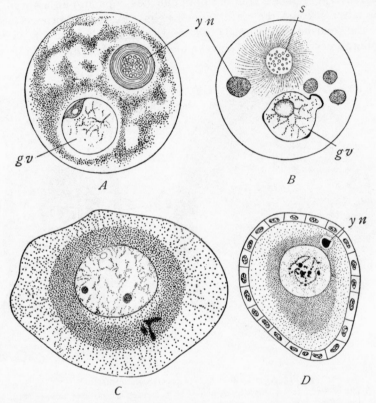

Fig. 59. — Young ovarian eggs, showing yolk-nuclei and deposit of deutoplasm.

A. Myriapod (*Geophilus*) with single " yolk-nucleus " (perhaps an attraction-sphere) and scattered deutoplasm.   [BALBIANI.]

B. The same, with several yolk-nuclei, and attraction-sphere, *s*.   [BALBIANI.]

C. Fish (*Scorpæna*), with deutoplasm forming a ring about the nucleus, and an irregular mass of "eliminated chromatin" (? yolk-nucleus).   [VAN BAMBEKE.]

D. Ovarian egg of young duck (3 months) surrounded by a follicle, and containing a "yolk-nucleus," *y.n.*   [MERTENS.]

Thus Jordan ('93) states that in the newt (*Diemyctylus*) the yolk may be first formed at one side of the egg and afterwards spread to other parts, or it may appear in more or less irregular separate patches which finally form an irregular ring about the nucleus, which at this period has an approximately central position.   In some amphibia the deutoplasm appears near the periphery and advances inwards towards the nucleus. More commonly it first appears in a zone surrounding the nucleus (Fig. 59, *C, D*) and advances thence towards the periphery (trout, Henneguy; cephalopods, Ussow). In still others (*e.g.* in myriapods, Balbiani) it appears in irregular patches scattered quite irregularly through the ovum (Fig. 59, *A*). In *Branchipus* the yolk is laid down at the centre of the egg, while the nucleus lies at the extreme periphery (Brauer). These variations show in general no definite relation to the ultimate arrangement — a fact which proves that the eccentricity of the nucleus and the polarity of the egg cannot be explained as the result of a simple mechanical displacement of the germinal vesicle by the yolk, as some authors have maintained. Neither do they support the view that the actual polarity of the egg exists from the beginning. They probably arise rather through the varying physiological conditions under which the egg-formation takes place; but these have not yet been sufficiently analyzed.[1]

The primary origin of the deutoplasm-grains is a question that really involves the whole theory of cell-action and the relation of nucleus and cytoplasm in metabolism. The evidence seems perfectly clear that in many cases the deutoplasm arises *in situ* in the cytoplasm like the zymogen-granules in gland-cells. But there is now a great body of evidence that seems to show with equal clearness that a part of the egg-cytoplasm is directly or indirectly derived from the nucleus. There is no question that a large part of the substance of the germinal vesicle is thrown out into the cytoplasm at the time of maturation, as shown with especial clearness in the eggs of amphibia, echinoderms, and some worms (*e.g.* in *Nereis*, Fig. 71). A large number of observers have maintained that a similar giving off of solid nuclear substance occurs during the earlier stages of growth; and these observations are so numerous and some of them are so careful, that it is impossible to doubt that this process really takes place. The portions thus cast out of the nucleus have been described by some authors as actual buds from the nucleus (Blochmann, Scharff, Balbiani, etc.), as separate chromatin-rods (Van Bambeke, Erlanger), as portions of the chromatic network (Calkins), or as nucleoli (Balbiani, Will, Leydig). There is no evidence that such eliminated nuclear materials directly give rise to deutoplasm-granules. They would seem, rather, to have the value of food-matters or formative substances which are afterwards absorbed and elaborated by the cytoplasm, the deutoplasm being a new deposit in the cytoplasmic substance. It is, however, a matter of great interest that formed nuclear elements should be given off into the cytoplasm, in view of the general *rôle* of the nucleus as discussed in Chapter VII.

[1] Cf. p. 288.

(c) *Yolk-nucleus.* — The term "yolk-nucleus" has been applied to various bodies or masses that appear in the cytoplasm of the growing ovarian egg; and it must be said that the word has at present no well-defined meaning.   We may distinguish two extreme types of "yolk-nuclei" which are connected by various transitional forms. At one extreme is the yolk-nucleus proper, as originally described by von Wittich ('45) in the eggs of spiders and later by Balbiani ('93) in

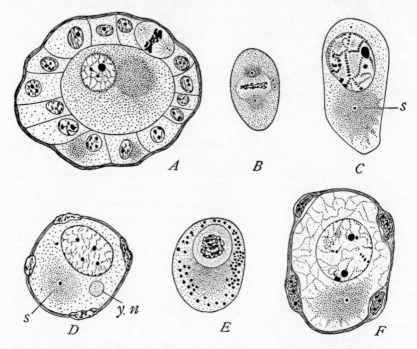

Fig. 60. — Young ovarian eggs of birds and mammals. [MERTENS.]

A. Egg of young magpie (8 days), surrounded by the follicle and containing germinal vesicle and attraction-sphere. *B.* Primordial egg (oögonium) of new-born cat, dividing. *C.* Egg of new-born cat containing attraction-sphere (*s*), and centrosome. *D.* Of young thrush surrounded by follicle and containing besides the nucleus an attraction-sphere and centrosome (*s*), and a yolk-nucleus (*y.n.*). *E.* Of young chick containing nucleus, attraction-sphere and fatty deutoplasm-spheres (black). *F.* Egg of new-born child, surrounded by follicle and containing nucleus and attraction-sphere.

those of myriapods, having the form of a single well-defined spheroidal mass which appears at a very early period and persists throughout the later ovarian history.   At the other extreme are "diffused yolk-nuclei" having the form of numerous irregular and ill-defined masses scattered through the cytoplasm, as described by Stuhlmann ('86) in the eggs of insects and more recently by Calkins and Foot in earthworms.   An intermediate form is represented in the amphibia

(Jordan, '93) and myriapods (Balbiani, '93), where the egg contains a number of fairly well defined yolk-nuclei. In *Lumbricus* the "yolk-nucleus" first appears as a single irregular deeply staining body closely applied to the nucleus and afterwards breaks up into numerous smaller bodies (Calkins, '95).

The most diverse accounts have been given of the structure and origin of these problematical bodies. This is in part owing to the fact, recently pointed out by Mertens, that two entirely different structures have been confounded under the one term. One of these is the attraction-sphere of the young egg with its centrosome. Such a "yolk-nucleus" has been described by Balbiani in the eggs of the myriapod *Geophilus* (Fig. 59, *B*). The other is a body, variously described as arising from the nucleus or in the cytoplasm, which is not improbably concerned in some manner with the constructive metabolism involved in the growth of the egg-cytoplasm and perhaps indirectly concerned with the formation of deutoplasm. It seems clear that the latter form alone should receive the name of yolk-nucleus, if indeed the term is worth retaining.

Mertens ('93) has recently described the ova of a number of birds and mammals (including man) as containing a very distinct attraction-sphere containing one or more intensely staining centrosomes (Fig. 60). This has, however, nothing to do with the true yolk-nucleus which may sometimes be seen in the same egg, lying beside the attraction-sphere (Fig. 60, *D*). The latter sooner or later fades away and disappears. The yolk-nucleus, on the other hand, may long persist. This observation probably explains the strange result reached by Balbiani in the case of myriapods (*Geophilus*), where the "yolk-nucleus" is described as arising by a budding of the nucleus, yet is identified with an attraction-sphere! The "yolk-nucleus" of Balbiani has here the typical appearance of an attraction-sphere, surrounded by rays and containing two or several centrosomes or centrioles. Besides this, however, the egg contains several other bodies which are described as arising by budding off from the nucleus and perhaps represent the true yolk-nuclei (Fig. 59, *B*).

The origin of the yolk-nucleus proper appears to differ in different cases. Jordan's observations on the newt seem to leave no doubt that the bodies described as yolk-nuclei in this animal arise *in situ* in the cytoplasm; and a similar origin of the yolk-nucleus has been described by a number of earlier observers. On the other hand, a number of observers have asserted its origin from the nucleus, either by a process of nuclear budding, by a casting out of the nucleolus of separate chromatin-rods, or of portions of the chromatic reticulum. That such a casting-out of nuclear substance occurs during the ovarian history of some eggs appears to be well established; but it is uncertain whether the bodies thus arising have the same physiological significance as the "yolk-nuclei" of cytoplasmic origin. Calkins ('95, 1), working in my laboratory, has brought forward strong evidence that the "yolk-nucleus" of *Lumbricus* is derived from a substance nearly related with chromatin (Fig. 61). The yolk-nucleus

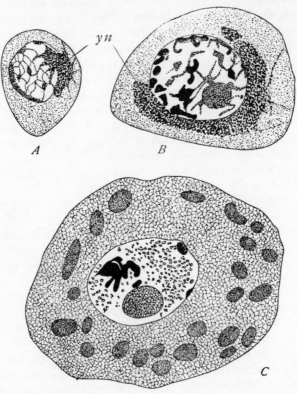

Fig. 61. — Young ovarian eggs of the earthworm (*Lumbricus*), showing yolk-nucleus. [CALKINS.]
    A. Very early stage; the irregular yolk-nucleus (*y. n.*) closely applied to the germinal vesicle and staining like chromatin. *B*. Later stage; the yolk-nucleus separating from the germinal vesicle and changing its staining-power. *C*. Still later stage; the yolk-nucleus broken up into rounded bodies staining like the cytoplasm.

here first appears as an irregular granular body lying directly on the nuclear wall, which in some cases appears to be interrupted, as if yolk-nucleus and chromatin were directly in continuity. Later the yolk-nucleus separates from the germinal vesicle and lies beside it in the cytoplasm. It finally breaks up into a considerable number of secondary yolk-nuclei scattered through the egg. The action of differential stains at different periods indicates that the substance of the yolk-nucleus is nearly related with chromatin, if not directly derived from it. When treated with the Biondi-Ehrlich mixture (basic methyl green, acid red fuchsin), the yolk-nucleus at first stains green like the chromatin, while the cytoplasm is red, and this is the case even after the yolk-nucleus has quite separated from the nuclear membrane. Later, however, as the yolk-nucleus breaks up, it loses its nuclear staining power, and stains red like the cytoplasm.

This conclusion is, however, disputed in a later work by Foot ('96), who maintains that the yolk-nucleus in *Allolobophora* is not of nuclear but of "archoplasmic" origin, though no relation between it and an attraction-sphere is established.[1] She adds the very interesting discovery that the "polar rings" (cf. p. 150) are probably to be identified with the yolk-nucleus, or are at least derived from a similar substance.

Calkins's observations taken in connection with those of Balbiani, Van Bambeke, and other earlier workers give, however, strong evidence, as I believe, that the "yolk-nucleus" of *Lumbricus* is derived, if not from the nucleus, at any rate from a substance nearly related with chromatin, which is afterwards converted into cytoplasmic substance. It is certain, in this case, that the appearance of the yolk-nucleus is coincident with a rapid growth of cytoplasm; but we cannot suppose that the latter grows entirely at the expense of the yolk-nucleus. More probably the yolk-nucleus supplies certain materials necessary to constructive metabolism, and it is not impossible that these may be ferments. We may perhaps interpret in the same manner the elimination of separate nuclear elements (*i.e.* not forming a definite yolk-nucleus) as described by Van Bambeke, Mertens, v. Erlanger, and many earlier writers.

The meaning of the yolk-nuclei of purely cytoplasmic origin is very obscure, and we have at present really no ground for assigning to them any particular function. It can only be said that their appearance coincides in time approximately with the period of greatest constructive activity in the cytoplasm, but there is no evidence of their direct participation in the yolk-formation, and we do not know whether they are active constructive physiological centres, or merely stores of reserve substances or degeneration-products.

[1] Miss Foot's use of the term "archoplasm" largely deprives the word of the definite meaning attached to it by Boveri. To identify as "archoplasm" everything stained by Lyons blue is indeed a broad use of the term.

2. *Formation of the Spermatozoön*

Owing to the extreme minuteness of the spermatozoön, the changes involved in the differentiation of its various parts have always been, and in some respects still remain, among the most vexed of cytological questions. The earlier observations of Kölliker, Schweigger-Seidel, and La Valette St. George, already mentioned, established the fact that the spermatozoön is a cell; but it required a long series of subsequent researches by many observers, foremost among them La Valette St. George himself, to make known the general course of spermatogenesis. This is, briefly, as follows: From the primordial germ-cells arise cells known as *spermatogonia*,[1] which at a certain period pause in their divisions and undergo a considerable growth. Each spermatogonium is thus converted into a *spermatocyte*, which by two rapidly succeeding divisions gives rise to four spermatozoa, as follows.[2] The primary spermatocyte first divides to form two daughter-cells known as spermatocytes of the second order or sperm mother-cells. Each of these divides again — as a rule, without pausing, and without the reconstruction of the daughter-nuclei — to form two *spermatids* or sperm-cells. Each of the four spermatids is then directly transformed into a single spermatozoön, its nucleus becoming very small and compact, its cytoplasm giving rise to the tail and to certain other structures. The number of chromosomes entering into the nucleus of each spermatid and spermatozoön is always one-half that characteristic of the tissue-cells, and this reduction in number is in many cases effected during the two divisions of the primary spermatocyte. In some cases, however (*e.g.* in the salamander), the reduced number appears during the division of the spermatogonia and may even appear in the very early germ-cells (cf. p. 194). The reduction of the chromosomes, which is the most interesting and significant feature of the process, will be considered in the following chapter, and we are here only concerned with the transformation of the spermatid into the spermatozoön. All observers are now agreed that the nucleus of the spermatid is directly transformed into that of the spermatozoön, the chromatin becoming extremely compact and losing, as a rule, all trace of its reticular structure. It is generally agreed, further, that the envelope of the tail-substance is derived from the cytoplasm of the spermatid. Beyond this point opinion is still far from unanimous, though it is probable that the other structures — viz. the axial filament, the

---

[1] The terminology, now almost universally adopted, is due to La Valette St. George. Cf. Fig. 90.

[2] See Fig. 91.

middle-piece, and the point — are likewise of cytoplasmic origin; and it is certain that the middle-piece is in some cases derived from the attraction-sphere of the spermatid, and contains the centrosome.

As the spermatid develops into the spermatozoön it assumes an elongate form, the nucleus lying at one end while the cytoplasm is drawn out to form the flagellum at the opposite end. The origin of the axial filament is still in doubt. Many authors (for example, Flemming and Niessing) have described it as growing out from the *nucleus;* but more recent work by Hermann, Moore, and others, shows that this is probably an error and that the axial filament is derived from the substance of the attraction-sphere.

The greatest uncertainty relates to the origin of the middle-piece and the apex. By one set of authors the centrosome is believed to pass into the point of the spermatozoön (Platner, Field, Benda, Prenant); by another set, into the middle-piece (Hermann, Wilcox, Calkins). That the latter is a correct view is absolutely demonstrated by the fact that during fertilization the centrosome in every accurately known case is derived from the middle-piece (amphibia, echinoderms, tunicates, earthworm, insects, mollusks, etc.). The observations of Platner and others in support of the other view are, however, too detailed to be rejected on this ground alone, and it is not impossible that the position of the centrosome may vary in different forms. The uncertainty is due to the difficulty of tracing out the fate of the centrosome and archoplasmic structures of the spermatid. It is certain that each spermatid receives a centrosome or attraction-sphere from the preceding amphiaster. But besides the centrosome (attraction-sphere) the spermatid may also contain a second "achromatic" body known as the *paranucleus* (Nebenkern) or *mitosome*, which has undoubtedly been mistaken for the attraction-sphere in some cases[1] and to this circumstance the existing confusion may be in part due. The concurrent results of La Valette St. George, Platner, and several others have shown that the "Nebenkern" is derived from the remains of the spindle-fibres; but the most divergent accounts of its later history have been given by different investigators. According to Platner's studies on the butterfly *Pygæra* ('89), it consists of a larger posterior and a smaller anterior body, which he calls respectively the large and small *mitosoma* (Fig. 62, *C*). The former gives rise to the investment of the axial filament of the tail, the latter to the middle-piece, while the "centrosome" lies at the anterior end of the nucleus at the "apex" (Fig. 62, *D*). Field ('95) reaches an essentially similar result in the echinoderm spermatozoön, the single "Nebenkern" forming the middle-piece, while the "centrosome" lies at the tip

[1] Compare the confusion between yolk-nucleus and attraction-sphere in the ovum, p. 119.

(Fig. 62, *B*). Benda describes the "Nebenkern" in the mammals as consisting of two parts, one of which passes backward and takes part in the formation of the tail-envelope, while the other passes forward to form the apex (head-cap or apical knob) and represents the attraction-sphere (archoplasm). A somewhat similar account was given by Platner of the "Nebenkern" of pulmonates. According to the more recent work of Moore on elasmobranchs, both middle-piece and apex are derived from the attraction-sphere, the centrosome passing into the former (Fig. 62, *A*).

The work of Platner and Field appears to have been carefully

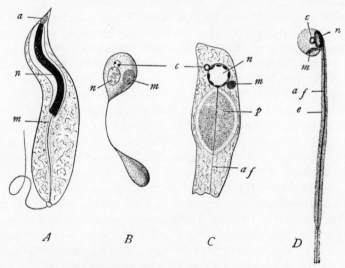

Fig. 62. — Formation of the spermatozoön from the spermatid.

A. Late stage of spermatid of the shark *Scyllium*. [MOORE.]
B. Spermatid of starfish *Chætaster*. [FIELD.]
C. Spermatid of butterfly *Pygæra*. *D*. Young spermatozoön of the same. [PLATNER.]
   a. apical body; *a.f.* axial filament; *c.* "centrosome;" *e.* envelope of tail; *m.* middle-piece ("small mitosoma" of Platner); *n.* nucleus; *p.* paranucleus ("Nebenkern," or "large mitosoma" of Platner).

done, yet there is good reason to believe that both these observers are in error, since their results are contradicted by the history of the spermatozoön in fertilization. As regards the insects, Henking's observations on the fertilization of the butterfly *Pieris* leave little doubt that the sperm-centrosome is here derived from the middle-piece; and, moreover, in the grasshopper *Caloptenus*, Wilcox ('95) has traced the centrosome of the spermatid into the middle-piece. In the case of echinoderms, Boveri, Mathews, and myself, confirmed by several later observers, have independently traced the sperm-centrosome to the middle-piece during fertilization, and have shown that

Fol was in error in referring it to the tip. Field's conclusion is therefore almost certainly erroneous, and he has probably confounded the centrosome with the " Nebenkern " or paranucleus.

Diametrically opposed, moreover, to the results of Platner and Field are those of Hermann ('89) and Calkins ('95, 2) on amphibia and earthworms, and both these observers have devoted especial attention to the origin of the middle-piece. The evidence brought forward by the last-named author, whose preparations I have critically examined, seems perfectly conclusive that the attraction-sphere or centrosome passes into the middle-piece. The "Nebenkern," which is rarely present, appears in this case to take no part in the formation of the flagellum, but degenerates without further change. In the salamander the origin of the middle-piece has been carefully studied by Flemming and Hermann. The latter ('89) has traced the middle-piece back to an "accessory body"

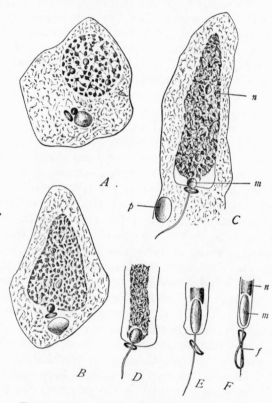

Fig. 63. — Formation of the spermatozoön from the spermatid in the salamander. [HERMANN.]

A. Young spermatid showing the nucleus above, and below the colorless sphere, the ring, and the chromatic sphere. *B.* Later stage, showing the chromatic sphere and ring at the base of the nucleus. *C, D, E, F.* Later stages, showing the transformation of the chromatic sphere into the middle-piece *m.*

(Nebenkörper), which he believes to be not a " Nebenkern " (derived from the spindle-fibres), but an attraction-sphere derived from the aster of the preceding division, as in *Lumbricus.* This body differs greatly from an ordinary attraction-sphere, consisting of the following three parts lying side by side in the cytoplasm (Fig. 63). These are: (*a*) a colourless sphere, (*b*) a minute rounded body which stains red with saffranin like the nucleoli or plasmosomes of the spermatid-nucleus, (c) a ring-shaped structure staining purple with gentian violet, like the chromatin. The colourless sphere ultimately vanishes, the red rounded body gives rise to the middle-piece, while the ring gives rise to the envelope (fin) of the flagellum. The apex or spur is developed from the nuclear membrane.[1] Hermann's results on the mouse agree in a general way with those on the salamander; but the apex (head-cap) is here derived from the cytoplasm. A "Nebenkörper" lies in the cytoplasm, consisting of a pale sphere and a smaller deeply staining body. From the latter arises the "end-knob," which Hermann accordingly homologizes with the middle-piece of the salamander spermatozoön, and from it the axial filament appears to grow out into the flagellum. The colourless sphere disappears as in the salamander, and the envelope of the axial filament is derived from the cytoplasm. Moore ('95) describes the flagellum of elasmobranchs as growing out from the attraction-sphere (archoplasm) of the spermatid (Fig. 62, A).

Summary. — The foregoing account shows that our positive knowledge of the formation of the spermatozoön still rests upon a somewhat slender basis. But despite the discrepancies in existing accounts, all agree that the spermatozoön arises by a direct metamorphosis of the spermatid, receiving from it a nucleus and a small amount of cytoplasm containing a centrosome or attraction-sphere. All agree, further, that the middle-piece is of archoplasmic origin, being derived, according to some authors, from a true attraction-sphere (or centrosome); according to others, from a "Nebenkern" formed from the spindle-fibres. The former account of its origin is certainly true in some cases. The latter cannot be accepted without reinvestigation, since it stands in contradiction to what is known of the middle-piece in fertilization, and is possibly due to a confusion between attraction-sphere and "Nebenkern." Similar doubts exist in regard to the origin of the apex, which is variously described as arising from the nuclear membrane, from the general cytoplasm, from the "Nebenkern," and from the centrosome.

Most late observers agree, further, that the flagellum is developed in intimate relation with the archoplasmic material (attraction-sphere or "Nebenkern"). This conclusion tallies with that of Strasburger, who regards the flagella of plant-spermatozoids as derived from the "kinoplasm" (archoplasm), and it is of especial interest in view of Van Beneden's hypothesis of the contractility of the archoplasm-fibrillæ. It is, however, possible that the axial filament may be derived from the nucleus, in which case it would have an origin comparable with that of the spindle-fibres in many forms of mitosis.

---

[1] Flemming described the middle-piece as arising inside the nucleus; but Hermann's observations leave no doubt that this was an error.

E. Staining-reactions of the Germ-nuclei

It was pointed out by Ryder in 1883 that in the oyster the germ-nuclei stain differently in the two sexes; for if the hermaphrodite gland of this animal be treated with a mixture of saffranin and methyl-green, the egg-nuclei are coloured red, the sperm-nuclei bluish-green. A similar difference was afterwards observed by Auerbach ('91) in the case of many vertebrate germ-cells, where the egg-nucleus was shown to have a special affinity for various red and yellow dyes (eosin, fuchsin, aurantia, carmin), while the sperm-nuclei were especially stained with blue and green dyes (methyl-green, aniline blue, hæmatoxylin).   He was thus led to regard the chromatin of the egg as especially "erythrophilous," and that of the sperm as "cyanophilous."   That the distinction as regards colour is of no value has been shown by Zacharias, Heidenhain, and others; for staining agents cannot be logically classed according to colour, but according to their chemical composition; and a red dye, such as saffranin, may in a given cell show the same affinity for the chromatin as a green or blue dye of different chemical nature, such as methyl-green or hæma-toxylin.   Thus Field has shown that the sperm-nucleus of *Asterias* may be stained green (methyl-green), blue (hæmatoxylin, gentian violet), red (saffranin), or yellow (iodine), and it is here a manifest absurdity to speak of "cyanophilous" chromatin (cf. p. 243).   It is certainly a very interesting fact that a difference of staining-reaction exists between the two sexes, as indicating a corresponding difference of chemical composition in the chromatin; but even this has been shown to be of a transitory character, for the staining-reactions of the germ-nuclei vary at different periods and are exactly alike at the time of their union in fertilization.   Thus Hermann has shown that when the spermatids and immature spermatozoa of the salamander are treated with saffranin (red) and gentian violet (blue),[1] the chromatic network is stained blue, the nucleoli and the middle-piece red; while in the mature spermatozoön the reverse effect is produced, the nuclei being clear red, the middle-piece blue.   A similar change of staining-capacity occurs in the mammals.   The great changes in the staining-capacity of the egg-nucleus at different periods of its history are described at pp. 245, 246.   Again, Watasé has observed in the newt that the germ-nuclei, which stain differently throughout the whole period of their maturation, and even during the earlier phases of fertilization, become more and more alike in the later phases and at the time of their union show identical staining-reactions.[2]   A very

---

[1] By Flemming's triple method.   [2] '92, p. 492.

similar series of facts has been observed in the germ-nuclei of plants by Strasburger (p. 163). These and many other facts of like import demonstrate that the chemical differences between the germ-nuclei are not of a fundamental but only of a secondary character. They are doubtless connected with the very different character of the metabolic processes that occur in the history of the two germ-cells; and the difference of the staining-reaction is probably due to the fact that the sperm-chromatin consists of pure or nearly pure nucleic acid, while the egg-chromatin is a nuclein containing a much higher percentage of albumin.

LITERATURE. III

Ballowitz, E. — Untersuchungen über die Struktur der Spermatozoen: 1. (*birds*) *Arch. Mik. Anat.* XXXII., 1888; 2. (*insects*) *Zeitschr. Wiss. Zool.*, L., 1890; 3. (*fishes, amphibia, reptiles*) *Arch. Mik. Anat.*, XXXVI., 1890; 4. (*mammals*) *Zeit. Wiss. Zool.*, LII., 1891.

Van Beneden, E. — Recherches sur la composition et la signification de l'œuf: *Mem. cour. de l'Acad. roy. de s. de Belgique*, 1870.

Boveri, Th. — Über Differenzierung der Zellkerne während der Furchung des Eies von *Ascaris meg.*: *Anat. Anz.*, 1887.

Brunn, M. von. — Beiträge zur Kenntniss der Samenkörper und ihrer Entwickelung bei Vögeln und Säugethieren: *Arch. Mik. Anat.*, XXXIII., 1889.

Häcker, V. — Die Eibildung bei Cyclops und Camptocanthus: *Zool. Jahrb.*, V., 1892. (See also List V.)

Hermann, F. — Urogenitalsystem; Struktur und Histiogenese der Spermatozoen: *Merkel und Bonnet's Ergebnisse*, II., 1892.

Kölliker, A. — Beiträge zur Kenntniss der Geschlechtsverhältnisse und der Samenflüssigkeit wirbelloser Tiere. *Berlin*, 1841.

Leydig, Fr. — Beiträge zur Kenntniss des thierischen Eies im unbefruchteten Zustande: *Zool. Jahrb.*, III. 1889.

Schweigger-Seidel, F. — Uber die Samenkörperchen und ihre Entwicklung: *Arch. Mik. Anat.*, I. 1865.

Strasburger, E. — Histologische Beiträge; Heft IV: Das Verhalten des Pollens und die Befruchtungsvorgänge bei den Gymnospermen, Schwärmsporen, pflanzliche Spermatozoiden und das Wesen der Befruchtung. *Fischer, Jena*, 1892.

Thomson, Allen. — Article, "Ovum," in Todd's Cyclopedia of Anatomy and Physiology. 1859.

Waldeyer, W. — Eierstock und Ei. *Leipzig*, 1870.

Id. — Bau und Entwickelung der Samenfäden: *Verh. d. Anat. Ges. Leipzig*, 1887.

CHAPTER IV

FERTILIZATION OF THE OVUM

"It is conceivable, and indeed probable, that every part of the adult contains molecules derived both from the male and from the female parent; and that, regarded as a mass of molecules, the entire organism may be compared to a web of which the warp is derived from the female and the woof from the male."   HUXLEY.[1]

IN mitototic cell-division we have become acquainted with the means by which, in all higher forms at least, not only the continuity of life, but also the maintenance of the species, is effected; for through this beautiful mechanism the cell hands on to its descendants an exact duplicate of the idioplasm by which its own organization is determined.   As far as we can see from an *a priori* point of view there is no reason why, barring accident, cell-division should not follow cell-division in endless succession in the stream of life.   It is possible, indeed probable, that such may be the fact in some of the lower and simpler forms of life where no form of sexual reproduction is known to occur.   In the vast majority of living forms, however, the series of cell-divisions tends to run in cycles in each of which the energy of division gradually comes to an end and is only *restored by an admixture of living matter derived from another cell.*   This operation, known as *fertilization* or *fecundation,* is the essence of sexual reproduction ; and in it we behold a process by which on the one hand the energy of division is restored, and by which on the other hand two independent lines of descent are blended into one.   Why this dual process should take place we are as yet unable to say, nor do we know which of its two elements is to be regarded as the primary and essential one.   According to the older and more familiar "dynamic" hypothesis, brought forward by Bütschli ('76) and Minot ('77, '79) and afterwards supported by such investigators as Engelmann, Hensen, Hertwig, and Maupas, the essential end of sexuality is *rejuvenescence, i.e.* the restoration of the growth-energy and the inauguration of a new cycle of cell-division.   Maupas's celebrated experiments on the conjugation of Infusoria, although not yet ade-

[1] Evolution, in *Science and Culture*, p. 296, from *Enc. Brit.*, 1878.

quately confirmed, have yielded very strong evidence that in these unicellular animals, even under normal conditions, the processes of growth and division sooner or later come to an end, undergoing a process of natural "senescence," which can only be counteracted by conjugation.   That conjugation or fertilization actually has such a dynamic effect is disputed by no one.   What is not determined is whether this is the primary motive for the process — *i.e.* whether the need of fertilization is a primary attribute of living matter — or whether it has been secondarily acquired in order to ensure a mixture of germ-plasms derived from different sources.   The latter view has been urged with great force by Weismann, who rejects the rejuve-nescence theory *in toto* and considers the essential end of fertilization to be a mixture of germ-plasms ("Amphimixis") as a means for the production, or rather multiplication, of variations which form the material on which selection operates.   On the other hand, Hatschek ('87, 1) sees in fertilization exactly the converse function of *checking* variations and holding the species true to the specific type.   The present state of knowledge does not, I believe, allow of a decision between these diverse views, and the admission must be made that the essential nature of sexual reproduction must remain undetermined until the subject shall have been far more thoroughly investigated, especially in the unicellular forms, where the key to the ultimate problem is undoubtedly to be sought.

A. General Sketch

Among the unicellular plants and animals, fertilization is effected by means of *conjugation*, a process in which two or more individuals permanently fuse together, or in which two unite temporarily and effect an exchange of nuclear matter, after which they separate.   *In all the higher forms fertilization consists in the permanent fusion of two germ-cells, one of paternal and one of maternal origin.*   We may first consider the fertilization of the animal egg, which appears to take place in essentially the same manner throughout the animal kingdom, and to be closely paralleled by the corresponding process in plants.

Leeuwenhoek, whose pupil Hamm discovered the spermatozoa (1677), put forth the conjecture that the spermatozoön must pene-trate into the egg; but the process was not actually seen until nearly two centuries later (1854), when Newport observed it in the case of the frog's egg; and it was described by Pringsheim a year later in one of the lower plants, *Œdigonium*.   The first adequate description of the process was given by Hermann Fol, in 1879,[1] though many

---

[1] See *l'Hénogénie*, pp. 124 ff., for a full historical account.

earlier observers, from the time of Martin Barry ('43) onwards, had seen the spermatozoa inside the egg-envelopes, or asserted its entrance into the egg.

In many cases the entire spermatozoön enters the egg (mollusks, insects, nematodes, some annelids, *Petromyzon*, axolotl, etc.), and in such cases the long flagellum may sometimes be seen coiled within the egg (Fig. 64). Only the nucleus and middle-piece, however, are concerned in the actual fertilization; and there are some cases (echinoderms) in which the tail is left outside the egg. At or near

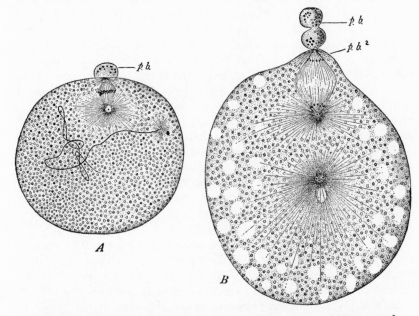

Fig. 64.—Fertilization of the egg of the snail *Physa*. [KOSTANECKI and WIERZEJSKI.]

A. The entire spermatozoön lies in the egg, its nucleus at the right, flagellum at the left, while the minute sperm-amphiaster occupies the position of the middle-piece. The first polar body has been formed, the second is forming. *B.* The enlarged sperm-nucleus and sperm-amphiaster lie near the centre; second polar body forming and the first dividing. The egg-centrosomes and asters afterwards disappear, their place being taken by those of the spermatozoön.

the time of fertilization, the egg successively segments off at the upper pole two minute cells, known as the *polar bodies* (Figs. 64, 65, 89) or directive corpuscles, which degenerate and take no part in the subsequent development. This phenomenon takes place, as a rule, immediately after entrance of the spermatozoön. It may, however, occur before the spermatozoön enters, and it forms no part of the process of fertilization proper. It is merely the final act in the process of *maturation*, by which the egg is prepared for fertilization, and we may defer its consideration to the following chapter.

1. The Germ-nuclei in Fertilization

The modern era in the study of fertilization may be said to begin with Oscar Hertwig's discovery, in 1875, of the fate of the spermatozoön within the egg. Earlier observers had, it is true, paved the way by showing that, at the time of fertilization, the egg contains *two nuclei* that fuse together or become closely associated before development begins. (Warneck, Bütschli, Auerbach, Van Beneden, Strasburger.) Hertwig discovered, in the egg of the sea-urchin (*Toxopneustes lividus*), that *one of these nuclei belongs to the egg, while the other is derived from the spermatozoön.* This result was speedily confirmed in a number of other animals, and has since been extended to every species that has been carefully investigated. The researches of Strasburger, De Bary, Schmitz, Guignard, and others have shown that the same is true of plants. *In every known case an essential phenomenon of fertilization is the union of a sperm-nucleus, of paternal origin, with an egg-nucleus, of maternal origin, to form the primary nucleus of the embryo. This nucleus, known as the cleavage- or segmentation-nucleus, gives rise by division to all the nuclei of the body, and hence every nucleus of the child may contain nuclear substance derived from both parents.* And thus Hertwig was led to the conclusion ('84), independently reached at the same time by Strasburger, Kölliker, and Weismann, that the nucleus is the most essential element concerned in hereditary transmission.

This conclusion received a strong support in the year 1883, through the splendid discoveries of Van Beneden on the fertilization of the thread-worm, *Ascaris megalocephala,* the egg of which has since ranked with that of the echinoderm as a classical object for the study of cell-problems. Van Beneden's researches especially elucidated the structure and transformations of the germ-nuclei, and carried the analysis of fertilization far beyond that of Hertwig. In *Ascaris,* as in all other animals, the sperm-nucleus is extremely minute, so that at first sight a marked inequality between the two sexes appears to exist in this respect. Van Beneden showed not only that the inequality in size totally disappears during fertilization, but that the two nuclei undergo a parallel series of structural changes which demonstrate their precise morphological equivalence down to the minutest detail; and here, again, later researches, foremost among them those of Boveri, Strasburger, and Guignard, have shown that, essentially, the same is true of the germ-cells of other animals and of plants. The facts in *Ascaris* (variety *bivalens*) are essentially as follows (Fig. 65): After the entrance of the spermatozoön, and during the formation of the polar bodies, the sperm-nucleus rapidly enlarges and

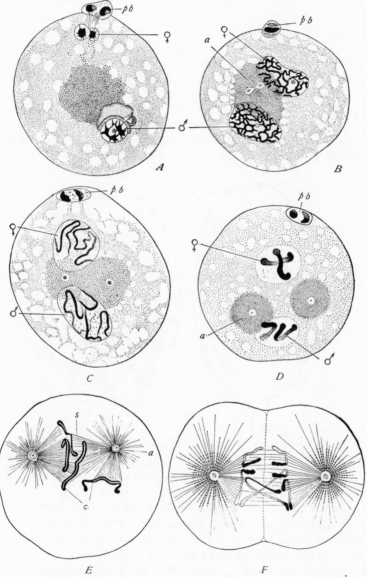

Fig. 65. — Fertilization of the egg of *Ascaris megalocephala*, var. *bivalens*. [BOVERI.] (For later stages see Fig. 104.)

A. The spermatozoön has entered the egg, its nucleus is shown at ♂; beside it lies the granular mass of "archoplasm" (attraction-sphere); above are the closing phases in the formation of the second polar body (two chromosomes in each nucleus). *B*. Germ-nuclei (♀, ♂) in the reticular stage; the attraction-sphere (*a*) contains the dividing centrosome. *C*. Chromosomes forming in the germ-nuclei; the centrosome divided. *D*. Each germ-nucleus resolved into two chromosomes; attraction-sphere (*a*) double. *E*. Mitotic figure forming for the first cleavage; the chromosomes (*c*) already split. *F*. First cleavage in progress, showing divergence of the daughter-chromosomes towards the spindle-poles (only three chromosomes shown).

finally forms a typical nucleus exactly similar to the egg-nucleus. The chromatin in each nucleus now resolves itself into two long, worm-like chromosomes, which are exactly similar in form, size, and staining reaction in the two nuclei.   Next, the nuclear membrane fades away, and the four chromosomes lie naked in the egg-substance. Every trace of sexual difference has now disappeared, and it is impossible to distinguish the paternal from the maternal chromosomes (Figs. 65, *D, E*).   Meanwhile an amphiaster has been developed which, with the four chromosomes, forms the mitotic figure for the first cleavage of the ovum, *the chromatic portion of which has been synthetically formed by the union of two equal germ-nuclei.*   The

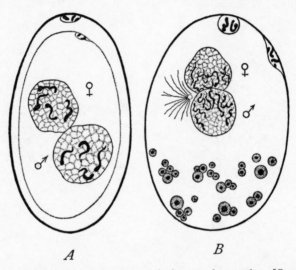

A   *B*

Fig. 66. — Germ-nuclei and chromosomes in the eggs of nematodes. [CARNOY.]

A. Egg of nematode parasitic in *Scyllium ;* the two germ-nuclei in apposition, each containing four chromosomes; the two polar bodies above. *B*. Egg of *Filaroides;* each germ-nucleus with eight chromosomes; polar bodies above, deutoplasm-spheres below.

later phases follow the usual course of mitosis.   Each chromosome splits lengthwise into equal halves, the daughter-chromosomes are transported to the spindle-poles, and here they give rise, in the usual manner, to the nuclei of the two-celled stage.   *Each of these nuclei, therefore, receives exactly equal amounts of paternal and maternal chromatin.*

These discoveries were confirmed and extended in the case of *Ascaris* by Boveri and by Van Beneden himself in 1887 and 1888 and in several other nematodes by Carnoy in 1887.   Carnoy found the number of chromosomes derived from each sex to be in *Coronilla* 4, in *Ophiostomum* 6, and in *Filaroides* 8.   A little later Boveri

('90) showed that the law of numerical equality of the paternal and maternal chromosomes held good for other groups of animals, being in the sea-urchin *Echinus* 9, in the worm *Sagitta* 9, in the medusa *Tiara* 14, and in the mollusk *Pterotrachea* 16 from each sex. Similar results were obtained in other animals and in plants, as first shown by Guignard in the lily ('91), where each sex contributes 12 chromosomes. In the onion the number is 8 (Strasburger); in the annelid *Ophryotrocha* it is only 2 from each sex (Korschelt). In all these cases the *number contributed by each is one-half the number characteristic of the body-cells.* The union of two germ-cells thus restores the normal number, and thus we find the explanation of the remarkable fact commented on at p. 48 that *the number of chromosomes in sexually produced organisms is always even.*[1]

These remarkable facts demonstrate the two germ-nuclei to be in a morphological sense precisely equivalent, and they not only lend very strong support to Hertwig's identification of the nucleus as the bearer of hereditary qualities, but indicate further that these qualities must be carried by the chromosomes; for their precise equivalence in number, shape, and size is the physical correlative of the fact that the two sexes play, on the whole, equal parts in hereditary transmission. And thus we are finally led to the view that chromatin is the physical basis of inheritance, and that the smallest visible units of structure by which inheritance is effected are to be sought in the chromatin-granules or chromomeres.

2. *The Centrosome in Fertilization*

The origin of the centrosomes and of the amphiaster, by means of which the paternal and maternal chromosomes are distributed and the egg divides, is still in some measure a matter of dispute. In a large number of cases, however, it is certainly known that *the egg-centrosome disappears before or during fertilization and its place is taken by a new centrosome which is introduced by the spermatozoön and divides into two to form the cleavage-amphiaster.* This has been conclusively demonstrated in several forms (various echinoderms, annelids, nematodes, tunicates, mollusks, and vertebrates) and established with a high degree of probability in many others (insects, crustacea). In every accurately known case, moreover, the centrosome has been traced to the middle-piece of the spermatozoön; *e.g.* in sea-urchins (Hertwig, Boveri, Wilson, Mathews, Hill), in the axolotl (Fick), in the tunicate *Phallusia* (Hill), probably in the earthworm,

[1] Cf. p. 154.

Allolobophora (Foot), in the butterfly *Pieris* (Henking), and in the gasteropod *Physa* (Kostanecki and Wierzejski). The agreement between forms so diverse is very strong evidence that this must be regarded as the typical derivation of the centrosome.[1]

The facts may be illustrated by a brief description of the phe-

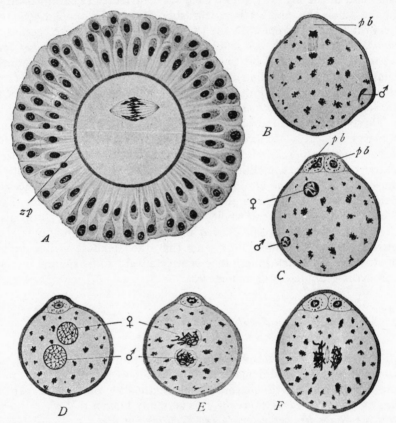

Fig. 67.—Maturation and fertilization of the egg of the mouse. [SOBOTTA.]

A. The ovarian egg still surrounded by the follicle-cells and the membrane (*z.p.*, zona pellucida); the polar spindle formed. *B.* Egg immediately after entrance of the spermatozoön (sperm-nucleus at ♂). *C.* The two germ-nuclei (♂, ♀) still unequal; polar bodies above. *D.* Germ-nuclei approaching, of equal size. *E.* The chromosomes forming. *F.* The minute cleavage-spindle in the centre; on either side the paternal and maternal groups of chromosomes.

nomena in the sea-urchin *Toxopneustes* (Fig. 69). As described at p. 146, the tail is in this case left outside, and only the head and middle-piece enter the egg. Within a few minutes after its entrance, and while still very near the periphery, the lance-shaped sperm-head, carrying the middle-piece at its base, rotates through nearly or quite

[1] Cf. p. 156.

180°, so that the pointed end is directed outward and the middle-piece is turned inward (Fig. 69 *A–F*).[1]   During the rotation a minute aster is developed about the middle-piece as a centre, and at the

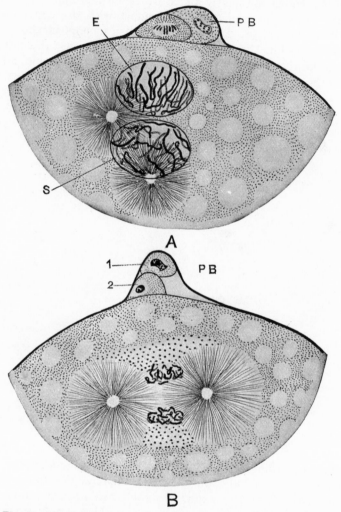

Fig. 68. — Fertilization of the egg of the gasteropod *Pterotrachea*. [BOVERI.]
A. The egg-nucleus (*E*) and sperm-nucleus (*S*) approaching after formation of the polar bodies; the latter shown above (*P.B.*); each germ-nucleus contains sixteen chromosomes; the sperm-amphiaster fully developed. *B.* The mitotic figure for the first cleavage nearly established; the nuclear membranes have disappeared leaving the maternal group of chromosomes above the spindle, the paternal below it.

[1] The first, as far as I know, to observe the rotation of the sperm-head was Flemming in the echinoderm-egg ('81, pp. 17–19). It has since been clearly observed in several other cases, and is probably a phenomenon of very general occurrence.

central point a minute intensely staining centrosome may be seen.[1]
As the sperm-nucleus advances, the aster leads the way, and at the
same time rapidly grows, its rays extending far out into the cytoplasm
and finally traversing nearly an entire hemisphere of the egg. The
central mass of the aster comes in contact with the egg-nucleus, divides into two, and the daughter-asters pass to opposite poles of the
egg-nucleus, while the sperm-nucleus flattens against the latter and
assumes the form of a biconvex lens (Fig. 70). The nuclei now fuse
to form the cleavage-nucleus. Shortly afterwards the nuclear membrane fades away, a spindle is developed between the asters, and

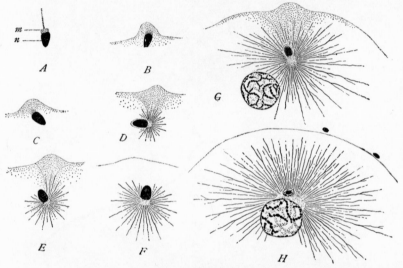

Fig. 69. — Entrance and rotation of the sperm-head and formation of the sperm-aster in the
sea-urchin *Toxopneustes* (*A.–F.*, × 1600; *G. H.*, × 800).

A. Sperm-head before entrance; *n*, nucleus; *m*, middle-piece and part of the flagellum.
B. C. Immediately after entrance, showing entrance-cone. *D.–F.* Rotation of the sperm-head,
formation of the sperm-aster about the middle-piece (the minute centrosome not shown).
G. H. Approach of the germ-nuclei; growth of the aster.

a group of chromosomes arises from the cleavage-nucleus. These
are 36 or 38 in number; and although their relation to the paternal
and maternal chromatin cannot in this case be accurately traced,
owing to the apparent fusion of the nuclei, there can be no doubt on
general grounds that one-half have been derived from each germ-
nucleus. Throughout these changes no trace of an egg-centrosome
is to be discovered. This centrosome, though present in earlier stages,
has been lost after the polar bodies were formed by the ovarian egg.

---

[1] I was unable to find such a centrosome in *Toxopneustes*, but the observations of Boveri
and Hill prove that it is certainly present in other sea-urchins, and I now believe my own
account to have been at fault in this respect.

The facts just described are now known to be typical of a large number of cases. We may, however, distinguish two types of ferti-

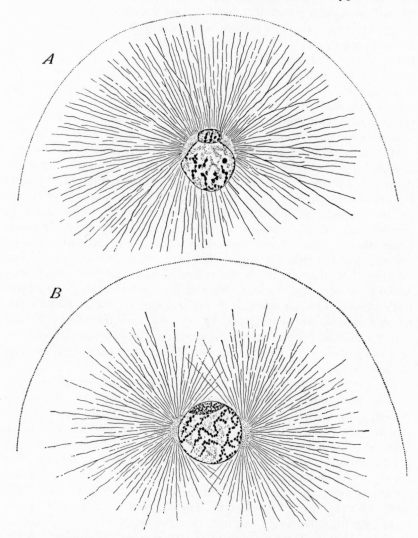

Fig. 70. — Conjugation of the germ-nuclei and division of the sperm-aster in the sea-urchin *Toxopneustes*, × 1000. (For later stages see Fig. 37.)

A. Union of the nuclei, extension of the aster. *B*. Flattening of the sperm-nucleus against the egg-nucleus, division of the aster.

lization according as the polar-bodies are formed before or after the entrance of the spermatozoön. In the first case, well illustrated by the sea-urchin (Fig. 69), the germ-nuclei conjugate immediately after entrance of the spermatozoön. In the second and more frequent case (*Ascaris*, Fig. 65 ; *Physa*, Fig. 64 ; *Nereis*, Fig. 71 ; *Cyclops*, Fig. 72), the sperm-nucleus penetrates for a certain distance, often to the centre of the egg, and then pauses while the polar bodies are formed. It then conjugates with the reformed egg-nucleus. In this case, the sperm-aster always divides to form an amphiaster before conjugation of the nuclei, while in the first case the aster may be still undivided at the time of union. This difference is doubtless due merely to a difference in the time elapsing between entrance of the spermatozoön and conjugation of the nuclei, the amphiaster having, in the second case, time to form during extrusion of the polar bodies.

It is an interesting and significant fact that the aster or amphiaster always leads the way in the march towards the egg-nucleus ; and in many cases it may be far in advance of the sperm-nucleus.[1] Boveri ('88, 1) has observed in sea-urchins that the sperm-nucleus may indeed be left entirely behind, the aster alone conjugating with the egg-nucleus and causing division of the egg *without union of the germ-nuclei*, though the sperm-nucleus afterwards conjugates with one of the nuclei of the two-cell stage. This process, known as " partial fertilization," is undoubtedly to be regarded as abnormal. It affords, however, a beautiful demonstration of the fact that *it is the centrosome alone that causes division of the egg, and it is therefore the fertilizing element proper* (Boveri, '87, 2). We may therefore conclude that the *end* of fertilization is the union of the germ-nuclei and the equal distribution of their substance, while the active *agent* in this process is the centrosome.

The earliest investigators of fertilization, such as Bütschli and Fol, had no knowledge of the centrosome, and hence no clear idea as to the origin of the asters, but Fol stated in 1873 that the asters represented "centres of attraction" lying outside and independent of the nucleus. Oscar Hertwig showed, in 1875, that in the sea-urchin egg the amphiaster arises by the division of a single aster that first appears near the sperm-nucleus and accompanies it in its progress toward the egg-nucleus. A similar observation was soon afterwards made by Fol ('79) in the eggs of *Asterias* and *Sagitta*, and in the latter case he determined the fact that the astral rays do not centre in the nucleus, as Hertwig described, *but at a point in advance of it,* — a fact afterwards confirmed by Hertwig himself and by Boveri ('88, 1). Hertwig and Fol afterwards found that in cases of polyspermy, when several spermatozoa enter the egg, each sperm-nucleus is accompanied by an aster, and Hertwig proved that each of these might give rise to an amphiaster (Fig. 75).

---

[1] Cf. Kostanecki and Wierzejski, '96.

It was Boveri ('87) who first accurately traced the complete history of the centrosome and clearly formulated the facts, proving that in *Ascaris* a single centrosome is brought in by the spermatozoön and that it divides to form two centres about which are developed the two

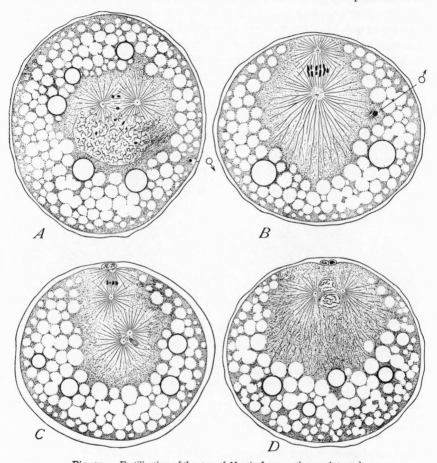

Fig. 71. — Fertilization of the egg of *Nereis*, from sections. (× 400.)

A. Soon after the entrance of the spermatozoön, showing the minute sperm-nucleus at ♀, the germinal vesicle disappearing, and the first polar mitotic figure forming. The empty spaces represent deutoplasm-spheres (slightly swollen by the reagents), the firm circles oil-drops. B. Sperm-nucleus (♂) advancing, a minute amphiaster in front of it; first polar mitotic figure established; polar concentration of the protoplasm. C. Later stage; second polar body forming. D. The polar bodies formed; conjugation of the germ-nuclei; the egg-centrosomes and asters have disappeared, leaving only the sperm-amphiaster (cf. Fig. 64).

asters of the cleavage-figure. He was thus led to the following conclusion, which I believe still accurately expresses the truth: "*The ripe egg possesses all of the organs and qualities necessary for division excepting the centrosome, by which division is initiated. The sperma-*

tozoön, on the other hand, is provided with a centrosome, but lacks the substance in which this organ of division may exert its activity. Through the union of the two cells in fertilization all of the essential organs necessary for division are brought together; the egg now contains a centrosome which by its own division leads the way in the embryonic development.[1] Boveri did not actually follow the disappearance of the egg-centrosome, but nearly at the same time this process was carefully described by Vejdovsky in the case of a fresh-water annelid *Rhynchelmis*. Here, again, very strong evidence was brought for-

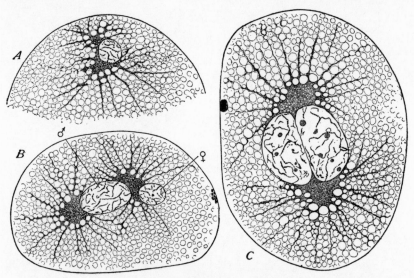

Fig. 72. — Fertilization of the egg in the copepod *Cyclops strenuus*.   [RÜCKERT.]
    A. Sperm-nucleus soon after entrance, the sperm-aster dividing. *B*. The germ-nuclei approaching; ♂, the enlarged sperm-nucleus with a large aster at each pole; ♀, the egg-nucleus reformed after formation of the second polar body, shown at the right. *C*. The apposed reticular germ-nuclei, now of equal size; the spindle is immediately afterwards developed between the two enormous sperm-asters; polar body at the left.

ward to show that the cleavage-amphiaster arises by the division of a single sperm-aster. Very numerous observations to the same effect have been made by later observers. Böhm could find in *Petromyzon* ('88) and the trout ('91) no radiations near the egg-nucleus after the formation of the polar-bodies, while a beautiful sperm-aster is developed near the sperm-nucleus and divides to form the amphiaster. Platner ('86) had already made similar observations in the snail *Arion*, and the same result was soon afterwards reached by Brauer ('92) in the case of *Branchipus*, and by Julin ('93) in *Styleopsis*. Fick's careful study of the fertilization of the axolotl ('93) proved in

[1] '87, 2, p. 155.

a very convincing manner not only that the amphiaster is a product of the sperm-aster, but also that the latter is developed about the *middle-piece* as a centre. The same result was indicated by Foot's observations on the earthworm ('94), and it was soon afterwards conclusively demonstrated in echinoderms through the independent and nearly simultaneous researches of myself on the egg of *Toxopneustes*, of Mathews on *Arbacia*, and of Boveri on *Echinus*. Nearly at the same time a careful study was made by Mead ('95) of the annelid *Chætopterus*, and of the starfish *Asterias* by Mathews, both observers independently showing that the polar spindle contains distinct centrosomes, which, however, degenerate after the formation of the polar bodies, their place being taken by the sperm-centrosome, which divides to form an amphiaster before union of the nuclei, as in *Rhynchelmis*. Exactly the same result has since been reached by Hill ('95) in *Sphærechinus* and the tunicate *Phallusia*, and by Kostanecki and Wierzejski ('96) in *Physa* (Fig. 64) ; and in all of these the centrosome is likewise shown to arise from the middle-piece. The origin of the centrosome from the spermatozoön alone has also been shown by Rückert ('95, 2) in *Cyclops* (Fig. 72), and is indicated by Sobotta's work ('95) on the fertilization of the mouse (Fig. 67).

Such an array of evidence, derived from the study of so many diverse groups, places Boveri's conception of fertilization (p. 141) on a very strong foundation, and justifies the conclusion that the origin of the first cleavage-centrosomes from the spermatozoön alone is a phenomenon of very wide, if not of universal, occurrence. The descendants of these centrosomes may be traced continuously into later cleavage-stages, and there can be little doubt that they are the progenitors of all the centrosomes of the adult body. Boveri and Van Beneden, followed by a number of later observers,[1] have followed the daughter-centrosomes through every stage of the first cleavage into the blastomeres of the two-cell stage, where they persist and give rise to the centrosomes of the four-cell stage, and so on in later stages. This is beautifully shown in the egg of *Thalassema* (Fig. 73), which has been carefully followed out in my laboratory by Mr. B. B. Griffin. The centrosome is here a minute granule at the focus of the sperm-aster, which divides to form an amphiaster soon after the entrance of the spermatozoön. During the early anaphase of the first cleavage each centrosome divides into two, passes to the outer periphery of the centrosphere, and there forms a minute amphiaster for the second cleavage before the first cleavage takes place (Fig. 73) ! The minute centrosomes of the second cleavage are therefore the direct descendants of the sperm-centrosome ; and there is good reason to believe that the

---

[1] See Mead on *Chætopterus*, '95, and Kostanecki and Wierzejski on *Physa*, '96.

continuity is not broken in later stages.   An exactly similar process is described by Kostanecki and Wierzejski in the egg of *Physa*. We thus reach the following remarkable conclusion : *During cleavage the cytoplasm of the blastomeres is derived from that of the egg, the centrosomes from the spermatozoön, while the nuclei (chromatin) are*

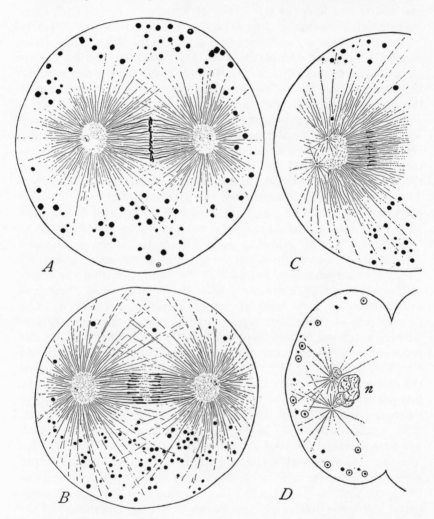

Fig. 73. — Persistence of the centrosomes from cell to cell, in the cleavage of the egg of the gephyrean *Thalassema*. [GRIFFIN.]

   A. Mitotic figure for the first cleavage ; the centrosome already double in each centrosphere (the small black bodies are deutoplasm-spheres). *B*. Early anaphase ; migration of the centrosomes to the periphery of the centrosphere. *C*. Middle anaphase (only one-half of the mitotic figure shown) ; daughter-amphiaster already formed. *D*. Telophase ; the egg dividing and nuclei reforming ; the old amphiaster has disappeared, leaving only the daughter-amphiaster in each cell.

equally derived from both germ-cells; and certainly it would be hard to find more convincing evidence that the chromatin is the controlling factor in the cell by which its specific character is determined.

We now proceed to a more detailed and critical examination of fertilization.

B. UNION OF THE GERM-CELLS

It does not lie within the scope of this work to consider the innumerable modes by which the germ-cells are brought together, further than to recall the fact that their union may take place inside the body of the mother or outside, and that in the latter case, both eggs and spermatozoa are as a rule discharged into the water, where fertilization and development take place. The spermatozoa may live for a long period, either before or after their discharge, without losing their fertilizing power, and their movements may continue throughout this period. In many cases they are motionless when first discharged, and only begin their characteristic swimming movements after coming in contact with the water. There is clear evidence of a definite attraction between the germ-cells, which is in some cases so marked (for example in the polyp *Renilla*) that when spermatozoa and ova are mixed in a small vessel, each ovum becomes in a few moments surrounded by a dense fringe of spermatozoa attached to its periphery by their heads and by their movements actually causing the ovum to move about. The nature of the attraction is not positively known, but Pfeffer's researches on the spermatozoids of plants leave little doubt that it is of a chemical nature, since he found the spermatozoids of ferns and of *Selaginella* to be as actively attracted by solutions of malic acid or malates (contained in capillary tubes) as by the substance extruded from the neck of the archegonium. Those of mosses, on the other hand, are indifferent to malic acid, but are attracted by cane-sugar. These experiments indicate that the specific attraction between the germ-cells of the same species is owing to the presence of specific chemical substances in each case. There is clear evidence, furthermore, that the attractive force is not exerted by the egg-nucleus alone, but by the egg-cytoplasm; for, as the Hertwigs and others have shown, spermatozoa will readily enter egg-fragments entirely devoid of a nucleus.

In naked eggs, such as those of some echinoderms, and cœlenterates, the spermatozoön may enter at any point; but there are some cases in which the point of entrance is predetermined by the presence of special structures through which the spermatozoön

L

enters (Fig. 74). Thus, the starfish egg, according to Fol, possesses before fertilization a peculiar protoplasmic "attraction-cone"
to which the head of the spermatozoön becomes attached, and through
which it enters the egg. In some of the hydromedusæ, on the other
hand, the entrance point is marked by a funnel-shaped depression at
the egg-periphery (Metschnikoff). When no preformed attraction-
cone is present, an "entrance-cone" is sometimes formed by a rush
of protoplasm towards the point at which the spermatozoön strikes
the egg and there forming a conical elevation into which the sperm-
head passes. In the sea-urchin (Fig. 74) this structure persists
only a short time after the spermatozoön enters, soon assuming a

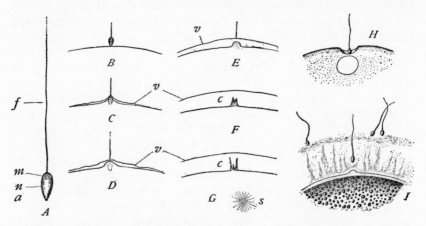

Fig. 74.—Entrance of the spermatozoön into the egg. *A.-G.* In the sea-urchin *Toxopneustes.*
H. In the medusa *Mitrocoma.* [METSCHNIKOFF.] *I.* In the star-fish *Asterias.* [FOL.]

A. Spermatozoön of *Toxopneustes*, × 2000; *a*, the apical body, *n*, nucleus, *m*, middle-piece,
f, flagellum. *B.* Contact with the egg-periphery. *C. D.* Entrance of the head, formation of the
entrance-cone and of the vitelline membrane (*v*), leaving the tail outside. *E. F.* Later stages.
G. Appearance of the sperm-aster (*s*) about 3-5 minutes after first contact; entrance-cone breaking up. *H.* Entrance of the spermatozoön into a preformed depression. *I.* Approach of the
spermatozoön, showing the preformed attraction-cone.

ragged flame-shape and breaking up into slender rays. In some
cases the egg remains naked, even after fertilization, as appears to
be the case in many cœlenterates. More commonly a vitelline membrane is quickly formed after contact of the spermatozoön, — *e.g.*
in *Amphioxus*, in the echinoderms, and in many plants, — and by
means of this the entrance of other spermatozoa is prevented. In
eggs surrounded by a membrane before fertilization, the spermatozoön either bores its way through the membrane at any point, as is
probably the case with mammals and amphibia, or may make its
entrance through a micropyle.

In some forms only one spermatozoön normally enters the ovum, as in echinoderms, mammals, many annelids, etc., while in others several may enter (insects, elasmobranchs, reptiles, the earthworm, *Petromyzon*, etc.). In the former case more than one spermatozoön may accidentally enter (pathological polyspermy), but development is then always abnormal. In such cases each sperm-centrosome gives rise to an amphiaster, and the asters may then unite to form the most complex polyasters, the nodes of which are formed by the

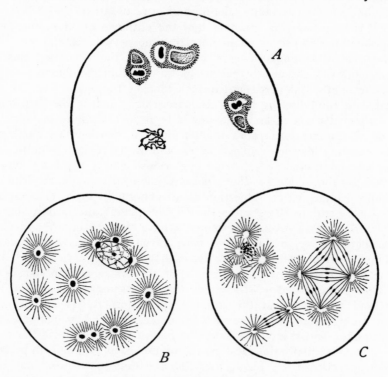

Fig. 75. — Pathological polyspermy.

A. Polyspermy in the egg of *Ascaris;* below, the egg-nucleus; above, three entire spermatozoa within the egg. [SALA.]

B. Polyspermy in sea-urchin egg treated with 0.005% nicotine-solution; ten sperm-nuclei shown, three of which have conjugated with the egg-nucleus. *C.* Later stage of an egg similarly treated, showing polyasters formed by union of the sperm-amphiasters. [O. and R. HERTWIG.]

centrosomes (Fig. 75). Such eggs either do not divide at all or undergo an irregular multiple cleavage and soon perish. If, however, only two spermatozoa enter, the egg may develop for a time. Thus Driesch has determined the interesting fact, which I have confirmed, that sea-urchin eggs into which two spermatozoa have accidentally entered undergo a double cleavage, dividing into four at the first cleavage, and forming eight instead of four micromeres at the fourth cleavage. Such embryos develop as far as the blastula stage, but never form a gastrula.[1] In cases where several spermatozoa normally enter the egg (physiological polyspermy), only one of the sperm-nuclei normally unites with the egg-nucleus, the supernumerary sperm-nuclei either degenerating, or in rare cases — *e.g.* in elasmo-branchs and reptiles — living for a time and even dividing to form "merocytes" or accessory nuclei. The fate of the latter is still in doubt; but they certainly take no part in fertilization.

It is an interesting question how the entrance of supernumerary spermatozoa is prevented in normal monospermic fertilization. In the case of echinoderm-eggs Fol advanced the view that this is mechanically effected by means of the vitelline membrane formed instantly after the first spermatozoön touches the egg. This is indicated by the following facts. Immature eggs, before the formation of the polar bodies, have no power to form a vitelline membrane, and the spermatozoa always enter them in considerable numbers. Polyspermy also takes place, as O. and R. Hertwig's beautiful experiments showed ('87), in ripe eggs whose vitality has been diminished by the action of dilute poisons, such as nicotine, strychnine, and morphine, or by subjection to an abnormally high temperature (31° C.); and in these cases the vitelline membrane is only slowly formed, so that several spermatozoa have time to enter.[2] Similar mechanical explanations have been given in various other cases. Thus Hoffman believes that in teleosts the micropyle is blocked by the polar-bodies after the entrance of the first spermatozoön; and Calberla suggested (*Petromyzon*) that the same result might be caused by the tail of the entering spermatozoön. It is, however, far from certain whether such rude mechanical explanations are adequate; and there is considerable reason to believe that the egg may possess a physiological power of exclusion called forth by the first spermatozoön. Thus Driesch found that spermatozoa did not enter fertilized sea-urchin eggs from which the membranes had been removed by shaking.[3] In some cases no membrane is formed (some cœlenterates), in others several spermatozoa are found inside the membrane (nemertines), in others the spermatozoön may penetrate the membrane at any point (mammals), yet monospermy is the rule.

---

[1] For an account of the internal changes, see p. 261.

[2] The Hertwigs attribute this to a diminished irritability on the part of the egg-substance. Normally requiring the stimulus of only a single spermatozoön for the formation of the vitelline membrane, it here demands the more intense stimulus of two, three, or more before the membrane is formed. That the membrane is not present before fertilization is admitted by Hertwig on the ground stated at p. 97.

[3] On the other hand, Morgan states ('95, 5, p. 270) that one or more spermatozoa will enter nucleated or enucleated egg-fragments whether obtained before or after fertilization.

I. *Immediate Results of Union*

The union of the germ-cells calls forth profound changes in both.

(a) *The Spermatozoön.* — Almost immediately after contact the tail ceases its movements. In some cases the tail is left outside, being carried away on the outer side of the vitelline membrane, and only the head and middle-piece enter the egg (echinoderms, Fig. 74). In other cases the entire spermatozoön enters (amphibia, earthworm, insects, etc., Fig. 64), but the tail always degenerates within the ovum and takes no part in fertilization. Within the ovum the sperm-nucleus rapidly grows, and both its structure and staining-capacity rapidly change (cf. p. 127). The most important and significant result, however, is *an immediate resumption by the sperm-nucleus and sperm-centrosome of the power of division* which has hitherto been suspended. This is not due to the union of the germ-nuclei; for, as the Hertwigs and others have shown, the supernumerary sperm-nuclei in polyspermic eggs may divide freely without copulation with the egg-nucleus, and they divide as freely after entering enucleated egg-fragments. The stimulus to division must therefore be given by the egg-cytoplasm. It is a very interesting fact that in some cases the cytoplasm has this effect on the sperm-nucleus *only after formation of the polar bodies ;* for when in sea-urchins the spermatozoa enter immature eggs, as they freely do, they penetrate but a short distance, and no further change occurs.

(b) *The Ovum.* — The entrance of the spermatozoön produces an extraordinary effect on the egg, which extends to every part of its organization. The rapid formation of the vitelline membrane, already described, proves that the stimulus extends almost instantly throughout the whole ovum.[1] At the same time the physical consistency of the cytoplasm may greatly alter, as for instance in echinoderm eggs, where, as Morgan has observed, the cytoplasm assumes immediately after fertilization a peculiar viscid character which it afterwards loses. In many cases the egg contracts, performs amœboid movements, or shows wave-like changes of form. Again, the egg-cytoplasm may show active streaming movements, as in the formation of the entrance-cone in echinoderms, or in the flow of peripheral protoplasm towards the region of entrance to form the germinal disc, as in many pelagic fish-eggs. An interesting phenomenon is the formation, behind the advancing sperm-nucleus, of a peculiar funnel-shaped mass of deeply staining material extending outwards to the periphery. This has been carefully described by Foot ('94) in the earthworm,

[1] I have often observed that the formation of the membrane, in *Toxopneustes*, proceeds like a wave from the entrance-point around the periphery, but this is often irregular.

where it is very large and conspicuous, and I have since observed it also in the sea-urchin (Fig. 69).

The most profound change in the ovum is, however, the migration of the germinal vesicle to the periphery, and the formation of the polar bodies. In many cases either or both these processes may occur before contact with the spermatozoön (echinoderms, some vertebrates). In others, however, the egg awaits the entrance of the spermatozoön (annelids, gasteropods, etc.), which gives it the necessary stimulus. This is well illustrated by the egg of *Nereis*. In the newly-discharged egg the germinal vesicle occupies a central position, the yolk, consisting of deutoplasm-spheres and oil-globules, is uniformly distributed, and at the periphery of the egg is a zone of clear perivitelline protoplasm (Fig. 43). Soon after entrance of the spermatozoön the germinal vesicle moves towards the periphery, its membrane fades away, and a radially directed mitotic figure appears, by means of which the first polar body is formed (Fig. 71). Meanwhile the protoplasm flows towards the upper pole, the perivitelline zone disappears, and the egg now shows a sharply marked polar differentiation. A remarkable phenomenon, described by Whitman in the leech ('78), and later by Foot in the earthworm ('94), is the formation of " polar rings," a process which follows the entrance of the spermatozoön and accompanies the formation of the polar bodies. These are two ring-shaped cytoplasmic masses which form at the periphery of the egg near either pole and advance thence towards the poles, the upper one surrounding the point at which the polar bodies are formed (Fig. 76). Their meaning is unknown, but Foot ('96) has made the interesting discovery that they are probably of the same nature as the yolk-nuclei (p. 121).

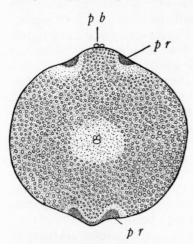

Fig. 76. — Egg of the leech *Clepsine*, during fertilization. [WHITMAN.]

p.b., polar bodies ; *p.r.*, polar rings ; cleavage-nucleus near the centre.

2. *Paths of the Germ-nuclei* (*Pro-nuclei*) [1]

After the entrance of the spermatozoön both germ-nuclei move through the egg-cytoplasm and finally meet one another. The paths traversed by each vary widely in different forms. In general two classes are to be distinguished, according as the polar-bodies are formed before or after entrance of the spermatozoön. In the former case (echinoderms) the germ-nuclei unite at once. In the latter case the sperm-nucleus advances a certain distance into the egg and then pauses while the germinal vesicle moves towards the periphery, and gives rise to the polar-bodies (*Ascaris*, annelids, etc.). This significant fact proves that the attractive force between the two nuclei is only exerted after the formation of the polar-bodies, and hence that the entrance-path of the sperm-nucleus is not determined by such attraction. A second important point, first pointed out by Roux, is that the path of the sperm-nucleus is *curved*, its "entrance-path" into the egg forming a considerable angle with its "copulation-path" towards the egg-nucleus.

These facts are well illustrated in the sea-urchin egg (Fig. 77), where the egg-nucleus occupies an eccentric position near the point at which the polar bodies are formed (before fertilization). Entering the egg at any point, the sperm-nucleus first moves rapidly inward along an entrance-path that shows no constant relation to the position of the egg-nucleus and is approximately but never exactly radial, *i.e.* towards a point near the centre of the egg. After penetrating a certain distance its direction changes slightly to that of the copulation-path, which, again, is directed not precisely towards the egg-nucleus, but towards a meeting-point where it comes in contact with the egg-nucleus. The latter does not begin to move until the entrance-path of the sperm-nucleus changes to the copulation-path. It then begins to move slowly in a somewhat curved path towards the meeting-point, often showing slight amœboid changes of form as it forces its way through the cytoplasm. From the meeting-point the apposed nuclei move slowly toward the point of final fusion, which in this case is near, but never precisely at, the centre of the egg.

These facts indicate that the paths of the germ-nuclei are deter-

---

[1] The terms "female pro-nucleus," "male pro-nucleus" (Van Beneden), are often applied to the germ-nuclei before their union. These should, I think, be rejected in favour of Hertwig's terms *egg-nucleus* and *sperm-nucleus*, on two grounds: (1) The germ-nuclei are true nuclei in every sense, differing from the somatic-nuclei only in the reduced number of chromosomes. As the latter character has recently been shown to be true also of the somatic nuclei in the sexual generation of plants (p. 196), it cannot be made the ground for a special designation of the germ-nuclei. (2) The germ-nuclei are not male and female in any proper sense (p. 183).

mined by at least two different factors, one of which is an attraction or other dynamical relation between the nuclei and the cytoplasm, the other an attraction between the nuclei. The former determines

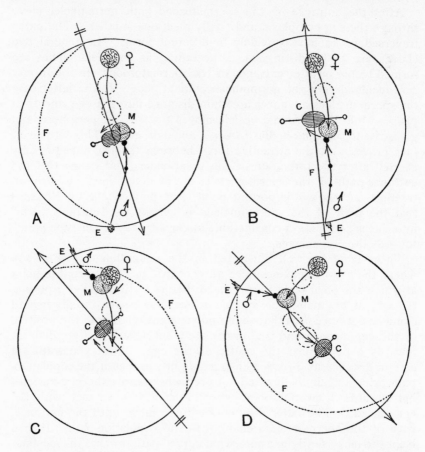

Fig. 77. — Diagrams showing the paths of the germ-nuclei in four different eggs of the sea-urchin *Toxopneustes*. From camera drawings of the transparent living eggs.

In all the figures the original position of the egg-nucleus (reticulated) is shown at ♀; the point at which the spermatozoön enters at *E* (entrance-cone). Arrows indicate the paths traversed by the nuclei. At the meeting-point (*M*) the egg-nucleus is dotted. The cleavage-nucleus in its final position is ruled in parallel lines, and through it is drawn the axis of the resulting cleavage-figure. The axis of the egg is indicated by an arrow, the point of which is turned away from the micromere-pole. Plane of first cleavage, passing near the entrance-point, shown by the curved dotted line.

the entrance-path of the sperm-nucleus, while both factors probably operate in the determination of the copulation-path along which it travels to meet the egg-nucleus. The real nature of neither factor is known.

Hertwig first called attention to the fact — which is easy to observe in the living sea-urchin egg — that the egg-nucleus does not begin to move until the sperm-nucleus has penetrated some distance into the egg and the sperm-aster has attained a considerable size; and Conklin ('94) has suggested that the nuclei are passively drawn together by the formation, attachment, and contraction of the astral rays. While this view has some facts in its favour, it is, I believe, untenable, for many reasons, among which may be mentioned the fact that neither the actual paths of the pro-nuclei nor the arrangement of the rays support the hypothesis; nor does it account for the conjugation of nuclei when no astral rays are developed (as in Protozoa), or are insignificant as compared with the nuclei (as in plants). I have often observed in cases of dispermy in the sea-urchin, that both sperm-nuclei move at an equal pace towards the egg-nucleus; but if one of them meets the egg-nucleus first, the movement of the other is immediately retarded, and only conjugates with the egg-nucleus, if at all, after a considerable interval; and in polyspermy, the egg-nucleus rarely conjugates with more than two sperm-nuclei. Probably, therefore, the nuclei are drawn together by an actual attraction which is neutralized by union, and their movements are not improbably of a chemotactic character.

3. *Union of the Germ-nuclei. The Chromosomes*

The earlier observers of fertilization, such as Auerbach, Strasburger, and Hertwig, described the germ-nuclei as undergoing a complete fusion to form the first embryonic nucleus, termed by Hertwig the *cleavage-* or *segmentation-nucleus*. As early as 1881, however, Mark clearly showed that in the slug *Limax* this is not the case, the two nuclei merely becoming apposed without actual fusion. Two years later appeared Van Beneden's epoch-making work on *Ascaris*, in which it was shown not only that the nuclei do not fuse, but that they give rise to two independent groups of chromosomes which separately enter the equatorial plate and whose descendants pass separately into the daughter-nuclei. Later observations have given the strongest reason to believe that, as far as the chromatin is concerned, a true fusion of the nuclei never takes place during fertilization, and that the paternal and maternal chromatin *may* remain separate and distinct in the later stages of development — possibly throughout life (p. 219). In this regard two general classes may be distinguished. In one, exemplified by some echinoderms, by *Amphioxus*, *Phallusia*, and some other animals, the two nuclei meet each other when in the reticular form, and apparently fuse in such a manner that the chromatin of the resulting nucleus shows no visible distinction between the paternal and maternal moieties. In the other class, which includes most accurately known cases, and is typically represented by *Ascaris* (Fig. 65) and other nematodes, by *Cyclops* (Fig. 72), and by *Pterotrachea* (Fig. 68), the two nuclei do not fuse, but only place themselves side by side, and in this position give rise each to its own group of chromosomes. On general grounds we may confidently maintain that the distinction between the two classes is only apparent, and probably is due to corresponding differences in the rate of development of the nuclei, or in the time that elapses before their union.[1]   If this time be very short, as in echinoderms, the nuclei unite before the chromosomes are formed.   If it be more prolonged, as in *Ascaris*, the chromosome-formation takes place before union.

With a few exceptions, which are of such a character as not to militate against the rule, *the number of chromosomes arising from the germ-nuclei is always the same in both, and is one-half the number characteristic of the tissue-cells of the species.   By their union, therefore, the germ-nuclei give rise to an equatorial plate containing the typical number of chromosomes.*   This remarkable discovery was first made by Van Beneden in the case of *Ascaris*, where the number of chromosomes derived from each sex is either one or two.   It has since been extended to a very large number of animals and plants, a partial list of which follows.

A Partial List showing the Number of Chromosomes Characteristic of the Germ-Nuclei and Somatic Nuclei in Various Plants and Animals.[2]

Germ-Nuclei.	Somatic Nuclei.	Name.	Group.	Authority.
I	2	Ascaris megalocephala, var. univalens.	Nematodes.	Van Beneden, Boveri.
2	4	Id., var. bivalens.	,,	,,
,,	,,	Ophryotrocha.	Annelids.	Korschelt.
,,	[,,]	Styleopsis.	Tunicates.	Julin.
4	8	Coronilla.	Nematodes.	Carnoy.
,,	,,	Pallavicinia.	Hepaticæ.	Farmer.
6	12	Spiroptera.	Nematodes.	Carnoy.
,,	[,,]	Gryllotalpa.	Insects.	vom Rath.
,,	,,	Caloptenus.	,,	Wilcox.
[,,]	,,	Æquorea.	Hydromedusæ.	Häcker.
8	16	Filaroides.	Nematodes.	Carnoy.
,,	,,	Hydrophilus.	Insects.	vom Rath.
,,	,,	Phallusia.	Tunicates.	Hill.
,,	,,	Limax.	Gasteropods.	vom Rath.
,,	[,,]	Rat.	Mammals.	Moore.
,,	[,,]	Ox, guinea-pig, man.	,,	Bardeleben.
,,	,,	Ceratozamia.	Cycads.	Overton.
,,	,,	Pinus.	Coniferæ.	Dixon.

[1] Indeed, Boveri has found that in *Ascaris* both modes occur, though the fusion of the germ-nuclei is exceptional.   (Cf. p. 216.)

[2] The above table is compiled from papers both on fertilization and maturation.   Numbers in brackets are inferred.

GERM-NUCLEI.	SOMATIC NUCLEI.	NAME.	GROUP.	AUTHORITY.
8	16	Scilla, Triticum.	Angiosperms.	Overton.
,,	,,	Allium.	,,	Strasburger, Guignard.
9	18	Echinus.	Echinoderms.	Boveri.
,,	,,	Sagitta.	Chætognaths.	,,
,,	,,	Ascidia.	Tunicates.	,,
11	[22]	Allolobophora.	Annelids.	Foot.
11 (12)	22 (24)	Cyclops strenuus.	Copepods.	Rückert.
12	24	,, brevicornis.	,,	Häcker.
,,	,,	Helix.	Gasteropods.	Platner, vom Rath.
,,	,,	Branchipus.	Crustacea.	Brauer.
,,	[,,]	Pyrrhocoris.	Insects.	Henking.
,,	,,	Salmo.	Teleosts.	Böhm.
,,	,,	Salamandra.	Amphibia.	Flemming.
,,	,,	Rana.	,,	vom Rath.
,,	,,	Mouse.	Mammals.	Sobotta.
,,	,,	Osmunda.	Ferns.	Strasburger.
,,	,,	Lilium.	Angiosperms.	Strasburger, Guignard.
,,	,,	Helleborus.	,,	Strasburger.
,,	,,	Leucojum, Pæonia, Aconitum.	,,	Overton.
14	28	Tiara.	Hydromedusæ.	Boveri.
16	32	Pterotrachea, Carinaria, Phyllirhoë.	Gastropods.	,,
,,	[,,]	Diaptomus, Heterocope.	Copepods.	Rückert.
,,	[,,]	Anomalocera, Euchæta.	,,	vom Rath.
,,	[,,]	Lumbricus.	Annelids.	Calkins.
18	36	Torpedo, Pristiurus.	Elasmobranchs.	Rückert.
[18 (19)]	36 (38)	Toxopneustes.	Echinoderms.	Wilson.
84	168	Artemia.	Crustacea.	Brauer.

The above data are drawn from sources so diverse and show so remarkable a uniformity as to establish the general law with a very high degree of probability. The few known exceptions are almost certainly apparent only and are due to the occurrence of plurivalent chromosomes. This is certainly the case with *Ascaris* (cf. p. 61). It is probably the case with the gasteropod *Arion*, where, as described by Platner, the egg-nucleus gives rise to numerous chromosomes, the sperm-nucleus to two only; the latter are, however, plurivalent, for Garnault showed that they break up into smaller chromatin-bodies, and that the germ-nuclei are exactly alike at the time of union.[1] We may here briefly refer to remarkable recent observations by Rückert and others, which seem to show that not only the paternal and mater-

[1] '89, pp. 10, 33.

nal chromatin, but also the chromosomes, may retain their individuality throughout development.[1] Van Beneden, the pioneer observer in this direction, was unable to follow the paternal and maternal chromatin beyond the first cleavage-nucleus, though he surmised that they remained distinct in later stages as well; and Rabl and Boveri brought forward evidence that the chromosomes did not lose their identity, even in the resting nucleus.   Rückert ('95, 3) and Häcker ('95, 1) have recently shown that in *Cyclops*, the paternal and maternal chromatin-groups not only remain distinctly separated during the anaphase, but give rise to double nuclei in the two-cell stage (Fig. 105). Each half again gives rise to a separate group of chromosomes at the second cleavage, and this is repeated at least as far as the blastula stage.   Herla and Zoja have shown furthermore that if in *Ascaris* the egg of variety *bivalens*, having two chromosomes, be fertilized with the spermatozoön of variety *univalens* having one chromosome, the three chromosomes reappear at each cleavage, at least as far as the twelve-cell stage (Fig. 106); and according to Zoja, the paternal chromosome is distinguishable from the two maternal at each step by its smaller size.   We have thus what must be reckoned as more than a possibility, that every cell in the body of the child may receive from each parent not only half of its chromatin substance, but one-half of its chromosomes, as distinct and individual descendants of those of the parents.

C. CENTROSOME AND ARCHOPLASM IN FERTILIZATION

We have now finally to consider more critically the history of the centrosomes in fertilization, already briefly reviewed at p. 135.   The account there given considers only the more usual and typical history of the centrosome, viz. the degeneration of the egg-centrosome and the introduction of a new centrosome by the spermatozoön.   There is, however, one phenomenon which indicates *a priori* the possibility that other modes of fertilization may occur, namely, *parthenogenesis*, in which the egg develops without fertilization.   In this case, as Brauer ('93) has clearly shown in *Artemia*, the egg-centrosome remaining after the formation of the polar bodies does not degenerate, but divides into two to form the cleavage-amphiaster.   The degeneration of the egg-centrosome is therefore not a necessary or invariable phenomenon, and as a matter of fact several accounts have been given of its persistence and active participation in the process of fertilization. These accounts fall under three categories, as follows: —

   1. Each germ-cell contributes a single centrosome, one of which

[1] Cf. p. 219.

forms the centre of each aster of the first mitotic figure (Van Beneden, in *Ascaris*, '83, '87, p. 270).

2. Each germ-cell contributes two centrosomes (or one which immediately divides into two), which conjugate, paternal with maternal, to form those of the cleavage-amphiaster (Fol, in sea-urchins, '91 ; Guignard, in flowering plants, '91 ; Conklin, in gasteropods, '93).

3. The centrosome is derived not from the spermatozoön, but from the egg (Wheeler, in the case of Myzostoma, '95).

The first of these accounts, which rested rather on surmise than on adequate observation, may probably be safely rejected, for it contradicts the universal law that the centrosome divides into two before cell-division, and is unsupported by later observers (Meyer, Erlanger, etc.). The second view, as embodied in the statements of Fol, Guignard, and Conklin, demands fuller consideration. All these authors agree that each germ-cell contributes two centrosomes, or one which divides into two during fertilization. The daughter-centrosomes thus formed conjugate two and two in such a manner that each of the centrosomes of the cleavage-spindle is formed by the union of a centrosome derived from each germ-cell. It is an interesting and significant fact that a conjugation of centrosomes was predicted by Rabl ('89) on the *a priori* ground that if the centrosome is a permanent cell-organ, as Boveri and Van Beneden maintain, then a union of germ-cells must involve a union not only of nuclei, but also of centrosomes. Unusual interest was therefore aroused when Fol, in 1891, under the somewhat dramatic title of the "Quadrille of Centres," described precisely such a conjugation of centrosomes as Rabl had predicted. The results of this veteran observer were very positively and specifically set forth, and were of so logical and consistent a character as to command instant acceptance on the part of many authorities. Moreover, a precisely similar result was reached through the careful studies, in the same year, of Guignard, on the lily, and of Conklin ('93), on the marine gasteropod *Crepidula*, a confirmation which seemed to place the quadrille on a firm basis. Fol's result was, however, opposed to the earlier conclusions of Boveri and Hertwig, and a careful re-examination of the fertilization of the echinoderm egg, independently made in 1894–5 by Boveri (*Echinus*), by myself (*Toxopneustes*), and Mathews (*Arbacia, Asterias*), demonstrated its erroneous character. In the echinoderm, as in so many other cases, the egg-centrosome disappears. The cleavage-amphiaster arises solely by division of the sperm-aster, and the centrosome of the latter is derived not from the tip of the spermatozoön, as asserted by Fol, but from the middle-piece, as already described. The same result has been since reached by Hill and Erlanger. Various attempts have been made to explain Fol's results as based

on double-fertilized eggs, on imperfect method, on a misinterpreta-
tion of the double centrosomes of the cleavage-spindle, yet they still
remain an inexplicable anomaly of scientific literature.

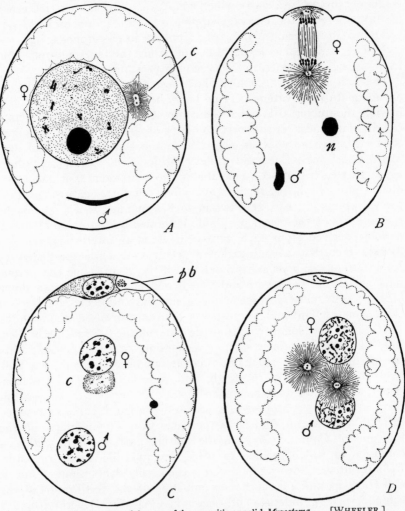

Fig. 78. — Fertilization of the egg of the parasitic annelid *Myzostoma*.   [WHEELER.]

A. Soon after entrance of the spermatozoön; the sperm-nucleus at ♂; at ♀ the germinal
vesicle; at *c* the double egg-centrosome. *B.* First polar body forming at ♀; *n*, the cast-out nucleolus or germinal spot. *C.* The polar bodies formed (*p.b.*); germ-nuclei of equal size; at *c* the
persistent egg-centrosomes. *D.* Approach of the germ-nuclei; the egg-amphiaster formed. In
all other known cases this amphiaster is derived from the *sperm*-amphiaster.

Serious doubt has also been thrown on Conklin's conclusions by
subsequent research.   Kostanecki and Wierzejski ('96) have recently
made a very thorough study, by means of serial sections, of the fertil-

ization of the gasteropod *Physa*, and have reached exactly the same result as that obtained in the echinoderms. Here also the egg-centre degenerates, and its place is taken by a centrosome brought in by the spermatozoön and giving rise to a sperm-amphiaster, which persists as the cleavage-amphiaster (Fig. 64). A strong presumption is thus created that Conklin was in error; and if this be the case, the last positive evidence of a conjugation of centrosomes in the animal egg disappears.[1]

In view of this result we may well hesitate to accept Guignard's conclusions in the case of flowering plants. The figures of this author show in the clearest manner four centrosomes lying in the neighbourhood of the apposed germ-nuclei (Fig. 80); but the conjugation of these centrosomes was an *inference*, not an observed fact, and has not been confirmed by any subsequent observer. Until such confirmation is forthcoming we must receive Guignard's results with scepticism.[2]

The third view, based upon the single case of *Myzostoma* as described by Wheeler ('95), apparently rests on strong evidence, though its force cannot be exactly estimated until a more detailed account has been published. In this case no sperm-aster can be seen at any period, with which is correlated the fact that no middle-piece can be made out in the spermatozoön. The egg-centrosome, on the other hand, is stated to persist after the formation of the second polar body, to become double at a very early period, and to give rise directly to the cleavage-amphiaster (Fig. 78). I can find no ground in Professor Wheeler's paper to doubt the accuracy of his conclusions. Nevertheless, an isolated case, which stands in contradiction to all that is known of other forms, must rest on irrefragable evidence in order to command acceptance. Since, moreover, the case involves the whole theory of fertilization based on other animals (cf. p. 141), it must, I think, await further investigation.

---

[1] Richard Hertwig has, however, recently published a very interesting observation which indicates that we may not yet have fully fathomed the facts in the case of echinoderms. If unfertilized echinoderm-eggs, after formation of the polar-bodies, lie for many hours in water or be treated with dilute poisons (strychnine), they may form a more or less perfectly developed amphiaster, and the nucleus may even make an abortive attempt at division. No centrosomes, however, could be discovered, even by the most approved methods. This remarkable phenomenon is probably of the same nature as the formation of artificial asters observed by Morgan (p. 226), but its meaning is not clear.

[2] Van der Stricht, in a recent paper on *Amphioxus* ('95), is inclined to believe that a fusion between the egg-centre and the sperm-centre occurs; but the evidence is very incomplete, and a comparison with the case of *Physa* indicates that his conclusion cannot be sustained. The same criticism applies to the earlier work of Blanc ('91, '93) on the trout's egg.

D. Fertilization in Plants

The investigation of fertilization in the plants has always lagged somewhat behind that of the animals, and even at the present time our knowledge of it is less complete, especially in regard to the history of the centrosome and the archoplasmic structures. It is, however, sufficient to show that the process is here essentially of the same nature as in animals in so far as it involves a union of two germ-nuclei derived from the two respective sexes. Many early observers from the time of Pringsheim ('55) onward described a conjugation of cells in the lower plants, but the union of *germ-nuclei,* as far as I can find, was first clearly made out in the flowering plants by Strasburger in 1877–8, and carefully described by him in 1884. Schmitz observed a union of the nuclei

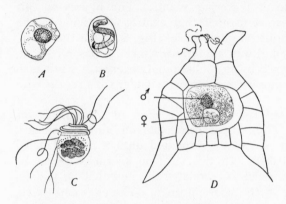

Fig. 79. — Fertilization in *Pibularia.* [Cambell.]

A. B. Early stages in the formation of the spermatozoid. *B.* The mature spermatozoid; the nucleus lies above in the spiral turns; below is a cytoplasmic mass containing starch-grains (*cf.* the spermatozoids of ferns and of *Marsilia*, Fig. 53). *D.* Archegonium during fertilization. In the centre the ovum containing the apposed germ-nuclei (♂, ♀).

of the conjugating cells of *Spirogyra* in 1879, and made similar observations on other algæ in 1884. The same has been shown to be true in *Muscineæ* and *Pteridophytes* by Strasburger, Cambell, and others (Fig. 79).

Up to the present time, however, the only thorough investigation of fertilization has been made in the case of the flowering plants, and our knowledge of the process here is due in the first instance to Strasburger ('84, '88) and Guignard ('91), supplemented by the work of Belajeff and Overton. The ovum or oösphere of the flowering plant is a large, rounded cell containing a large nucleus and numerous minute colourless plastids from which arise, by division, the plastids of the embryo (chromatophores, amyloplasts). The ovum lies in the "embryo-sac," which represents morphologically the female prothallium or sexual generation of the Pteridophyte, and is itself embedded in the ovule within the ovary. The male germ-cell is here non-motile, and is represented by a "generative nucleus," with a small quantity of cytoplasm and two centrosomes (Guignard), lying near the tip of the pollen-tube (Fig. 80, *A*), which is developed as an outgrowth from the pollen-grain and represents, with the latter, a rudimentary male prothallium or sexual generation. The formation

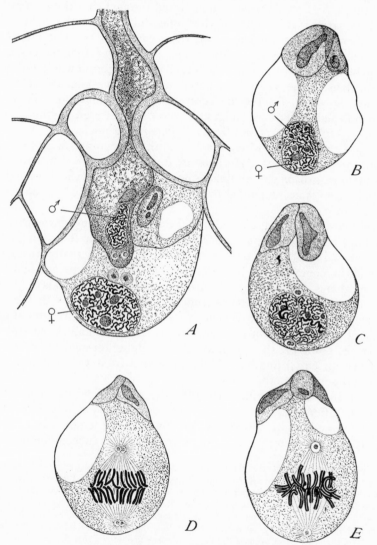

Fig. 80. — Fertilization of the lily. [GUIGNARD.]

A. The tip of the pollen-tube entering the embryo-sac; below, the ovum (oösphere) with its nucleus at ♀ and two centrosomes; at the tip of the pollen-tube the sperm-nucleus (♂) with two centrosomes near it. *B.* Union of the germ-nuclei. *C.* Later stage of the same, showing the asserted fusion of the centrosomes. *E.* The first cleavage-figure in the metaphase. *D.* Early anaphase of the same; precocious division of the centrosomes.

M

of the pollen-tube, and its growth down through the tissue of the pistil to the ovule, was observed by Amici ('23), Brogniard ('26), and Robert Brown ('31); and in 1833–34 Corda was able to follow its tip through the micropyle into the ovule.[1]

Strasburger ('77–88) first demonstrated the fact that the generative nucleus carried at the tip of the pollen-tube enters the ovum and unites with the egg-nucleus. On the basis of these observations he reached, in 1884, the same conclusion as Hertwig, that the essential phenomena of fertilization is a union of two germ-nuclei, and that the nucleus is the vehicle of hereditary transmission. Strasburger did not, however, observe the centrosome in fertilization. This was accomplished in 1891 by Guignard, who demonstrated in the case of the lily (*Lilium Martagon*) that the generative nucleus as it enters the egg is accompanied by a small quantity of cytoplasm and by two centrosomes (Fig. 80). He showed further that the egg also contains two centrosomes; and according to his account the conjugation of the nuclei is accompanied by a conjugation of the centrosomes, as already described.

Guignard also first cleared up the history of the chromosomes, reaching results closely in accord with those of Van Beneden in the case of *Ascaris*. The two germ-nuclei do not actually fuse, but remain in contact, side by side, and give rise each to one-half the chromosomes of the equatorial plate, precisely as in animals (Fig. 80). The number of chromosomes from each germ-nucleus is, in the lily, twelve. The later history is identical with that of the animal egg, each chromosome splitting lengthwise, and the halves passing to opposite poles of the spindle. Each daughter-nucleus therefore receives an equal number of chromosomes from the maternal and paternal germ-nuclei.[2]

As in the case of animals (p. 127), the germ-nuclei of plants show marked differences in structure and staining-reaction before their union, though they ultimately become exactly equivalent. Thus, according to Rosen ('92, p. 443), on treatment by fuchsin-methyl-blue

---

[1] It is interesting to note that the botanists of the eighteenth century engaged in the same fantastic controversy regarding the origin of the embryo as that of the zoölogists of the time. Moreland (1703), followed by Etienne François Geoffroy, Needham, and others, placed himself on the side of Leeuwenhoek and the spermatists, maintaining that the pollen supplied the embryo which entered the ovule through the micropyle. (The latter had been described by Grew in 1672.) It is an interesting fact that even Schleiden adopted a similar view. On the other hand, Adanson (1763) and others maintained that the ovule contained the germ which was excited to development by an aura or vapour emanating from the pollen and entering through the tracheæ of the pistil.

[2] Guignard's observations on the conjugation of the centrosomes have already been considered at p. 159. They stand at present isolated as the only precise account of the history of the centrosomes in plant-fertilization, and no general conclusions on this subject can therefore at present be drawn.

the male germ-nucleus of phanerogams is "cyanophilous," the female "erythrophilous," as described by Auerbach in animals. Strasburger, while confirming this observation in some cases, finds the reaction to be inconstant, though the germ-nuclei usually show marked differences in their staining-capacity. These are ascribed by Strasburger ('92, '94) to differences in the conditions of nutrition; by Zacharias and Schwarz to corresponding differences in chemical composition, the male nucleus being in general richer in nuclein, and the female nucleus poorer. This distinction disappears during fertilization, and Strasburger has observed, in the case of gymnosperms (after treatment with a mixture of fuchsin-iodine-green) that the paternal nucleus, which is at first "cyanophilous," becomes "erythrophilous," like the egg-nucleus before the pollen-tube has reached the egg. Within the egg both stain exactly alike. These facts indicate, as Strasburger insists, that the differences between the germ-nuclei of plants are as in animals of a temporary and non-essential character.

E. Conjugation in Unicellular Forms

The conjugation of unicellular organisms possesses a peculiar interest, since it is undoubtedly a prototype of the union of germ-cells in the multicellular forms. Bütschli and Minot long ago maintained that cell-divisions tend to run in cycles, each of which begins and ends with an act of conjugation. In the higher forms the cells produced in each cycle cohere to form the multicellular body; in the unicellular forms the cells separate as distinct individuals, but those belonging to one cycle are collectively comparable with the multicellular body. The validity of this comparison, in a morphological sense, is generally admitted.[1] No process of conjugation, it is true, is known to occur in many unicellular and in some multicellular forms, and the cyclical character of cell-division still remains *sub judice*.[2] It is none the less certain that a key to the fertilization of higher forms must be sought in the conjugation of unicellular organisms.

The difficulties of observation are, however, so great that we are as yet acquainted with only the outlines of the process, and have still no very clear idea of its finer details or its physiological meaning. The phenomena have been most closely followed in the Infusoria by Bütschli, Maupas, and Richard Hertwig, though many valuable observations on the conjugation of unicellular plants have been made by De Bary, Schmitz, Klebahn, and Overton. All these observers have reached the same general result as that attained through study of the fertilization of the egg; namely, that an essential phenomenon

[1] Cf. p. 41.　　　　　　[2] Cf. p. 129.

of conjugation is *a union of the nuclei of the conjugating cells.*
Among the unicellular plants both the cell-bodies and the nuclei
completely fuse. Among animals this may occur; but in many of
the Infusoria union of the cell-bodies is only temporary, and the conjugation consists of a mutual exchange and fusion of nuclei. It is

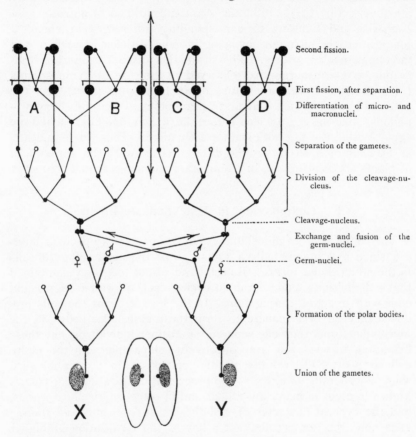

Fig. 81. — Diagram showing the history of the micronuclei during the conjugation of *Paramœcium.* [Modified from MAUPAS.]

X and *Y* represent the opposed macro- and micronuclei in the two respective gametes; circles
represent degenerating nuclei; black dots, persisting nuclei.

impossible within the limits of this work to attempt more than a
sketch of the process in a few forms.

We may first consider the conjugation of Infusoria. Maupas's
beautiful observations have shown that in this group the life-history
of the species runs in cycles, a long period of multiplication by cell-
division being succeeded by an "epidemic of conjugation," which
inaugurates a new cycle, and is obviously comparable in its physio-

logical aspect with the union of germ-cells in the Metazoa. If conjugation do not occur, the race rapidly degenerates and dies out; and Maupas believes himself justified in the conclusion that conjugation counteracts the tendency to senile degeneration and causes rejuvenescence, as maintained by Bütschli and Minot.[1]

In *Stylonychia pustulata*, which Maupas followed continuously from the end of February until July, the first conjugation occurred on April 29th, after 128 bi-partitions; and the epidemic reached its height three weeks later, after 175 bi-partitions. The descendants of individuals prevented from conjugation died out through "senile degeneracy," after 316 bi-partitions. Similar facts were observed in many other forms. The degeneracy is manifested by a very marked reduction in size, a partial atrophy of the cilia, and especially by a more or less complete *degradation of the nuclear apparatus*. In *Stylonychia pustulata* and *Onychodromus grandis* this process especially affects the micronucleus, which atrophies, and finally disappears, though the animals still actively swim, and for a time divide. Later, the macronucleus becomes irregular, and sometimes breaks up into smaller bodies. In other cases, the degeneration first affects the macronucleus, which may lose its chromatin, undergo fatty degeneration, and may finally disappear altogether (*Stylonychia mytilus*), after which the micronucleus soon degenerates more or less completely, and the race dies. It is a very significant fact that towards the end of the cycle, as the nuclei degenerate, the animals become incapable of taking food and of growth; and it is probable, as Maupas points out, that the degeneration of the cytoplasmic organs is due to disturbances in nutrition caused by the degeneration of the nucleus.

The more essential phenomena occurring during conjugation are as follows. The Infusoria possess two kinds of nuclei, a large *macronucleus* and one or more small *micronuclei*. During conjugation the macronucleus degenerates and disappears, and the micronucleus alone is concerned in the essential part of the process. The latter divides several times, one of the products, the *germ-nucleus*, conjugating with a corresponding germ-nucleus from the other individual, while the others degenerate as "corpuscules de rebut." The dual nucleus thus formed, which corresponds with the cleavage-nucleus of the ovum, then gives rise by division to both macronuclei and micronuclei of the offspring of the conjugating animals (Fig. 81).

These facts may be illustrated by the conjugation of *Paramœcium caudatum*, which possesses a single macronucleus and micronucleus, and in which conjugation is temporary and fertilization mutual. The two animals become united by their ventral sides and the macronucleus of each begins to degenerate, while the micronucleus divides twice to form four spindle-shaped bodies (Fig. 82, *A*, *B*). Three of these degenerate, forming the "corpuscules de rebut," which play no further part. The fourth divides into two, one of which, the "female pronucleus," remains in the body, while the other, or "male pronucleus," passes into the other animal and fuses with the female

[1] Cf. p. 129.

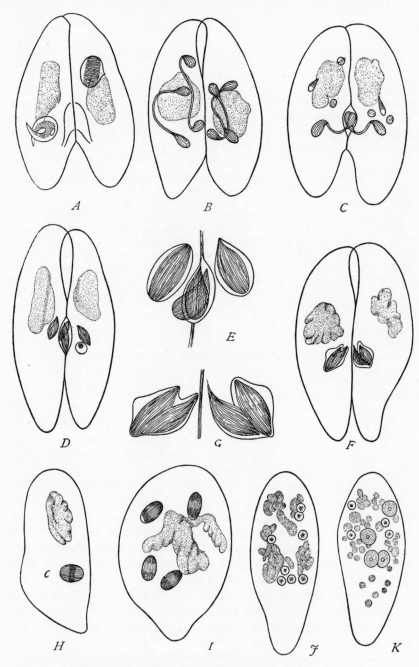

Fig. 82. — Conjugation of *Paramœcium caudatum*. [*A–C,* after R. HERTWIG; *D–K,* after MAUPAS.] (The macronuclei dotted in all the figures.)

A. Micronuclei preparing for their first division. *B.* Second division. *C.* Third division: three polar bodies or "corpuscules de rebut," and one dividing germ-nucleus in each animal. *D.* Exchange of the germ-nuclei. *E.* The same, enlarged. *F.* Fusion of the germ-nuclei. *G.* The same, enlarged. *H.* Cleavage-nucleus (*c*), preparing for the first division. *I.* The cleavage-nucleus has divided twice. *J.* After three divisions of the cleavage-nucleus; macronucleus breaking up. *K.* Four of the nuclei enlarging to form new macronuclei. The first fission soon takes place.

pronucleus (Fig. 82, *C–H*). Each animal now contains a cleavage-nucleus equally derived from both the conjugating animals, and the latter soon separate. The cleavage-nucleus in each divides three times successively, and of the eight resulting bodies four become macronuclei and four micronuclei (Fig. 82, *H–K*). By two succeeding fissions the four macronuclei are then distributed, one to each of the four resulting individuals. In some other species the micro-nuclei are equally distributed in like manner, but in *P. cauda-tum* the process is more complicated, since three of them degenerate, and the fourth divides twice to produce four new micronuclei. In either case at the close of the process each of the conjugating individuals has given rise to four descendants, each containing a macro-nucleus and micro-nucleus derived from the cleavage-nucleus. From this time forward fission follows fission in the usual manner, both nuclei dividing at each fission, until, after many generations, conjugation recurs.

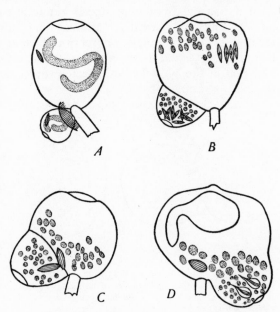

Fig. 83.—Conjugation of Vorticellids. [MAUPAS.]

A. Attachment of the small free-swimming microgamete to the large fixed macrogamete; micronucleus dividing in each (*Carchesium*). *B.* Microgamete containing eight micronuclei; macrogamete four (*Vorticella*). *C.* All but one of the micro-nuclei have degenerated as polar bodies or "corpuscules de rebut." *D.* Each of the micronuclei of the last stage has divided into two to form the germ-nuclei; two of these, one from each gamete, have conjugated to form the cleavage-nucleus seen at the left; the other two, at the right, are degenerating.

Essentially similar facts have been observed by Richard Hertwig and Maupas in a large number of forms. In cases of permanent conjugation, as in *Vorticella*, where a smaller *microgamete* unites with a larger *macrogamete*, the process is essentially the same, though the details are still more complex. Here the germ-nucleus derived from each gamete is in the macrogamete one-fourth and in the microgam-ete one-eighth of the original micronucleus (Fig. 83). Each germ-nucleus divides into two, as usual, but one of the products of each degenerates, and the two remaining pronuclei conjugate to form a cleavage-nucleus.

The facts just described show a very close parallel to those observed in the maturation and fertilization of the egg. In both cases there is a union of two similar nuclei to form a cleavage-nucleus or its equivalent, equally derived from both gametes, and this is the progenitor of all the nuclei of the daughter-cells arising by subsequent divisions. In both cases, moreover (if we confine the comparison to the egg) the original nucleus does not conjugate with its fellow until it has by division produced a number of other nuclei all but one of which degenerate. Maupas does not hesitate to compare these degenerating nuclei or "corpuscules de rebut" with the polar bodies (p. 175), and it is a remarkable coincidence that their number, like that of the polar bodies, is often three, though this is not always the case.

A remarkable peculiarity in the conjugation of the Infusoria

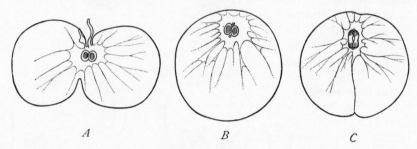

Fig. 84.—Conjugation of *Noctiluca*. [ISHIKAWA.]

A. Union of the gametes, apposition of the nuclei. *B.* Complete fusion of the gametes. Above and below the apposed nuclei are the centrosomes. *C.* Cleavage-spindle, consisting of two separate halves.

is the fact that *the germ-nuclei unite when in the form of spindles or mitotic figures.* These spindles consist of achromatic fibres, or "archoplasm," and chromosomes, but no asters or undoubted centrosomes have been thus far seen in them. During union the spindles join side by side (Fig. 82, *G*), and this gives good reason to believe that the chromatin of the two gametes is equally distributed to the daughter-nuclei as in Metazoa. In the conjugation of some other Protozoa the nuclei unite while in the resting state; but very little is known of the process save in the cystoflagellate *Noctiluca*, which has been studied with some care by Cienkowsky and Ishikawa (Fig. 84). Here the conjugating animals completely fuse, but the nuclei are merely apposed and give rise each to one-half of the mitotic figure. At either pole of the spindle is a centrosome, the origin of which remains undetermined.

It is an interesting fact that in *Noctiluca*, in the Gregarines, and probably in some other Protozoa, conjugation is followed by a very rapid multiplication of the nucleus followed by a corresponding division of the cell-body to form "spores," which remain for a time closely aggregated before their liberation. The resemblance of this process to the fertilization and subsequent cleavage of the ovum is particularly striking.

The conjugation of unicellular plants shows some interesting

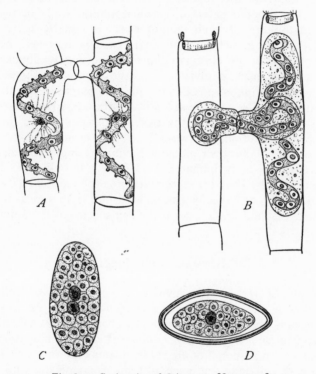

Fig. 85. — Conjugation of *Spirogyra.* [OVERTON.]

A. Union of the conjugating cells (*S. communis*). *B.* The typical, though not invariable, mode of fusion in *S. Weberi ;* the chromatophore of the "female" cell breaks in the middle, while that of the "male" cell passes into the interval. *C.* The resulting zygospore filled with pryrenoids, before union of the nuclei. *D.* Zygospore after fusion of the nuclei and formation of the membrane.

features. Here the conjugating cells completely fuse to form a "zygospore" (Figs. 85, 99), which as a rule becomes surrounded by a thick membrane, and, unlike the animal conjugate, may long remain in a quiescent state before division. Not only do the nuclei unite, but in many cases the plastids also (chromatophores). In *Spirogyra* some interesting variations in this regard have been observed. In some species De Bary has observed that the long band-shaped chromatophores unite end to end so that in the zygote the paternal and maternal chromatophores lie at opposite ends. In *S. Weberi*, on the other hand, Overton has found that the single maternal chromatophore breaks in two in the middle and the paternal chromatophore is interpolated between the two halves, so as to lie in the middle of the zygote (Fig. 85). It follows from this, as De Vries has pointed out, that the origin of the chromatophores in the daughter-cells differs in the two species, for in the former case one receives a maternal, the other a paternal, chromatophore, while in the latter, the chromatophore of each daughter-cell is equally derived from those of the two gametes. The final result is, however, the same; for, in both cases, the chromatophore of the zygote divides in the middle at each ensuing division. In the first case, therefore, the maternal chromatophore passes into one, the paternal into the other, of the daughter-cells. In the second case the same result is effected by two succeeding divisions, the two middle-cells of the four-celled band receiving paternal, the two end-cells maternal, chromatophores. In the case of a *Spirogyra* filament having a single chromatophore it is therefore "wholly immaterial whether the individual cells receive the chlorophyll-band from the father or the mother" (De Vries), — a result which, as Wheeler has pointed out, is in a measure analogous to that reached in the case of the centrosome of the animal egg.[1]

F. Summary and Conclusion

All forms of fertilization involve a conjugation of cells by a process that is the exact converse of cell-division. In the lowest forms, such as the unicellular algæ, the conjugating cells are, in a morphological sense, precisely equivalent, and conjugation takes place between corresponding elements, nucleus uniting with nucleus, cell-body with cell-body, and even, in some cases, plastid with plastid. Whether this is true of the centrosomes is not known, but in the Infusoria there is a conjugation of the achromatic spindles which certainly points to a union of the centrosomes or their equivalents. As we rise in the scale, the conjugating cells diverge more and more, until in the higher plants and animals they differ widely not only in form and size, but also in their internal structure, and to such an extent that they are no longer equivalent either morphologically or physiologically. Both in animals and in plants the paternal germ-cell loses most of its cytoplasm, the main bulk of which, and hence the main body of the embryo, is now supplied by the egg. But,

---

[1] De Vries's conclusion is, however, not entirely certain; for it is impossible to determine, save by analogy, whether the chromatophores maintain their individuality in the zygote.

more than this, the germ-cells come to differ in their morphological composition; for in plants the male germ-cell loses its plastids, which are supplied by the mother alone, while in most if not all animals the egg loses its centrosome, which is then supplied by the father. The loss of the centrosome by the egg is, I believe, to be regarded as a provision to guard against parthenogenesis and to ensure amphimixis.

The equivalence of the germ-cells is thus finally lost. Only the germ-nuclei retain their primitive morphological equivalence. Hence we find the essential fact of fertilization and sexual reproduction to be a union of equivalent nuclei; and to this all other processes are tributary. The substance of the germ-nuclei, giving rise to the same number of chromosomes in each, is equally distributed to the daughter-cells and probably to all the cells of the body.

As regards the most highly differentiated type of fertilization and development we thus reach the following conception: From the mother comes in the main the cytoplasm of the embryonic body which is the principal substratum of growth and differentiation. From both parents comes the hereditary basis or chromatin by which these processes are controlled and from which they receive the specific stamp of the race. From the father comes the centrosome to organize the machinery of mitotic division by which the egg splits up into the elements of the tissues, and by which each of these elements receives its quota of the common heritage of chromatin. Huxley hit the mark two score years ago when in the words that head this chapter he compared the organism to a web of which the warp is derived from the female and woof from the male. What has since been gained is the knowledge that this web is to be sought in the chromatic substance of the nuclei, and that the centrosome is the weaver at the loom.

LITERATURE IV

Van Beneden, E. — Recherches sur la maturation de l'œuf, la fécondation et la division cellulaire: *Arch. Biol.*, IV. 1883.

Van Beneden and Neyt. — Nouvelles recherches sur la fécondation et la division mitosique chez l'Ascaride mégalocephale: *Bull. Acad. roy. de Belgique*, III. 14, No. 8, 1887.

Boveri, Th. — Über den Anteil des Spermatozoön an der Teilung des Eies: *Sitz.-Ber. d. Ges. f. Morph. u. Phys. in München*, B. III., Heft 3. 1887.

Id. — Zellenstudien, II. 1888.

Id. — Befruchtung: *Merkel und Bonnet's Ergebnisse*, I. 1891.

Id. — Über das Verhalten der Centrosomen bei der Befruchtung des Seeigeleies, etc.: *Verhandl. Phys. Med. Ges. Wurzburg*, XXIX. 1895.

Fick, R. — Über die Reifung und Befruchtung des Axolotleies: *Zeitschr. Wiss. Zoöl.*, LVI. 4. 1893.

Guignard, L. — Nouvelles études sur la fécondation : *Ann. d. Sciences nat. Bot.*, XIV. 1891.

Hartog, M. M. — Some Problems of Reproduction, etc. : *Quart. Journ. Mic. Sci.*, XXXIII. 1891.

Hertwig, O. — Beiträge zur Kenntniss der Bildung, Befruchtung und Teilung des tierischen Eies, I. : *Morph. Jahrb.*, I. 1875.

Hertwig, R. — Über die Konjugation der Infusorien : *Abh. d. bayr. Akad. d. Wiss.*, II. Cl. XVII. 1888–89.

Id. — Über Befruchtung und Konjugation : *Verh. deutsch. Zoöl. Ges. Berlin*, 1892.

Kostanecki, K. v., and Wierzejski, A. — Über das Verhalten der sogen. achromatischen Substanzen im befruchteten Ei (of *Physa*) : *Arch. mik. Anat.*, XLVII. 2. 1896.

Mark, E. L. — Maturation, Fecundation, and Segmentation of *Limax campestris* : *Bull. Mus. Comp. Zoöl. Harvard College, Cambridge, Mass.*, VI. 1881.

Maupas. — Le rejeunissement karyogamique chez les Ciliés : *Arch. d. Zoöl.*, 2me série, VII. 1889.

Rückert, J. — Über das Selbständigbleiben der väterlichen und mütterlichen Kernsubstanz während der ersten Entwicklung des befruchteten Cyclops-Eies : *Arch. mik. Anat.*, XLV. 3. 1895.

Strasburger, E. — Neue Untersuchungen über den Befruchtungsvorgang bei den Phanerogamen, als Grundlage für eine Theorie der Zeugung. *Jena*, 1884.

Id. — Über Kern- und Zellteilung im Pflanzenreich, nebst einem Anhang über Befruchtung. *Jena*, 1888.

Vejdovský, F. — Entwickelungsgeschichtliche Untersuchungen, Heft 1, Reifung, Befruchtung und Furchung des Rhynchelmis-Eies. *Prag*, 1888.

Wilson, Edm. B. — Atlas of Fertilization and Karyokinesis. *New York*, 1895.

CHAPTER V

OOGENESIS AND SPERMATOGENESIS.   REDUCTION OF THE CHROMOSOMES

" Es kommt also in der Generationenreihe der Keimzelle irgendwo zu einer Reduktion der ursprünglich vorhandenen Chromosomenzahl auf die Hälfte, und diese *Zahlen*-reduktion ist demnach nicht etwa nur ein theoretisches Postulat, sondern eine Thatsache."

BOVERI.[1]

VAN BENEDEN'S epoch-making discovery that the nuclei of the conjugating germ-cells contain each one-half the number of chromosomes characteristic of the body-cells has now been extended to so many plants and animals that it may probably be regarded as a universal law of development.   The process by which the reduction in number is effected, forms the most essential part of the phenomena of *maturation* by which the germ-cells are prepared for their union.   No phenomena of cell-life possess a higher theoretical interest than these. For, on the one hand, nowhere in the history of the cell do we find so unmistakable and striking an adaptation of means to ends or one of so marked a prophetic character, since maturation looks not to the present but to the future of the germ-cells.   On the other hand, the chromatin-reduction suggests problems relating to the morphological constitution of nucleus and chromatin which have an important bearing on all theories of development, and which now stand in the foreground of scientific discussion among the most debatable and interesting of biological problems.

It must be said at the outset that the phenomena of maturation belong to one of the most difficult fields of cytological research, and one in which we are confronted not only by diametrically opposing theoretical views, but also by apparently contradictory results of observation.

Two fundamentally different views have been held of the manner in which the reduction is effected.   The earlier and simpler view, which was somewhat doubtfully suggested by Boveri ('87, 1), and has been more recently supported by Van Bambeke ('94) and some others,

---

[1] *Zellenstudien*, III. p. 62.

assumed an actual degeneration or casting out of half the chromosomes during the growth of the germ-cells — a simple and easily
intelligible process.   The whole weight of the evidence now goes to
show, however, that this view cannot be sustained, and that *reduction
is effected by a rearrangement and redistribution of the nuclear substance* without loss of any of its essential constituents.   It is true
that a large amount of chromatin is lost during the growth of the
egg.[1]   It is nevertheless certain that this loss is not directly connected with the process of reduction; for, as Hertwig and others
have shown, no such loss occurs during spermatogenesis, and even
in the oögenesis the evidence is clear that an explanation must be
sought in another direction.   We have advanced a certain distance
towards such an explanation and, indeed, apparently have found it

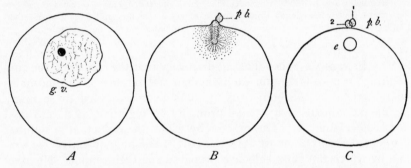

Fig. 86. — Formation of the polar bodies before entrance of the spermatozoön, as seen in the
living ovarian egg of the sea-urchin *Toxopneustes* (× 365).
    A. Preliminary change of form in the germinal vesicle. *B.* The first polar body formed, the
second forming. *C.* The ripe egg, ready for fertilization, after formation of the two polar bodies
(*p. b.,* 1, 2) ; *e,* the egg-nucleus. In this animal the second polar body fails to divide. For
division of the second polar body see Fig. 64.

in a few specific cases.   Yet when the subject is regarded as a
whole, the admission must be made that the time has not yet come
for an understanding of the phenomena, and the subject must therefore be treated in the main from an historical point of view.

A. General Outline

    The general phenomena of maturation fall under two heads ; viz.
oögenesis, which includes the formation and maturation of the ovum,
and *spermatogenesis,* comprising the corresponding phenomena in
case of the spermatozoön.   Recent research has shown that maturation conforms to the same type in both sexes, which show as close a
parallel in this regard as in the later history of the germ-nuclei.   Stated

[1] Cf. Figs. 71, 88.

in the most general terms, this parallel is as follows:[1] In both sexes the final reduction in the number of chromosomes is effected in the course of the last two cell-divisions by which the definitive germ-cells arise, each of the four cells thus formed having but half the usual number of chromosomes. In the female but one of the four cells forms the "ovum" proper, while the other three, known as the *polar bodies*, are minute, rudimentary, and incapable of development (Figs. 64, 71, 86). In the male, on the other hand, all four of the cells become functional spermatozoa. This difference between the two sexes is probably due to the physiological division of labour between the germ-cells, the spermatozoa being motile and very small, while the egg contains a large amount of protoplasm and yolk, out of which the

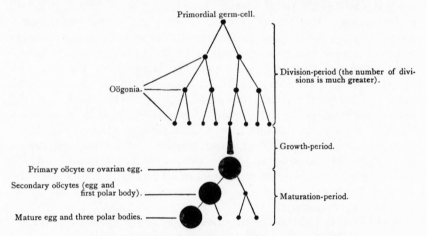

Fig. 87. — Diagram showing the genesis of the egg. [After BOVERI.]

main mass of the embryonic body is formed. In the male, therefore, all of the four cells may become functional; in the female the functions of development have become restricted to but one of the four, while the others have become rudimentary (cf. p. 182). The polar bodies are therefore to be regarded as *abortive eggs* — a view first put forward by Mark in 1881, and ultimately adopted by nearly all investigators.

1. *Reduction in the Female. Formation of the Polar Bodies*

As described in Chapter III., the egg arises by the division of cells descended from the primordial egg-cells of the maternal organism, and these may be differentiated from the somatic cells at a very early

[1] The parallel was first clearly pointed out by Platner in 1889, and was brilliantly demonstrated by Oscar Hertwig in the following year.

period, sometimes even in the cleavage-stages.   As development proceeds, each primordial cell gives rise, by division of the usual mitotic
type, to a number of descendants known as *oögonia* (Fig. 87), which
are the immediate predecessors of the ovarian egg.   At a certain
period these cease to divide.   Each of them then grows to form an
ovarian egg, its nucleus enlarging to form the germinal vesicle, its
cytoplasm becoming more or less laden with food-matters (yolk or
deutoplasm), while egg-membranes may be formed around it.   The
ovum may now be termed the *oöcyte* (Boveri) or ovarian egg.

In this condition the egg-cell remains until near the time of fertilization, when the process of maturation proper — *i.e.* the formation of
the polar bodies — takes place.   In some cases, *e.g.* in the sea-urchin,
the polar bodies are formed before fertilization while the egg is still
in the ovary.   More commonly, as in annelids, gasteropods, nematodes, they are not formed until after the spermatozoön has made its
entrance ; while in a few cases one polar body may be formed before
fertilization and one afterwards, as in the lamprey-eel, the frog, and
Amphioxus.   In all these cases, the essential phenomena are the
same.   Two minute cells are formed, one after the other, near the
upper or animal pole of the ovum (Figs. 71, 86) ; and in many cases
the first of these divides into two as the second is formed (Fig. 64).

A group of four cells thus arises, namely, the mature egg, which
gives rise to the embryo, and three small cells or polar bodies which
take no part in the further development, are discarded, and soon die
without further change.   The egg-nucleus is now ready for union
with the sperm-nucleus.

A study of the nucleus during these changes brings out the following facts.   During the multiplication of the oögonia the number of
chromosomes is, in some cases at any rate, the same as that occurring
in the division of the somatic cells,[1] and the same number enters into
the formation of the chromatic reticulum of the germinal vesicle.
During the formation of the polar bodies this number becomes
reduced to one-half, the nucleus of each polar body and the egg-
nucleus receiving the reduced number.   In some manner, therefore,
the formation of the polar bodies is connected with the process by
which the reduction is effected.   The precise nature of this process
is, however, a matter which has been certainly determined in only a
few cases.

We need not here consider the history of opinion on this subject
further than to point out that the early observers, such as Purkinje,
von Baer, Bischoff, had no real understanding of the process and
believed the germinal vesicle to disappear at the time of fertilization.

---

[1] See, however, p. 194.

To Bütschli ('76,) Hertwig, and Giard ('77) we owe the discovery that the formation of the polar bodies is through *mitotic division*, the chromosomes of the equatorial plate being derived from the chro-

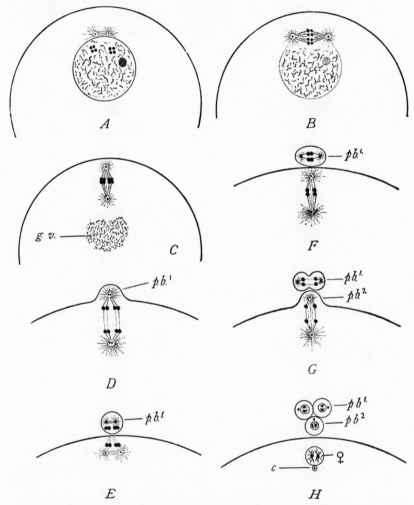

Fig. 88. — Diagrams showing the essential facts in the maturation of the egg. The somatic number of chromosomes is supposed to be four.

A. Initial phase; two tetrads have been formed in the germinal vesicle. *B*. The two tetrads have been drawn up about the spindle to form the equatorial plate of the first polar mitotic figure. *C*. The mitotic figure has rotated into position, leaving the remains of the germinal vesicle at *g. v*. *D*. Formation of the first polar body; each tetrad divides into two dyads. *E*. First polar body formed; two dyads in it and in the egg. *F*. Preparation for the second division. *G*. Second polar body forming and the first dividing; each dyad divides into two single chromosomes. *H*. Final result; three polar bodies and the egg-nucleus (♀), each containing two single chromosomes (half the somatic number); *c*, the egg-centrosome which now degenerates and is lost.

N

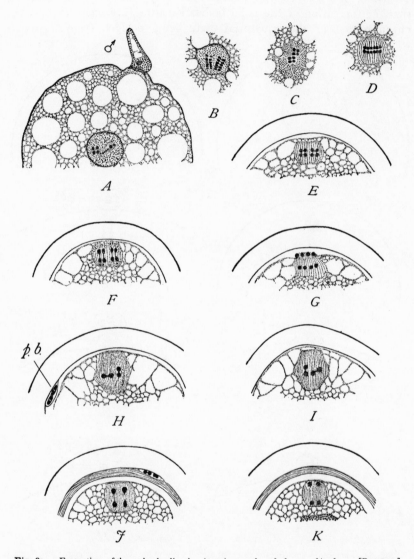

Fig. 89. — Formation of the polar bodies in *Ascaris megalocephala*, var. *bivalens*.   [BOVERI.]

    A. The egg with the spermatozoön just entering at ♂ ; the germinal vesicle contains two rod-shaped tetrads (only one clearly shown), the number of chromosomes in earlier divisions having been four. *B*. The tetrads seen in profile. *C*. The same in end view. *D*. First spindle forming (in this case inside the germinal vesicle). *E*. First polar spindle. *F*. The tetrads dividing. *G*. First polar body formed, containing, like the egg, two dyads. *H. I*. The dyads rotating into position for the second division. *J*. The dyads dividing. *K*. Each dyad has divided into two single chromosomes, completing the reduction.   (For later stages see Fig. 65.)

matin of the germinal vesicle.[1] In the formation of the first polar body the group of chromosomes splits into two daughter-groups, and this process is immediately repeated in the formation of the second *without an intervening reticular resting stage.* The egg-nucleus therefore receives, like each of the polar bodies, one-fourth of the *mass* of chromatin derived from the germinal vesicle.

But although the formation of the polar bodies was thus shown to be a process of true cell-division, the history of the chromosomes was found to differ in some very important particulars from that of the tissue-cells. The essential facts, which were first accurately determined by Boveri in *Ascaris* ('87, 1), are in a typical case as follows (Figs. 88, 89) : As the egg prepares for the formation of the first polar body, the chromatin of the germinal vesicle groups itself in a number of masses, each of which splits up into a group of four bodies united by linin-threads to form a "quadruple group" or tetrad (Vierergruppe). *The number of tetrads is always one-half the usual number of chromosomes.* Thus in *Ascaris* (*megalocephala, bivalens*) the germinal vesicle gives rise to two tetrads, the normal number of chromosomes in the earlier divisions being four; in the salamander and the frog there are twelve tetrads, the somatic number of chromosomes being twenty-four (Fleming, vom Rath), etc. As the first polar body forms, each of the tetrads is halved to form two double groups, or *dyads,* one of which remains in the egg while the other passes into the polar body. Both the egg and the first polar body therefore receive each a number of dyads equal to one-half the usual number of chromosomes. The egg now proceeds at once to the formation of the second polar body without previous reconstruction of the nucleus. Each dyad is halved to form two single chromosomes, one of which, again, remains in the egg while its sister passes into the polar body. Both the egg and the second polar body accordingly receive two single chromosomes (one-half the usual number), each of which is one-fourth of an original tetrad group. From the two remaining in the egg a reticular nucleus, much smaller than the original germinal vesicle, is now formed.[2]

Essentially similar facts have now been determined in a considerable number of animals, though the form of the tetrads varies greatly, and there are some cases in which no actual tetrad-formation has been observed (apparently in the flowering plants). It is clear from the

---

[1] The early accounts asserting the disappearance of the germinal vesicle were based on the fact that in many cases only a small fraction of the chromatic network gives rise to chromosomes, the remainder disintegrating and being scattered through the yolk.

[2] It is nearly certain that the division of the first polar body (which, however, may be omitted) is analogous to that by which the second is formed, *i.e.* each of the dyads is similarly halved.

foregoing account that the numerical reduction of chromatin-*masses* takes place before the polar bodies are actually formed, through the operation of forces which determine the number of tetrads within the germinal vesicle. The numerical reduction is therefore determined in the grandmother-cell of the egg. The actual divisions by which the polar bodies are formed merely distribute the elements of the tetrads.

2. *Reduction in the Male. Spermatogenesis*

The researches of Platner ('89), Boveri, and especiàlly of Oscar Hertwig ('90, 1) have demonstrated that reduction takes place in the

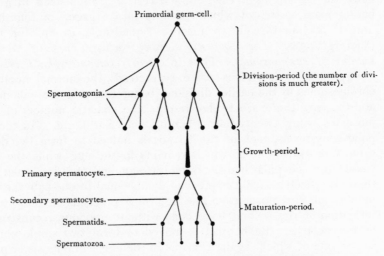

Fig. 90. — Diagram showing the genesis of the spermatozoön. [After BOVERI.]

male in a manner almost precisely parallel to that occurring in the female. Platner first suggested ('89) that the formation of the polar bodies is directly comparable to the last two divisions of the sperm mother-cells (spermatocytes). In the following year Boveri reached the same result in *Ascaris*, stating his conclusion that reduction in the male must take place in the "grandmother-cell of the spermatozöon, just as in the female it takes place in the grandmother-cell of the egg," and that the egg-formation and sperm-formation really agree down to the smallest detail ('90, p. 64). Later in the same year appeared Oscar Hertwig's splendid work on the spermatogenesis of *Ascaris*, which established this conclusion in the most striking manner. Like the ova, the spermatozoa are descended from primordial germ-cells which by mitotic division give rise to the *spermatogonia* from which the spermatozoa are ultimately formed (Fig. 90). Like the oögonia, the spermatogonia continue for a time to divide with the usual (somatic) number of chromosomes; *i.e.* four in *Ascaris megalocephala bivalens*. Ceasing for a time to divide, they

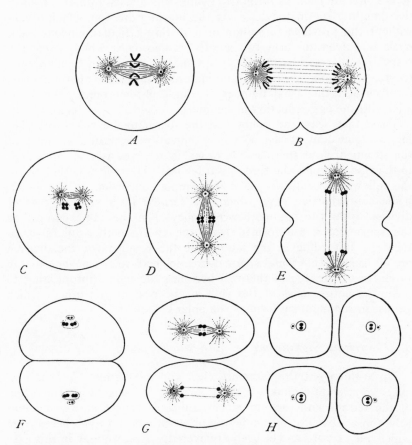

Fig. 91. — Diagrams showing the essential facts of reduction in the male. The somatic number of chromosomes is supposed to be four.

A. B. Division of one of the spermatogonia, showing the full number (four) of chromosomes. C. Primary spermatocyte preparing for division; the chromatin forms two tetrads. D. E. F. First division to form two secondary spermatocytes each of which receives two dyads. G. H. Division of the two secondary spermatocytes to form four spermatids. Each of the latter receives two single chromosomes and a centrosome which persists in the middle-piece of the spermatozoön.

now enlarge considerably to form *spermatocytes*, each of which is morphologically equivalent to an unripe ovarian ovum, or *oöcyte*. Each spermatocyte finally divides twice in rapid succession, giving rise first to two daughter-spermatocytes and then to four *spermatids*, each of which is directly converted into a single spermatozoön. *The history of the chromatin in these two divisions is exactly parallel to that in the formation of the polar bodies* (Figs. 91, 92). From the chromatin of the spermatocyte are formed a number of tetrads equal to one-half the usual number of chromosomes. Each tetrad is halved at the first division to form two dyads which pass into the respective daughter-spermatocytes. At the ensuing division, which occurs without the previous formation of a resting reticular nucleus, each dyad is halved to form two single chromosomes which enter the respective spermatids (ultimately spermatozoa). From each spermatocyte, therefore, arise four spermatozoa, and each sperm-nucleus receives half the usual number of single chromosomes. The parallel with the egg-reduction is complete.

These facts leave no doubt that the spermatocyte is the morphological equivalent of the oöcyte or immature ovarian egg, and that the group of four spermatozoa to which it gives rise is equivalent to the ripe egg plus the three polar bodies. Hertwig was thus led to the following beautifully clear and simple conclusion: "The polar bodies are abortive eggs which are formed by a final process of division from the egg-mother-cell (oöcyte) in the same manner as the spermatozoa are formed from the sperm-mother-cell (spermatocyte). But while in the latter case the products of the division are all used as functional spermatozoa, in the former case one of the products of the egg-mother-cell becomes the egg, appropriating to itself the entire mass of the yolk at the cost of the others which persist in rudimentary form as the polar bodies."[1]

3. *Theoretical Significance of Maturation*

Up to this point the facts are clear and intelligible. When, however, we attempt a more searching analysis by considering the origin of the tetrads and the ultimate meaning of reduction, we find ourselves in a labyrinth of conflicting observations and hypotheses from which no exit has as yet been discovered. And we may in this case most readily approach the subject by considering its theoretical aspect at the outset.

The process of reduction is very obviously a provision to hold constant the number of chromosomes characteristic of the species; for if it did not occur, the number would be doubled in each succeeding generation through union of the germ-cells. But why should the number be constant?

In its modern form this problem was first attacked by Weismann in 1885, and again in 1887, though many earlier hypotheses regard-

[1] '90, I, p. 126.

ing the meaning of the polar bodies had been put forward.[1] His interpretation was based on a remarkable paper published by Wilhelm Roux in 1883,[2] in which are developed certain ideas which afterwards formed the foundation of Weismann's whole theory of inheritance and development. Roux argued that the facts of mitosis are only explicable under the assumption that chromatin is not a uniform and homogeneous substance, but differs qualitatively in different regions of the nucleus ; that the collection of the chromatin into a thread and its accurate division into two halves is meaningless unless the chromatin in different regions of the thread represents different *qualities* which are to be divided and distributed to the daughter-cells according to some definite law. He urged that if the chromatin were qualitatively the same throughout the nucleus, direct division would be as efficacious as indirect, and the complicated apparatus of mitosis would be superfluous. Roux and Weismann, each in his own way, subsequently elaborated this conception to a complete theory of inheritance and development, but at this point we may confine our attention to the views of Weismann. The starting-point of his theory is the hypothesis of De Vries that the chromatin is a congeries or colony of invisible self-propagating vital units or *biophores* somewhat like Darwin's "gemmules" (p. 303), each of which has the power of determining the development of a particular quality. Weismann conceives these units as aggregated to form units of a higher order known as "determinants," which in turn are grouped to form

[1] Of these we need only consider at this point the very interesting suggestion of Minot ('77), afterwards adopted by Van Beneden ('83), that the ordinary cell is hermaphrodite, and that maturation is for the purpose of producing a unisexual germ-cell by dividing the mother-cell into its sexual constituents, or "genoblasts." Thus, the male element is removed from the egg *in the polar bodies*, leaving the mature egg a female. In like manner he believed the female element to be cast out during spermatogenesis (in the "Sertoli cells"), thus rendering the spermatozoa male. By the union of the germ-cells in fertilization the male and female elements are brought together so that the fertilized egg or oösperm is again hermaphrodite or neuter. This ingenious view was independently advocated by Van Beneden in his great work on *Ascaris* ('83). A fatal objection to it, on which both Strasburger and Weismann have insisted, lies in the fact that male as well as female qualities are transmitted by the egg-cell, while the sperm-cell also transmits female qualities. The germ-cells are therefore non-sexual; they are physiologically as well as morphologically equivalent. The researches of Hertwig, Brauer, and Boveri show, moreover, that in *Ascaris*, at any rate, all of the four spermatids derived from a spermatocyte become functional spermatozoa, and the beautiful parallel between spermatogenesis and oögenesis thus established becomes meaningless under Minot's view. This hypothesis must, therefore, in my opinion, be abandoned.

Balfour probably stated the exact truth when he said, "In the formation of the polar cells part of the constituents of the germinal vesicle, which are requisite for its functions as a complete and independent nucleus, is removed to make room for the supply of the necessary parts to it again by the spermatic nucleus " ('80, p. 62). He fell, however, into the same error as Minot and Van Beneden in characterizing the germ-nuclei as "male" and "female."

[2] *Über die Bedeutung der Kerntheilungsfiguren.*

"ids," the latter being identified with the visible chromomeres or chromatin-granules. The ids finally are associated in linear groups to form the "idants" or chromosomes. Since the biophores differ qualitatively, it follows that the same must be true of the higher units

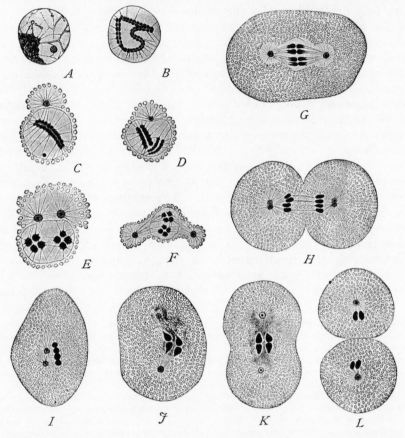

Fig. 92. — Reduction in the spermatogenesis of *Ascaris megalocephala*, var. *bivalens*. [BRAUER.][1]

A–G. Successive stages in the division of the primary spermatocyte. The original reticulum undergoes a very early division of the chromatin-granules which then form a doubly split spireme-thread, *B.* This shortens (*C*), and breaks in two to form the two tetrads (*D* in profile, *E* viewed endwise). *F. G. H.* First division to form two secondary spermatocytes, each receiving two dyads. *I.* Secondary spermatocyte. *J. K.* The same dividing. *L.* Two resulting spermatids, each with two single chromosomes and a centrosome.

formed by their. aggregation. Hence each chromosome has a distinct and definite character of its own, representing a particular group of hereditary qualities. From this it follows that the number of

[1] For division of the spermatogonia see Fig. 39 ; for the corresponding phenomena in var. *univalens* see Fig. 107.

specifically distinct chromosomes is doubled by the union of two germ-cells, a process which if unchecked would quickly lead to an infinite complexity of the chromatin or germ-plasm. The end of maturation, or reduction, is therefore to prevent "the excessive accumulation of different kinds of hereditary tendencies or germ-plasms"[1] through the progressive summation of ancestral chromatins.

We now come to the vital point of Weismann's hypothesis of reduction, about which all later researches have revolved. Assuming with Roux that the different qualities or "ancestral germ-plasms" are arranged in a linear manner in the spireme-thread and in the chromosomes derived from it, he ventured the prediction ('87) that two kinds of mitosis would be found to occur. The first of these is characterized by a longitudinal splitting of the thread, as in ordinary cell-division, "by means of which all the ancestral germ-plasms are equally distributed in each of the daughter-nuclei after having been divided into halves." This form of division, which he called "equal division" (Aequationstheilung), was then a known fact. The second form, at that time a purely theoretical postulate, he assumed to be of such a character that each daughter-nucleus should receive only half the number of ancestral germ-plasms possessed by the mother-nucleus. This he termed a "reducing division" (Reduktionstheilung), and suggested[2] that this might be effected either by a *transverse* division of the chromosomes, or by the divergence and separation of entire chromosomes without division. By either method the number of "ids" would be reduced; and Weismann argued that such reducing divisions must be involved in the formation of the polar bodies, and in the parallel phenomena of spermatogenesis.

The fulfilment of Weismann's prediction is one of the most interesting results of recent cytological research. It has been demonstrated, in a manner which I believe is incontrovertible, that the reducing divisions postulated by Weismann actually occur, though not precisely in the manner conceived by him. Unfortunately, however, this demonstration has been made in only a few specific cases, — the complete demonstration, indeed, in but a single group, namely, the copepod crustacea, — while careful studies by the most accomplished observers have led to an entirely different result in other cases; namely, in *Ascaris* and the flowering plants. We are in fact confronted by an apparent contradiction of so absolute a character that no middle ground between the conflicting results can at present be discovered. We may best appreciate the nature of this contradiction by a preliminary consideration of the tetrad groups; for it is plain that the nature of the maturation-divisions can only be approached through a study of the origin of the tetrads.

[1] Essay VI., p. 366. [1] *l.c.*, p. 375.

B. ORIGIN OF THE TETRADS

1. *General Sketch*

It is generally agreed that each tetrad arises by a double division of a single primary chromatin-rod.   Nearly all observers agree further that the number of primary rods at their first appearance in the germinal vesicle or in the spermatocyte-nucleus is *one-half the usual number of chromosomes*, and that this numerical reduction is due to the fact that the spireme-thread segments into one-half the usual number of pieces.   The contradiction relates to the manner in which the primary rod divides to form the tetrad.   According to one account, mainly based on the study of *Ascaris* by Boveri, Hertwig, and Brauer, and supported in principle by the observations of Guignard and Strasburger on the flowering plants, each tetrad arises by *a double longitudinal splitting of the primary chromatin-rod* caused by the division of each chromatin-granule into four parts.   In this case the four resulting bodies — *i.e.* the four chromosomes of the tetrad — must be exactly equivalent, since all are derived from the same region of the spireme-thread and consist of equivalent groups of ids or chromatin-granules (Fig. 102, *A*).   No reducing division can therefore occur in Weismann's sense.   There is only a reduction in the number of *chromosomes*, not a reduction in the number of qualities represented by the chromatin-granules.   This may be graphically expressed as follows: —

If the original spireme-thread be represented by *abcd*, normal mitosis consists in its segmentation into the four chromosomes $a-b-c-d$, which split lengthwise to form $\frac{a}{a}, \frac{b}{b}, \frac{c}{c}, \frac{d}{d}$.   In maturation the thread segments into *two* portions, $ab-cd$, each of which then split into four equivalent portions, giving the equivalent tetrads, thus, $\frac{ab|ab}{ab|ab}$ and $\frac{cd|cd}{cd|cd}$; or $\frac{x|x}{x|x}, \frac{y|y}{y|y}$, since it is not known whether *ab* really is equal to $a + b$.

The second account, which finds its strongest support in the observations of Rückert, Häcker, and vom Rath on the maturation of arthropods, asserts that each tetrad arises by *one longitudinal and one transverse division of each primary chromatin-rod* (Fig. 102, *B*).   Thus the spireme *abcd* segments as before into two segments *ab* and *cd*. These first divide longitudinally to form $\frac{ab}{ab}$ and $\frac{cd}{cd}$ and then transversely to form $\frac{a|b}{a|b}$ and $\frac{c|d}{c|d}$.   Each tetrad therefore consists, not of four equivalent chromosomes, but of two different pairs; and the second or transverse division by which *a* is separated from *b*, or *c* from *d*, is the reducing division demanded by Weismann's hypothesis. The observations of Rückert and Häcker prove that the transverse division is accomplished during the formation of the second polar body.

2. *Detailed Evidence*

We may now consider some of the evidence in detail, though the limits of this work will only allow the consideration of some of the best known cases. We may first examine the case of *Ascaris*, on which the first account is based. In the first of his classical cell-studies Boveri showed that each tetrad appears in the germinal vesicle in the form of four parallel rods, each consisting of a row of chromatin-granules (Fig. 89, *A–C*). He believed these rods to arise by the double longitudinal splitting of a single primary chromatin-rod, each cleavage being a preparation for one of the polar bodies. In his opinion, therefore, the formation of the polar bodies differs from ordinary mitosis only in the fact that the chromosomes split very early, and not once, but twice, in preparation for two rapidly succeeding divisions without an intervening resting period. He supported this view by further observations in 1890 on the polar bodies of *Sagitta* and several gasteropods, in which he again determined, as he believed, that the tetrads arose by double longitudinal splitting. An essentially similar view of the tetrads was taken by Hertwig in 1890, in the spermatogenesis of *Ascaris*, though he could not support this conclusion by very convincing evidence. In 1893, finally, Brauer made a most thorough and apparently exhaustive study of their origin in the spermatogenesis of *Ascaris*, which seemed to leave no doubt of the correctness of Boveri's result. Every step in the origin of the tetrads from the reticulum of the resting spermatocytes was traced with the most painstaking care. The first step observed was a double splitting of the chromatin-threads in the reticulum, caused by a division of the chromatin-granules into four parts (Fig. 92, *A*). From the reticulum arises a continuous spireme-thread, which from its first appearance is split into four longitudinal parts, and ultimately breaks in two to form the two tetrads characteristic of the species. These have at first the same rod-like form as those of the germinal vesicle. Later they shorten to form compact groups, each consisting of four spherical chromosomes. Brauer's figures are very convincing, and, if correct, seem to leave no doubt that the tetrads here arise by a double longitudinal splitting of the spireme-thread, initiated even in the reticular stage before a connected thread has been formed. If this really be so, there can be here no reducing division in Weismann's sense.   The reduction of chromatin, caused by the ensuing cell-division, is therefore only a quantitative mass-reduction, as Hertwig and Brauer insist, not a qualitative sundering of different elements, as Weismann's postulate demands.[1]   The work of Strasburger and Guignard, considered at p. 195, has given in principle the same general result in the flowering plants, though the details of the process are here considerably modified, and apparently no tetrads are formed.

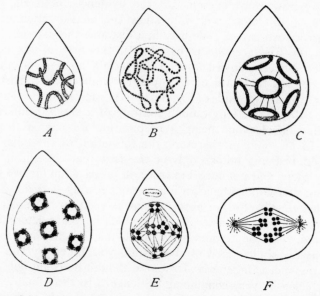

Fig. 93. — Origin of the tetrads by ring-formation in the spermatogenesis of the mole-cricket *Gryllotalpa*. [VOM RATH.]

A. Primary spermatocyte, containing six double rods, each of which represents two chromosomes united end to end and longitudinally split except at the free ends. *B. C.* Opening out of the double rods to form rings. *D.* Concentration of the rings. *E.* The rings broken up into tetrads. *F.* First division-figure established.

We now return to the second view, referred to at p. 186, which accords with Weismann's hypothesis, and flatly contradicts the conclusions drawn from the study of *Ascaris*.   This view is based mainly on the study of arthropods, especially the crustacea and insects, but has been confirmed by the facts observed in some of the lower vertebrata.   In many of these forms the tetrads first appear in the form of closed rings, each of which finally breaks into four parts.   First observed by Henking ('91) in the insect *Pyrrochoris*, they have since been found in other insects by vom Rath and Wilcox, in various cope-

[1] In an earlier paper on *Branchipus* ('92) Brauer reached an essentially similar result, which was, however, based on far less convincing evidence.

pods by Rückert, Häcker, and vom Rath, in the frog by vom Rath, and in elasmobranchs by Moore. The genesis of the ring was first determined by vom Rath in the mole-cricket (*Gryllotalpa*, '92), and has been thoroughly elucidated by the later work of Rückert ('94) and Häcker ('95, 1). All these observers, excepting Wilcox and

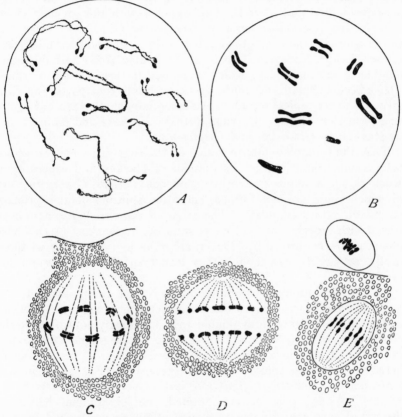

Fig. 94. — Formation of the tetrads and polar bodies in *Cyclops*, slightly schematic. (The full number of tetrads is not shown.) [RÜCKERT.]

A. Germinal vesicle containing eight longitudinally split chromatin-rods (half the somatic number). *B.* Shortening of the rods; transverse division (to form the tetrads) in progress. *C.* Position of the tetrads in the first polar spindle, the longitudinal split horizontal. *D.* Anaphase; longitudinal division of the tetrads. *E.* The first polar body formed; second polar spindle with the eight dyads in position for the ensuing division, which will be a *transverse* or reducing division.

Moore (see p. 201), have reached the same conclusion; namely, that the ring arises by the longitudinal splitting of a primary chromatin-rod, the two halves remaining united by their ends, and opening out to form a ring. The ring-formation is, in fact, a form of heterotypical mitosis (p. 60). The breaking of the ring into four parts involves first the separation of these two halves (corresponding with the original longitudinal split), and second, the *transverse* division of each half, the latter being the reducing division of Weismann. The number of primary rods, from which the rings arise, is one-half the somatic number. Hence each of them is conceived by vom Rath, Häcker, and Rückert as bivalent or double; *i.e.* as representing two chromosomes united end to end. This appears with the greatest clearness in the spermatogenesis of *Gryllotalpa* (Fig. 93). Here the spireme-thread splits lengthwise before its segmentation into rods. It then divides transversely to form six double rods (half the usual number of chromosomes), which open out to form six closed rings. These become small and thick, break each into four parts, and thus give rise to six typical tetrads. An essentially similar account of the ring-formation is given by vom Rath in *Euchæta* and *Calanus*, and by Rückert in *Heterocope* and *Diaptomus*.

That the foregoing interpretation of the rings is correct, is beautifully demonstrated by the observations of Häcker, and especially of Rückert, on a number of other copepods (*Cyclops, Canthocamptus*), in which rings are not formed, since the splitting of the primary chromatin-rods is complete. The origin of the tetrads has here been traced with especial care in *Cyclops strenuus*, by Rückert ('94), whose observations, confirmed by Häcker, are quite as convincing as those of Brauer on *Ascaris*, though they lead to a diametrically opposite result.

The normal number of chromosomes is here twenty-two. In the germinal vesicle arise eleven threads, which split lengthwise (Fig. 94), and finally shorten to form double rods, manifestly equivalent to the closed rings of *Diaptomus*. Each of these now segments *transversely* to form a tetrad group, and the eleven tetrads then place themselves in the equator of the spindle for the first polar body (Fig. 94, *C*), in such a manner that the *longitudinal split* is transverse to the axis of the spindle. As the polar body is formed, the longitudinal halves of the tetrad separate, and the formation of the first polar body is thus demonstrated to be an "equal division" in Weismann's sense. The eleven dyads remaining in the eggs now rotate (as in *Ascaris*), so that the transverse division lies in the equatorial plane, and are halved during the formation of the second polar body. The division is accordingly a "reducing division," which leaves eleven single chromosomes in the egg, and it is a curious fact that this conclusion, which apparently rests on irrefragable evidence, completely confirms Weismann's earlier views, published in 1887,[1] and contradicts the later interpretation upheld in his book on the germ-plasm.

[1] Essay VI.

Häcker ('92) has reached exactly similar results in the case of *Canthocamptus* and draws the same conclusion. In *Cyclops strenuus* he finds in the case of first-laid eggs a variation of the process which seems to approach the mode of tetrad formation in some of the lower vertebrates. In such eggs the primary double rods become sharply

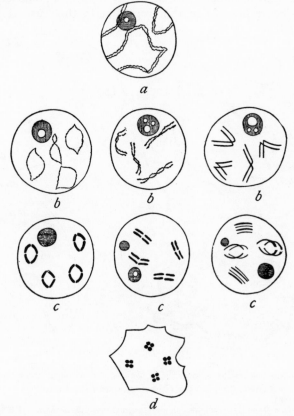

Fig. 95.—Diagrams of various modes of tetrad-formation. [HÄCKER.]

a. Common starting-point, a double spireme-thread in the germinal vesicle; *d.* common result, the typical tetrads; *b. c.* intermediate stages: at the left the ring-formation (as in *Diaptomus, Gryllotalpa, Heterocope*); middle series, complete splitting of the rods (as in *Cyclops* according to Rückert, and in *Canthocamptus*); at the right by breaking of the V-shaped rods (as in *Cyclops strenuus,* according to Häcker, and in the salamander, according to vom Rath).

bent near the middle to form **V**-shaped loops (Fig. 96, *C*), which finally break transversely near the apex to form the tetrad [1] — a process which clearly gives the same result as before. An exactly similar process seems to occur in the salamander as described by Flemming and

[1] Häcker upholds this account ('95, 1) in spite of the criticisms of Rückert and vom Rath.

vom Rath.   Flemming observed the double **V**-shaped loops in 1887,
and also the tetrads derived from them, but regarded the latter as
"anomalies."   Vom Rath ('93) subsequently found that the double
V's break at the apex, and that the four rods thus formed then draw
together to form four spheres grouped in a tetrad precisely like
those of the arthropods.   Still later ('95, 1) the same observer traced
a nearly similar process in the frog; but in this case the four ele-

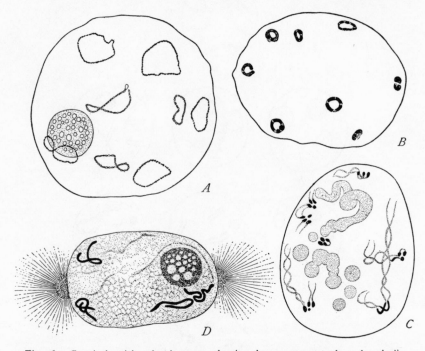

Fig. 96. — Germinal vesicles of various eggs, showing chromosomes, tetrads, and nucleoli.

   A.   A copepod (*Heterocope*) showing eight of the sixteen ring-shaped tetrads and the nucleolus.   [RÜCKERT.]

   B.   Later stage of the same, condensation and segmentation of the rings.   [RÜCKERT.]

   C. "*Cyclops strenuus,*" illustrating Häcker's account of the tetrad-formation from elongate
double rods; a group of "accessory nucleoli."   [HÄCKER]

   D.   Germinal vesicle of an annelid (*Ophryotrocha*) showing nucleolus and four chromosomes.
[KORSCHELT.]

ments appear to remain for a short time united to form a ring before
breaking up into separate spheres.

   To sum up: The researches of Rückert, Häcker, and vom Rath,
on insects, crustacea, and amphibia have all led to the same result.
However the tetrad-formation may differ in matter of detail, it is in
all these forms the same in principle.   Each primary chromatin-rod
has the value of a bivalent chromosome; *i.e.* two chromosomes
joined end to end, *ab*.   By a longitudinal division a ring or double

rod is formed, which represents two equivalent pairs of chromosomes
$\frac{ab}{ab}$. During the two maturation-divisions the four chromosomes
are split apart, $\frac{a\,|\,b}{a\,|\,b}$, and Rückert's observations demonstrate that
the first division separates the two equivalent dyads, *ab* and *ab*, which
by the second division are split apart into the two separate chromosomes, *a* and *b*. Weismann's postulate is accordingly realized in the
second division. It is clear from this account that the primary
halving of the number of chromatin-rods is not an actual reduction,
since each rod represents two chromosomes. Rückert therefore
proposes the convenient term "pseudo-reduction" for this preliminary halving.[1] The actual reduction is not effected until the
dyads are split apart during the second maturation-division.

C. THE EARLY HISTORY OF THE GERM-NUCLEI

We may for the present defer a consideration of accounts of reduction differing from the two already described and pass on to a
consideration of the earlier history of the germ-nuclei. A considerable number of observers are now agreed that the primary chromatin-
rods appear at a very early period in the germinal vesicle and are
longitudinally split from the first. (Häcker, vom Rath, Rückert, in
copepods; Rückert in selachians; Born and Fick in amphibia;
Holl in the chick; Rückert in the rabbit.) Häcker ('92, 2) made the
interesting discovery that in some of the copepods (*Canthocamptus,
Cyclops*) these double rods could be traced back continuously to a
double spireme-thread, following immediately upon the division of the
last generation of oögonia, and that *at no period is a true reticulum
formed in the germinal vesicle* (Fig. 97). In the following year Rückert ('93, 2) made a precisely similar discovery in the case of selachians.
After division of the last generation of oögonia the daughter-chromosomes do not give rise to a reticulum, but split lengthwise, and
persist in this condition throughout the entire growth-period of the
egg. Rückert therefore concluded that the germinal vesicle of the
selachians is to be regarded as a "daughter-spireme of the oögonium
(*Ur-ei*) grown to enormous dimensions, the chromosomes of which
are doubled and arranged in pairs."[2] In the following year ('93)
vom Rath, following out the earlier work of Flemming, discovered
an exactly analogous fact in the spermatogenesis of the salamander.
The tetrads were here traced back to double chromatin-rods, individually identical with the daughter-chromosomes of the preceding

---

[1] '93, 2, p. 541.   [2] '92, 2, p. 51.

o

spermatogonium-division, which split lengthwise during the anaphase and pass into the spermatocyte-nucleus without forming a reticulum. Flemming had observed in 1887 that these daughter-chromosomes split in the anaphase, but could not determine their further history. Vom Rath found that each double daughter-chromosome breaks in two at the apex to form a tetrad, which passes into the ensuing spermatocyte without the intervention of a resting stage.[1]

It is clear that in such cases the "pseudo-reduction" must take place at an earlier period than the penultimate generation of cells. In the salamander Flemming ('87) found that the "chromosomes" of the *spermatogonia* appeared in the reduced number (twelve) in at least three cell-generations preceding the penultimate. Vom Rath ('93)

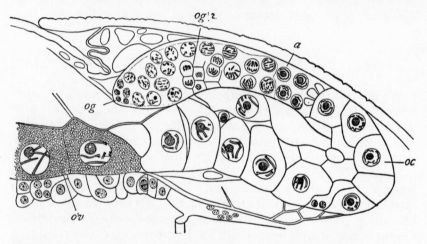

Fig. 97. — Longitudinal section through the ovary of the copepod *Canthocamptus*. [HÄCKER.]
og. The youngest germ-cells or oögonia (dividing at *og.*[2]) ; *a.* upper part of the growth-zone ; *oc.* oöcyte, or growing ovarian egg ; *ov.* fully formed egg, with double chromatin-rods.

traced the pseudo-reduction in both sexes back to much earlier stages, not only in the larvæ, but even in the embryo (!). This very remarkable discovery showed that *the pseudo-reduction might appear in the early progenitors of the germ-cells during embryonic life — perhaps even during the cleavage.* This conjecture has apparently been substantiated by Häcker ('95, 3), who finds that in *Cyclops brevicornis* the

[1] It is certain that these facts do not represent a universal type of maturation, for in *Ascaris* there is no doubt that a true reticular resting stage occurs in the primary spermatocytes, and probably also in the germinal vesicle. Häcker found, moreover, that the same species might show differences in this regard; for in *Cyclops strenuus* the first-laid eggs have no resting stage, the double daughter-chromosome passing directly into the tetrads, while in later broods of eggs a daughter-spireme, composed of long double threads, is formed. The difference is believed by Häcker to be due to the fact that the earlier eggs are quickly laid, while the later broods are long retained in the oviduct.

reduced number of chromosomes (twelve) appears in the primordial germ-cells which are differentiated in the blastula-stage (Fig. 56). He adds the interesting discovery that in this form the *somatic* nuclei of the cleavage-stages show the same number, and hence concludes that all the chromosomes of these stages are bivalent. As development proceeds, the germ-cells retain this character, while the somatic cells acquire the usual number (twenty-four) — a process which, if the conception of bivalent chromosomes be valid, must consist in the division of each bivalent rod into its two elements. We have here a wholly new light on the historical origin of reduction; for the pseudo-reduction of the germ-nuclei seems to be in this case a persistence of the embryonic condition, and we may therefore hope for a future explanation of the process by which it has in other cases been deferred until the penultimate cell-generation, as is certainly the fact in *Ascaris*.[1] The foregoing facts pave the way to an examination of reduction in the plants, to which we now proceed.

D. REDUCTION IN THE PLANTS

Guignard's and Strasburger's observations on reduction in the flowering plants gave a result which in substance agrees with that obtained by Boveri and Brauer in the case of *Ascaris*. These observers could find absolutely no evidence of a transverse or reducing division, and asserted that the reduction in number is directly effected by a segmentation of the spireme-thread into half the usual number of chromosomes; *i.e.* by a process exactly corresponding with the "pseudo-reduction" of Rückert (see Fig. 25). These observers find that in the male the chromosomes suddenly appear in the reduced number (twelve in the lily, eight in the onion) at the first division of the pollen-mother-cell, from which arise four pollen-grains. In the female the same process takes place at the first division of the mother-cell of the embryo-sac. Strasburger and Guignard agree that *in the subsequent divisions these chromosomes do not form tetrads, but undergo simple longitudinal splitting at each successive division.* In case of the male there are at least four of these divisions; viz. two divisions to form the four pollen-grains, a third division to form the vegetative and generative cell of the pollen-grain, and finally a fourth division of the generative nucleus in the pollen-tube. In all these mitoses the reduced number of chromosomes appears, and each division is followed by a return of the nucleus to the resting state. In the

---

[1] It may be recalled that in *Ascaris* Boveri proved that the primordial germ-cells have the full number of chromosomes, and Hertwig clearly showed that this number is retained up to the last division of the spermatogonia.

mother-cell of the embryo-sac the number of divisions before fertilization is three, four, five, or sometimes even more, the reduced number persisting throughout. These facts led to the suspicion, first expressed by Overton in 1892, that the reduced number of chromosomes might be found in the sexual generation of higher cryptogams (which corresponds with the cells derived from the pollen-grain, or from the mother-cell of the embryo-sac). This surmise quickly became a certainty. Overton himself discovered ('93) that the cells of the endosperm in the Gymnosperm *Ceratozamia* divide with the reduced number, namely eight; and Dixon observed the same fact in *Pinus* at the same time. In the following year Strasburger brought the matter to a definite conclusion in the case of a fern (*Osmunda*), showing that *all the cells of the prothallium, from the original spore-mother-cell onwards to the formation of the germ-cells, have one-half the number of chromosomes found in the asexual generation,* namely twelve instead of twenty-four; in other words, the reduction takes place in the formation of the spore from which the sexual generation arises, scores of cell-generations before the germ-cells are formed, indeed before the formation of the body from which these cells arise. Similar facts were determined by Farmer in *Pallavicinia,* one of the Hepaticæ, where all of the nuclei of the asexual generation (sporogonium) show four chromosomes during division, those of the sexual generation (thallus) eight. It now seems highly probable that this will be found a general rule.

The striking point in these, as in vom Rath's and Häcker's observations, is that the numerical reduction takes place so long before the fertilization for which it is the obvious preparation. Speculating on the meaning of this remarkable fact, Strasburger advances the hypothesis that the reduced number is *the ancestral number* inherited from the ancestral type. The normal, *i.e.* somatic, number arose through conjugation by which the chromosomes of two germ-cells were brought together. Strasburger does not hesitate to apply the same conception to animals, and suggests that the four cells arising by the division of the oögonium (egg plus three polar-bodies) represent the remains of a separate generation, now a mere remnant included in the body in somewhat the same manner that the rudimentary prothallium of angiosperms is included in the embryo-sac. This may seem a highly improbable conclusion, but it must not be forgotten that so able a zoölogist as Whitman expressed a nearly related thought, as long ago as 1878: "I interpret the formation of polar globules as *a relic of the primitive mode of asexual reproduction.*"[1] Could Strasburger's hypothesis be substantiated, it would place the entire problem, not merely of maturation, but of sexuality itself, in a new light.

[1] '78, p. 262.

Strasburger's hypothesis is, however, open to a very serious *a priori* objection, as Häcker has pointed out; for if the account of "reduction" in the plants given by Guignard and Strasburger be correct, it corresponds exactly to the "pseudo-reduction" in animals, and the "chromosomes" of the sexual generation must be bivalent like those of the early germ-cells in animals. The recent observations of Belajeff, Farmer, and especially those of Sargant, give, however, good reason to believe that both Guignard and Strasburger have overlooked some of the most essential phenomena of reduction. These observations have not yet revealed the exact nature of the process, yet they show that the first division of the pollen-mother-cells (in the lily) *is of the heterotypical form ; i.e. that the chromosomes have the form of rings.* It is impossible to avoid the suspicion that these rings may be of the same nature as the ring-shaped tetrads in animals, though apparently they do not actually break up into a tetrad. Until this point has been cleared up by further investigation the nature of reduction in the plants remains an open question. Belajeff and Farmer showed that as the daughter-chromosomes diverge after the first division they assume a **V**-shape, and Miss Sargant's very interesting observations give some reason to believe

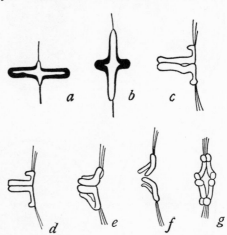

Fig. 98. — Division of the chromosomes (? tetrad-formation) in the first division of the pollen-mother-cell of the lily. (*a. b.* after FARMER and MOORE; *c–g.* after SARGANT.)

a. b. Two stages in the ring-formation (heterotypical mitosis). *c–f.* Successive stages, in profile view, of the separation of the daughter-chromosomes. *g.* The daughter-chromosomes, seen *en face*, at the moment of separation; this stage is perhaps to be interpreted as a tetrad like those occurring in the salamander.

that the **V** breaks at the apex precisely as described by Häcker in *Cyclops* and vom Rath in the salamander (Fig. 98, *g*). Should this prove to be the case the way would be opened for an interpretation of reduction in the plants agreeing in principle with that of Rückert, Häcker, and vom Rath; and as far as the plants are concerned, the *a priori* objection to Strasburger's interesting hypothesis might be removed.

E.   Reduction in Unicellular Forms

A reduction of the number of chromosomes as a preparation for conjugation in the one-celled forms has not yet been certainly determined, but there are many facts that render it highly probable.   In

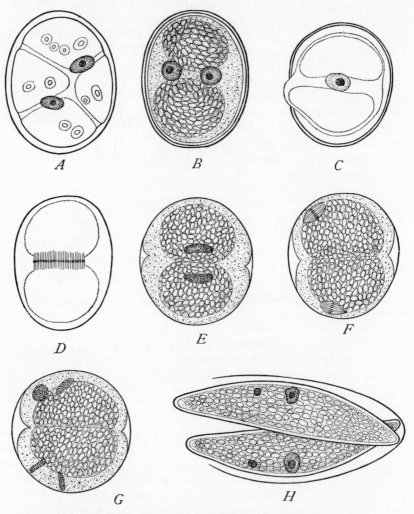

Fig. 99. — Conjugation of *Closterium*.   [KLEBAHN.]

A. Soon after union, four chromatophores.   *B*. Chromatophores reduced to two, nuclei distinct.   *C*. Fusion of the nuclei.   *D*. First cleavage of the zygote.   *E*. Resulting 2-cell stage. *F*. Second cleavage.   *G*. Resulting stage, each cell bi-nucleate.   *H*. Separation of the cells; one of the nuclei in each enlarging to form the permanent nucleus, the other (probably representing a polar body) degenerating.

the conjugation of infusoria, as already described (p. 165), the original nucleus divides several times before union, and only one of the resulting nuclei becomes the conjugating germ-nucleus, while the others perish, like the polar bodies. The numerical correspondence between the rejected nuclei or " corpuscles de rebut" has already been pointed out (p. 168). Hertwig could not count the chromosomes with absolute certainty, yet he states ('89) that in *Paramœcium caudatum*, during the final division, the number of spindle-fibres and of the corresponding chromatic elements is but 4–6, while in the earlier divisions the number is approximately double this (8–9). This observation makes it nearly certain that a numerical reduction of chromosomes occurs in the Protozoa in a manner similar to that of the higher forms; but the reduction here appears to be deferred until the final division.[1]   In the gregarines Wolters ('91) has observed the formation of an actual polar body as a small cell segmented off from each of the two conjugating animals soon after their union; but the number of chromosomes was not determined.

In the unicellular plants there are indications of a similar process, but the few facts at our command indicate that the reduction may here take place not before, but *after*, conjugation of the nuclei.   Thus in the dermids *Closterium* and *Cosmarium*, according to Klebahn (Fig. 99), the nuclei first unite to form a cleavage-nucleus, after which the zygote divides into two.   Each of the new nuclei now divides, one of the products persisting as the permanent nucleus, while the other degenerates and disappears.   Chmielewski asserts that a similar process occurs in *Spirogyra*.   Although the numerical relations of the chromosomes have not been determined in these cases, it appears probable that the elimination of a nucleus in each cell is a process of reduction occurring after fertilization.

F. Divergent Accounts of Reduction

We can only touch on a few of the accounts of reduction which differ from both the modes already considered.   Of these the most interesting are observations which indicate the possibility of,

1. *The Formation of Tetrads by Conjugation*

A considerable number of observers have maintained that reduction may be effected by the union or conjugation of chromosomes that were previously separate.   This view agrees in principle with that of Rückert, Häcker, and vom Rath; for the bivalent chromo-

---

[1] Cf. Moore on the spermatogenesis of mammals, p. 201.

somes assumed by these authors may be conceived as two conjugated chromosomes. It seems to be confirmed by the observations of Born and Fick on amphibia and those of Rückert on selachians (*Pristiurus*); for in all these cases the number of chromatin-masses at the time the first polar body is formed is but half the number observed in younger stages of the germinal vesicle. In *Pristiurus* there are at first thirty-six double segments in the germinal vesicle. At a later period these give rise to a close spireme, which then becomes more open, and is found to form a double thread segmented into eighteen double segments; *i.e.* the reduced number. In this case, therefore, the preliminary pseudo-reduction is almost certainly effected by the union of the original thirty-six double chromosomes, two by two. The most specific accounts of such a mode of origin have, however, been given by Calkins (earthworm) and Wilcox (grasshopper). The latter author asserts ('95) that in *Caloptenus* the spireme of the first spermatocyte first segments into the normal number (twelve) of dumb-bell-shaped segments, which then become associated in pairs to form six tetrads. Each of these dumb-bell-shaped bodies is assumed to be a bivalent chromosome, and the tetrad-formation is therefore interpreted as follows : —

$$a\,b\,c\,d-l \atop \text{(spireme)}, \qquad ab-cd-kl \atop \text{(segmented spireme)}, \qquad \frac{a\,|\,b}{c\,|\,d} \qquad \frac{e\,|\,f}{g\,|\,h}, \text{ etc. (tetrads).}$$

There is, therefore, no longitudinal splitting of the chromosomes. A careful examination of the figures does not convince me of the correctness of this conclusion, which is, moreover, inconsistent with itself on Wilcox's own interpretation. Since each germ-nucleus receives six chromosomes, the somatic number must be 12, and Wilcox has observed this number in the divisions of the spermatogonia. The 12 dumb-bell-shaped primary segments must therefore represent *single* chromosomes, not bivalent ones, as Wilcox assumes, and his primary tetrad must therefore be not $\dfrac{a\,|\,b}{c\,|\,d}$, as he assumes, but either $\dfrac{a}{b}$ or (if we assume that the normal number of chromosomes undergoes a preliminary doubling) $\dfrac{a\,|\,a}{b\,|\,b}$. Until this contradiction is cleared up Wilcox's results must be received with considerable scepticism.

The second case, which is perhaps better founded, is that of the earthworm (*Lumbricus terrestris*), as described by Calkins ('95, 2), whose work was done under my own direction. Calkins finds, in accordance with all other spermatologists save Wilcox, that the spireme-thread splits longitudinally and then divides transversely into 32 double segments. These then unite, two by two, to form 16 tetrads. The 32 primary double segments therefore represent chromosomes of the normal number that have split longitudinally, *i.e.* $\dfrac{a}{a} - \dfrac{b}{b}$, etc., and the formula for a tetrad is $\dfrac{a}{a}\bigg|\dfrac{b}{b}$ or $\dfrac{a}{a}\bigg|\dfrac{x}{x}$. Such a tetrad, therefore, agrees as to its composition with the formulas of Häcker, vom Rath, and Rückert, and agrees in mode of origin with the process described by Rückert in the eggs of *Pristiurus*. While these observations are not absolutely conclusive, they nevertheless rest on strong evidence, and they do not stand in actual contradiction of what is known in the copepods and vertebrates. The possibility of such a mode of origin in other forms must, I think, be held open.

Under the same category must be placed Korschelt's unique results in the egg-reduction of the annelid *Ophryotrocha* ('95), which are very difficult to reconcile with anything known in other forms. The typical somatic number of chromosomes is here four. The *same number* of chromosomes appear in the germinal vesicle (Fig. 96, *D*). They are at first single, then double by a longitudinal split, but afterwards single again by a reunion of the halves. The four chromosomes group themselves in a single tetrad, two passing into the first polar-body, while two remain in the egg, but meanwhile each of them again splits into two. Of the four chromosomes thus left in the egg two are passed out into the second polar body, while the two remaining in the egg give rise to the germ-nucleus. From this it follows that the formation of the *first* polar body is a reducing division (!) — a result which agrees with the earlier conclusions of Henking on *Pyrrochoris*, but differs entirely from those of Rückert, Häcker, and vom Rath. The meaning of this remarkable result cannot here be discussed. A clue to its interpretation is perhaps given by Häcker's interesting observations on the two modes of maturation in *Canthocamptus*, for which the reader is referred to Häcker's paper ('95, 1).

Moore ('95) has given an account of reduction in the spermatogenesis of mammals and elasmobranchs which differs widely in many respects from those of all other observers. In both cases there is said to be a resting stage between the two spermatocyte-divisions, and in mammals (rat) the reduced number of chromosomes first appears in the prophase of the *last* division. In elasmobranchs *both* spermatocyte-divisions are of the heterotypical form, with ring-shaped chromosomes. On all these points Moore's account contradicts those of all other investigators of reduction in the animals, and he is further in contradiction with Rückert on the number of chromosomes. His general interpretation accords with that of Brauer and Strasburger, reducing divisions being totally denied. The evidence on which this interpretation rests will be found in his original papers.

G.   Maturation of Parthenogenetic Eggs

The maturation of eggs that develop without fertilization is a subject of special interest, partly because of its bearing on the general theory of fertilization, partly because it is here, as I believe, that one of the strongest supports is found for the hypothesis of the individuality of chromosomes.   In an early article by Minot ('77) on the theoretical meaning of maturation the suggestion is made that parthenogenesis may be due to failure on the part of the egg to form the polar bodies, the egg-nucleus thus remaining hermaphrodite, and hence capable of development without fertilization.   This suggestion forms the germ of all later theories of parthenogenesis.   Balfour ('80) suggested that the function of forming polar cells has been acquired by the ovum for the express purpose of preventing parthenogenesis, and a nearly similar view was afterwards maintained by Van Beneden.[1]   These authors assumed accordingly that in parthenogenetic eggs no polar bodies are formed.   Weismann ('86) soon discovered, however, that the parthenogenetic eggs of *Polyphemus* (one of the Daphnidæ) produce a *single* polar-body.   This observation was quickly followed by the still more significant discovery by Blochmann ('88) that *in Aphis the parthenogenetic eggs produce a single polar body while the fertilized eggs produce two.* Weismann was able to determine the same fact in ostracodes and rotifera, and was thus led to the view[2] which later researches have entirely confirmed, that it is the *second* polar body that is of special significance in parthenogenesis.   Blochmann observed that in insects the polar bodies were not actually thrown out of the egg, but remained embedded in its substance near the periphery.   At the same time Boveri ('87, 1) discovered that in *Ascaris* the second polar body might in exceptional cases remain in the egg and there give rise to a resting-nucleus indistinguishable from the egg-nucleus or sperm-nucleus.   He was thus led to the interesting suggestion that parthenogenesis might be due to the retention of the second polar body in the egg and its union with the egg-nucleus.   "The second polar body would thus, in a certain sense, assume the *rôle* of the spermatozoön, and it might not without reason be said : *Parthenogenesis is the result of fertilization by the second polar body.*"[3]

This conclusion received a brilliant confirmation through the observations of Brauer ('93) on the parthenogenetic egg of *Artemia*, though it appeared that Boveri arrived at only a part of the truth. Blochmann ('88–89) had found that in the parthenogenetic eggs of the honey-bee, *two* polar-bodies are formed, and Platner discovered the

[1] '83, p. 622.   [2] Essay VI., p. 359.   [3] *l.c.*, p. 73.

same fact in the butterfly *Liparis* ('89) — a fact which seemed to contradict Boveri's hypothesis. Brauer's beautiful researches resolved the contradiction by showing that there are *two types* of *parthenogenesis* which may occur in the same animal. In the one case Boveri's

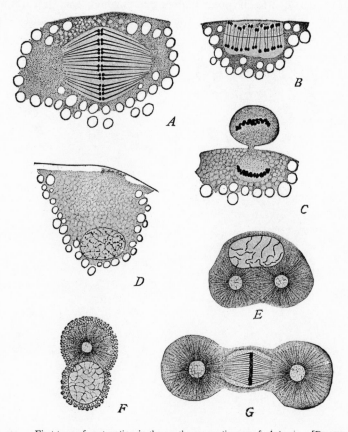

Fig. 100. — First type of maturation in the parthenogenetic egg of *Artemia*. [BRAUER.]

A. The first polar spindle; the equatorial plate contains 84 tetrads. *B. C.* Formation of the first polar body; 84 dyads remain in the egg and these give rise to the egg-nucleus, shown in *D*. *F*. Appearance of the egg-centrosome and aster. *E. G.* Division of the aster and formation of the cleavage-figure; the equatorial plate consists of 84 apparently single but in reality bivalent chromosomes.

conception is exactly realized, while the other is easily brought into relation with it.

(*a*) In both modes typical tetrads are formed in the germ-nucleus to the number of eighty-four. In the first and more frequent case (Fig. 100) but one polar body is formed, which removes eighty-four dyads, leaving eighty-four in the egg. There may be an abortive attempt to form a second polar spindle, but no division results, and the eighty-four dyads give rise to a reticular cleavage-nucleus.   From this arise eighty-four thread-like chromosomes, and *the same number appears in later cleavage-stages.*

(*b*) It is the second and rarer mode that realizes Boveri's conception (Fig. 101).   Both polar bodies are formed, the first removing eighty-four dyads and leaving the same number in the egg.   In the

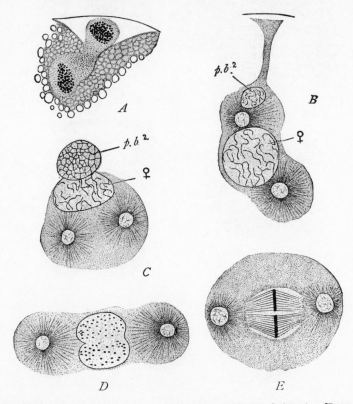

Fig. 101. — Second type of ,maturation in the parthenogenetic egg of *Artemia*.   [BRAUER.]
   A. Formation of second polar body. *B.* Return of the second polar nucleus (*p. b.*²) into the egg; development of the egg-amphiaster. *C.* Union of the egg-nucleus (♀) with the second polar nucleus (*p. b.*²). *D.* Cleavage-nucleus and amphiaster. *E.* First cleavage-figure with equatorial plate containing 168 chromosomes in two groups of 84 each.

formation of the second, the eighty-four dyads are halved to form two daughter-groups, each containing eighty-four single chromosomes. *Both these groups remain in the egg, and each gives rise to a single reticular nucleus, as described by Boveri in Ascaris.   These two nuclei place themselves side by side in the cleavage figure, and give rise each to eighty-four chromosomes, precisely like two germ-nuclei in ordinary fertilization.*   The one hundred and sixty-eight chromosomes split lengthwise, and are distributed in the usual manner, *and reappear in the same number in all later stages.* In other words, the second polar body here plays the part of a sperm-nucleus, precisely as maintained by Boveri.

In all individuals arising from eggs of the first type, therefore, the somatic number of chromosomes is eighty-four; in all those arising from eggs of the second type, it is one hundred and sixty-eight. It is impossible to doubt that the chromosomes of the first class are bivalent; *i.e.* represent two chromosomes joined together — for that the dyads have this value is not a theory, but a known fact. It remains to be seen whether these facts apply to other parthenogenetic eggs; but the single case of *Artemia* is little short of a demonstration not only of Häcker's and vom Rath's conception of bivalent chromosomes, but also of the more general hypothesis of the individuality of chromosomes (Chapter VI.). Only on this hypothesis can we explain the persistence of the original number of chromosomes, whether eighty-four or one hundred and sixty-eight, in the later stages. How important a bearing this case has on Strasburger's theory of reduction (p. 196) is obvious.

H. Summary and Conclusion

The one fact of maturation that stands out with perfect clearness and certainty amid all the controversies surrounding it is a *reduction in the number of chromosomes in the ultimate germ-cells to one-half the number characteristic of the somatic cells.* It is equally clear that this reduction is a preparation of the germ-cells for their subsequent union, and a means by which the number of chromosomes is held constant in the species. As soon, however, as we attempt to advance beyond this point we enter upon doubtful ground, which becomes more and more uncertain as we proceed. With a few exceptions the reduction in number first appears in the direct progenitors of the germ-cells by a *segmentation of the spireme-thread into one-half the usual number of rods.* This process is, however, not an actual reduction in the number of *chromosomes*, but only a preliminary "pseudo-reduction" in the number of chromatin-*masses.* In what we may regard as the typical case (*e.g. Ascaris*) the pseudo-reduction first appears at the penultimate division; *i.e.* in the grandmother-cell of the germ-cell (primary oöcyte or spermatocyte). It may, however, appear at a very much earlier period, even in the embryonic germ-cells, the reduced number appearing in every succeeding division until the germ-cells are formed. This is the case in the salamander and in *Cyclops.* It appears in its most striking form in the higher plants, where the reduced number appears in all the cells of the sexual generation (pro-thallium, pollen-tube, embryo-sac), beginning with the mother-cell of the asexual spores from which this generation arises.

In every case we must distinguish carefully between the primary pseudo-reduction in the number of chromatin-masses, and the actual reduction in the number of chromosomes; for the former is in some cases certainly not an actual halving of the number of *chromosomes*, since each of the primary chromatin-rods is proved by its later history to be bivalent, representing two chromosomes united end to end (sal-amander, copepods). In these cases the actual reduction takes place in the course of the last two divisions (formation of the polar bodies and of the spermatids), each bivalent chromatin-rod di-viding transversely into the two chromosomes which it repre-sents, and at the same time (or earlier) splitting lengthwise. Each primary rod thus gives rise to a tetrad consisting of two pairs of chromosomes which, by the two final divisions, are distributed one to each of the four resulting cells. In the copepods the first division sepa-rates the longitudinal halves of the chromosomes and is there-fore an "equal division" (Weis-mann). The second division corresponds with the transverse division of the primary rod, and therefore is the "reducing division" postulated by Weismann.

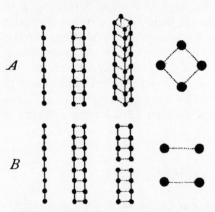

Fig. 102.— Diagram contrasting the two modes of tetrad-formation.

A. Ascaris-type. Double longitudinal split-ting of the primary rod; no reduction in the number of granules ("ids"). *B*. Copepod-type. A longitudinal followed by a transverse division of the primary rod; the number of granules halved by the second division.

This result gives a perfectly clear conception of the process of actual reduction and its relation to the preparatory pseudo-reduction that precedes it. It has, however, been absolutely demonstrated in only two groups of animals, viz. the copepods and the vertebrates (amphibia), and a diametrically opposite result has been reached in the case of *Ascaris* (Boveri, Hertwig, Brauer) and in the plants (Gui-gnard, Strasburger). In *Ascaris* typical tetrads are formed, but all observers agree that they arise by a double longitudinal splitting of the original chromatin-rod. In the plants no tetrads have been ob-served, but the precise nature of the maturation-divisions is still in doubt.

We have thus two diametrically opposing results. In the one

case the primary halving in number is a pseudo-reduction, and each tetrad arises by one longitudinal and one transverse division of a bivalent chromosome, representing two different regions of the spireme-thread (Häcker, vom Rath, Rückert, Weismann). In the other case the primary halving appears to be an actual reduction, and if tetrads are formed, they arise (*Ascaris*) by a double longitudinal splitting of the primary rod, and all of its four derivatives represent the same region of the spireme-thread. Since the latter consists primarily of a single series of granules ("ids" of Weismann, or chromomeres), by the fission of which the splitting takes place, the difference between the two views comes to this: that in the second case the four chromosomes of each tetrad must represent identical groups of granules, while in the first case they represent two different groups (Fig. 102). In the second case the maturation-divisions cannot cause a reduction in the number of different kinds of ids. In the first case the number of ids is reduced to one-half by the second division by which the second polar body is formed, or by which two spermatids arise from the daughter-spermatocyte (Rückert, Häcker, vom Rath).

The first view must obviously stand or fall with the conception of the primary chromatin-rods as bivalent chromosomes. That this is a valid conception is in my judgment demonstrated by Brauer's remarkable observations on *Artemia;* for in this case it is impossible to escape the conclusion that the "chromosomes" of those parthenogenetic embryos in which the number is halved are bivalent, — *i.e.* have the value of two chromosomes united by their ends, — and they lend the strongest support to vom Rath's and Häcker's hypothesis. For if the number of chromosomes be merely the expression of a formative tendency, like the power of crystallization, inherent in each specific kind of chromatin, why should the chromatin of the same animal differ in the two cases though *derived from the same source* in both? Yet if the cleavage-nucleus arises from eighty-four dyads the same number of chromatin-rods appears in all later stages; whereas if the dyads break each into two separate chromosomes before their union, the number is thenceforward one hundred and sixty-eight. So great is the force of this evidence that I think we must still hesitate to accept the results thus far attained in *Ascaris* and the plants, and must await further research in this direction. Until the contradiction is cleared up the problem of reduction remains unsolved.

APPENDIX

1. *Accessory Cells of the Testis*

It is necessary to touch here on the nature of the so-called "Sertoli-cells," or supporting cells of the testis in mammals, partly because of the theoretical significance attached to them by Minot, partly because of their relations to the question of amitosis in the testis. In the seminiferous tubules of the mammalian testis, the parent-cells of the spermatozoa develop from the periphery inwards towards the lumen, where the spermatozoa are finally formed and set free. At the periphery is a layer of cells next the basement-membrane, having flat, oval nuclei. Within this, the cells are arranged in columns alternating more or less regularly with long, clear cells, containing large nuclei. The latter are the *Sertoli-cells*, or supporting cells; they extend nearly through from the basement-membrane to the lumen, and to their inner ends the young spermatozoa are attached by their heads, and there complete their growth. The spermatozoa are developed from cells which lie in columns between the Sertoli-cells, and which undoubtedly represent spermatogonia, spermatocytes, and spermatids, though their precise relationship is, to some extent, in doubt. The innermost of these cells, next the lumen, are spermatids, which, after their formation, are found attached to the Sertoli-cells, and are there converted into spermatozoa without further division. The deeper cells from which they arise are spermatocytes, and the spermatogonia lie deeper still, being probably represented by the large, rounded cells.

Two entirely different interpretations of the Sertoli-cells were advanced as long ago as 1871, and both views still have their adherents. Von Ebner ('71) at first regarded the Sertoli-cell as the parent-cell of the group of spermatozoa attached to it, and the same view was afterwards especially advocated by Biondi ('85), and is still maintained by Minot ('92), who regards the nucleus of the Sertoli-cell as the physiological analogue of the polar bodies, *i.e.* as containing the female nuclear substance ('92, p. 77). According to the opposing view, first suggested by Merkel ('71), the Sertoli-cell is not the parent-cell, but a nurse-cell, the spermatozoa developing from the columns of rounded cells, and becoming *secondarily* attached to the Sertoli-cell, which serves merely as a support and a means of conveying nourishment to the growing spermatozoa. This view was advocated by Brown ('85), and especially by Benda ('87). In the following year ('88), von Ebner himself abandoned his early hypothesis and strongly advocated Benda's views, adding the very significant result that *four spermatids arise from each spermatocyte*, precisely as was afterwards shown to be the case in *Ascaris*, etc. The very careful and thorough work of Benda and von Ebner leaves no doubt, in my opinion, that mammalian spermatogenesis conforms, in its main outlines, with that of *Ascaris*, the salamander, and other forms, and that Biondi's views, which Minot unfortunately adopts, are without foundation. If this be the case, Minot's theoretical interpretation of the Sertoli-cell as the physiological equivalent of the polar bodies, of course collapses.

Various other attempts have been made to discover in the spermatogenesis a casting out of material which might be compared with the polar bodies, but these attempts have now only an historical interest. Van Beneden and Julin sought such material in the " residual corpuscles." left behind in the division of the sperm-forming cells of *Ascaris*. Other authors have regarded in the same light the " Nebenkern " (Waldeyer) and the "residual globules " (Lankester, Brown) thrown off by the developing spermatozoa of mammals. All of these views are, like Minot's, wide of the mark, and they were advanced before the real parallel between spermatogenesis and ovogenesis had been made known by Platner and Hertwig.

2. *Amitosis in the Early Sex-Cells*

Whether the progenitors of the germ-cells ever divide amitotically is a question of high theoretical interest. Numerous observers have described amitotic division in testis-cells, and a few also in those of the ovary. The recent observations of Meves ('91), vom Rath ('93), and Preusse ('95), leave no doubt whatever that such divisions occur in the testis of many animals. Vom Rath, however, maintains, after an extended investigation, that all cells so dividing do not belong in the cycle of development of the germ-cells ('93, p. 164) ; that amitosis occurs only in the supporting or nutritive cells (Sertoli-cells, etc.), or in such as are destined to degenerate, like the "residual bodies" of Van Beneden. Meves has, however, produced strong evidence ('94) that in the salamander the spermatogonia may, in the autumn, divide by amitosis, and in the ensuing spring may again resume the process of mitotic division, and give rise to functional spermatozoa. On the strength of these observations, Flemming ('93) himself now admits the possibility that amitosis may form part of a normal cycle of development, and Preusse has recently shown that amitosis may continue through several generations in the early ovarian cells of Hemiptera without a sign of degeneration.

LITERATURE. V

Van Beneden, E. — Recherches sur la maturation de l'œuf, la fécondation et la division cellulaire : *Arch. Biol.*, IV. 1883.

Boveri, Th. — Zellenstudien, I., III. *Jena*, 1887–90. See also "Befruchtung" (List IV.).

Brauer, A. — Zur Kenntniss der Spermatogenese von *Ascaris megalocephala : Arch. mik. Anat.*, XLII. 1893.

Id. — Zur Kenntniss der Reifung der parthenogenetisch sich entwickelnden Eies von *Artemia Salina : Arch. mik. Anat.*, XLIII. 1894.

Häcker, V. — Die Vorstadien der Eireifung (General Review) : *Arch. mik. Anat.*, XLV. 2. 1895.

Hertwig, O. — Vergleich der Ei- und Samenbildung bei Nematoden. Eine Grundlage für celluläre Streitfragen : *Arch. mik. Anat.*, XXXVI. 1890.

Mark, E. L. — (See List IV.)

Platner, G. — Über die Bedeutung der Richtungskörperchen : *Biol. Centralb.*, VIII. 1889.

vom Rath, O. — Zur Kenntniss der Spermatogenese von *Gryllotalpa vulgaris : Arch. mik. Anat.*, XL. 1892.

Id. — Neue Beiträge zur Frage der Chromatinreduction in der Samen- und Eireife : *Arch. mik. Anat.*, XLVI. 1895.

Ruckert, J. — Die Chromatinreduktion der Chromosomenzahl im Entwicklungsgang der Organismen : *Ergebn. d. Anat. u. Entwick.*, III. 1893 (1894).

Strasburger, E. — Über periodische Reduktion der Chromosomenzahl im Entwicklungsgang der Organismen : *Biol. Centralb.*, XIV. 1894.

P

CHAPTER VI

SOME PROBLEMS OF CELL–ORGANIZATION

"Wir müssen deshalb den lebenden Zellen, abgesehen von der Molecularstructur der organischen Verbindungen, welche sie enthält, noch eine andere und in anderer Weise complicirte Structur zuschreiben, und diese es ist, welche wir mit dem Namen *Organization* bezeichnen." BRÜCKE.[1]

"Was diese Zelle eigentlich ist, darüber existieren sehr verschiedene Ansichten." HÄCKEL.[2]

The remarkable history of the chromatic substance in the maturation of the germ-cells forces upon our attention the problem of the ultimate morphological organization of the nucleus, and this in its turn involves our whole conception of protoplasm and the cell. The grosser and more obvious organization is revealed to us by the microscope as a differentiation of its substance into nucleus, cytoplasm, and centrosome. But, as Strasburger has well said, it would indeed be a strange accident if the highest powers of our present microscopes had laid bare the ultimate organization of the cell. Brücke insisted more than thirty years ago that protoplasm must possess a far more complicated morphological organization than is revealed to us in the visible structure of the cell, and suggested the possible existence of vital units ranking between the molecule and the cell. Many biological thinkers since Brücke's time have in one form or other accepted this conception, which indeed lies at the root of nearly all recent attempts to analyze exhaustively the phenomena of cell-life. I shall make no attempt to review the *a priori* arguments that have been urged in favour of this conception,[3] but will rather inquire what are the extreme conclusions justified by the known facts of cell-structure.

[1] *Elementarorganismen*, 1861, p. 386.
[2] *Anthropogenie*, 1891, p. 104.
[3] For an exhaustive review of the subject see Yves Delage, *La Structure du protoplasma, et les théories sur l'hérédité.* Paris, 1895.

A. THE NATURE OF CELL-ORGANS

The cell is, in Brücke's words, an *elementary organism*, which may by itself perform all the characteristic operations of life, as is the case with the unicellular organisms, and in a sense also with the germ-cells. Even when the cell is but a constituent unit of a higher grade of organization, as in multicellular forms, it is no less truly an organism, and in a measure leads an independent life, even though its functions be restricted and subordinated to the common life. It is true that the earlier conception of the multicellular body as a colony of one-celled forms cannot be accepted without certain reservations.[1] Nevertheless, all the facts at our command indicate that the tissue-cell possesses the same morphological organization as the egg-cell, or the protozoan, and the same fundamental physiological properties as well. Like these the tissue-cell has its differentiated structural parts or organs, and we have now to inquire how these cell-organs are to be conceived.

The visible organs of the cell fall under two categories according as they are merely temporary structures, formed anew in each successive cell-generation out of the common structural basis, or permanent structures whose identity is never lost since they are directly handed on by division from cell to cell. To the former category belong, in general, such structures as cilia, pseudopodia, and the like; to the latter, the nucleus, probably also the centrosome, and the plastids of plant-cells. A peculiar interest attaches to the permanent cell-organs. Closely inter-related as these organs are, they nevertheless have a remarkable degree of morphological independence. They assimilate food, grow, divide, and perform their own characteristic actions like coexistent but independent organisms, of a lower grade than the cell, living together in colonial or symbiotic association. So striking is this morphological and physiological autonomy in the case of the green plastids or chromatophores that neither botanists nor zoölogists are as yet able to distinguish with absolute certainty between those that form an integral part of the cell, as in the higher green plants, and those that are actually independent organisms living symbiotically within it, as is probably the case with the yellow cells of Radiolaria. Even so acute an investigator as Watasé ('93, 1) has not hesitated to regard the nucleus itself — or rather the chromosome — as a distinct organism living in symbiotic association with the cytoplasm, but having had, in an historical sense, a different origin. It is but a short step from this con-

[1] Cf. p. 41.

clusion to the view that the centrosome, too, is such an independent organism and that the cell is a symbiotic association of at least three dissimilar living beings! Such a conception would, however, as I believe, be in the highest degree misleading, even if with Watasé we limit it to the nucleus and the cytoplasm. The facts point rather to the conclusion that all cell-organs arise as differentiated areas in the common structural basis of the cell, and that their morphological character is the outward expression of localized and specific forms of metabolic activity.

It is certain that some of the cell-organs are the seat of specific chemical changes. Chromatin (nuclein) is formed only in the nucleus. The various forms of plastids have specific metabolic powers, giving rise to chlorophyll, to pigment, or to starch, according to their nature. The centrosome, as Bütschli, Strasburger, and Heidenhain have insisted, possesses a specific chemical character to which its remarkable effect on the cytoplasm must be due.[1] Even in regions of the cytoplasm not differentiated into distinct cell-organs the metabolic activities may show specific and constant localization, as shown by the deposit of zymogen-granules, the secretion of membranes, the formation of muscle-fibres, and a multitude of related facts. Physiologically, therefore, no line of demarcation can be drawn between permanent cell-organs, transient cell-organs, and areas of the cell-substance that are physiologically specialized but not yet morphologically differentiated into organs. When we turn to the structural relations of cell-organs, we find, I think, reason to accept the same conclusion in a morphological sense. The subject may best be approached by a consideration of the structural basis of the cell and the morphological relations between nucleus and cytoplasm.

B.   STRUCTURAL BASIS OF THE CELL

It has been pointed out in Chapter I. that the ultimate structural basis of the cell is still an open question; for there is no general agreement as to the configuration of the protoplasmic network, and we do not yet know whether the fibrillar or the alveolar structure is the more fundamental. This question is, however, of minor importance as compared with the microsome-problem, which is, I think, the most fundamental question of cell-morphology, and which is equally pressing whatever view we may hold regarding the configuration of the network.

Are the granules described as " microsomes " accidental and non-essential bodies, produced, it may be, by the coagulating effects of

[1] *Cf.* p. 77.

the reagents, as Fischer's experiments suggest? Or are they normal and constant morphological elements that have a definite significance in the life of the cell? It is certain that the microsomes are not merely nodes of the network, or optical sections of the threads, as the earlier authors maintained; for the fibrillæ may often be seen to consist of regular rows of granules. Van Beneden gave the first clear description of the microsomes in this regard in the following words: "I have often had occasion to note facts that establish the essential identity of the moniliform fibrillæ and the homogeneous fibrillæ of the protoplasm. In my opinion every fibrilla, though it appear under the microscope as a simple line devoid of varicosities, is formed at the expense of a moniliform fibril composed of microsomes connected with one another by segments of uniting fibrils." [1] Again, in a later work he says of the fibrils of the astral system in *Ascaris:* "It is easy to see that the achromatic fibrils are moniliform, that they are formed of microsomes united by inter-fibrils." [2] Similar observations have been made by many later writers. In the eggs of sea-urchins and annelids, which I have carefully studied, there is no doubt that after some reagents, *e.g.* sublimate-acetic, picroacetic, chromo-formic, the entire astral system has exactly the structure described by Van Beneden in *Ascaris*. Although the basal part of the astral ray appears like a continuous fibre, its distal.part may be resolved into a single series of microsomes, like a string of beads, which passes insensibly into the cytoreticulum. The latter is composed of irregular rows of distinct granules which stain intensely blue with hæmatoxylin, while the substance in which they are embedded, left unstained by hæmatoxylin, is colored by red acid aniline dyes, such as Congo red or acid fuchsin.

The difficulty is to determine whether this appearance represents the normal structure or is produced by a coagulation and partial disorganization of the threads through the action of the reagents. A justifiable scepticism exists in regard to this point; for it is perfectly certain that such coagulation-effects actually occur in the proteids of the cell-substance, and that some of the granules there observed have such an origin. It is very difficult to determine this point in the case of the cyto-microsomes, owing to their extreme minuteness. The question must, therefore, be approached indirectly by way of an examination of the nucleus and its relation to the cytoplasm. Here we find ourselves on more certain ground and are able to make an analysis that in a certain measure justifies the hypothesis that the cyto-microsomes may be true morphological elements having the power of growth and division like the cell-organs formed by their aggregation.

[1] '83, p. 576, 577. [2] '87, p. 266.

1. *Nucleus and Cytoplasm*

From the time of the earlier writings of Frommann ('65, '67), Arnold ('67), Heitzmann ('73), and Klein ('78), down to the present, an increasing number of observers have held that the nuclear reticulum is to be conceived as a modification of the same structural basis as that which forms the cytoplasm. The latest researches indicate, indeed, that true chromatin (nuclein) is confined to the nucleus.[1] But the whole weight of the evidence now goes to show that the linin-network is of the same nature, both chemically and physically, as the cyto-reticulum, and that the achromatic nuclear membrane is formed as a condensation of the same substance. Many investigators, among whom may be named Frommann, Leydig, Klein, Van Beneden, and Reinke, have described the threads of both the intra- and extra-nuclear network as terminating in the nuclear membrane; and the membrane itself is described by these and other observers as being itself reticular in structure, and by some (Van Beneden) as consisting of closely crowded microsomes arranged in a network. The clearest evidence is, however, afforded by the origin of the spindle-fibres in mitotic division; for it is now well established that these may be formed either inside or outside the nucleus, and there is a pretty general agreement among cytologists, with the important exception of Boveri, that both spindle-fibres and astral rays arise by a direct rearrangement of the pre-existing structures.[2] At the close of mitosis the central portion of the spindle appears always to give rise to a portion of the cytoplasm lying between the daughter-nuclei; and in the division of the egg in the sea-urchin I have obtained strong evidence that the spindle-fibres are directly resolved into a portion of the general reticulum. These fibres are in this case formed inside the nucleus from the linin-network; and we have therefore proof positive of a direct genetic continuity between the latter and the cytoplasmic structures. But more than this, I have found reason to conclude that in this case a considerable part of the linin-network is derived from the *chromatin*, that the entire nuclear reticulum is a continuous structure, and that it is no more than a specially differentiated area of the general cell-network ('95, 2). This conclusion finds, I believe, a very strong support in the studies of Van Beneden, Heidenhain, and Reinke reviewed beyond (p. 223); but the bearing of these only becomes plain after considering the morphological differentiations of the nuclear network ·and its transformations during mitosis.

[1] Cf. Hammarsten ('95).

[2] The long-standing dispute as to the origin of the nuclear membrane (whether nuclear or cytoplasmic) is therefore of little moment.

C. Morphological Composition of the Nucleus

1. *The Chromatin*

(*a*) *Hypothesis of the Individuality of the Chromosomes.* — It may now be taken as a well-established fact that the nucleus is never formed *de novo*, but always arises by the division of a pre-existing nucleus. In the typical mode of division by mitosis the chromatic substance is resolved into a group of chromosomes, always the same in form and number in a given species of cell, and having the power of assimilation, growth, and division, as if they were morphological individuals of a lower order than the nucleus. That they are such individuals or units has been maintained as a definite hypothesis, especially by Rabl and Boveri. As a result of a careful study of mitosis in epithelial cells of the salamander, Rabl ('85) concluded that *the chromosomes do not lose their individuality at the close of division, but persist in the chromatic reticulum of the resting nucleus.* The reticulum arises through a transformation of the chromosomes, which give off anastomizing branches, and thus give rise to the appearance of a network. Their loss of identity is, however, only apparent. They come into view again at the ensuing division, at the beginning of which "the chromatic substance flows back, through predetermined paths, into the primary chromosome-bodies" (Kernfäden), which reappear in the ensuing spireme-stage in nearly or quite the same position they occupied before. Even in the resting nucleus, Rabl believed that he could discover traces of the chromosomes in the configuration of the network, and he described the nucleus as showing a distinct polarity having a "pole" corresponding with the point towards which the apices of the chromosomes converge (*i.e.* towards the centrosome), and an "anti-pole" (Gegenpol) at the opposite point (*i.e.* towards the equator of the spindle) (Fig. 17). Rabl's hypothesis was precisely formulated and ardently advocated by Boveri in 1887 and 1888, and again in 1891, on the ground of his own studies and those of Van Beneden on the early stages of *Ascaris*. The hypothesis was supported by extremely strong evidence, derived especially from a study of abnormal variations in the early development of *Ascaris*, the force of which has, I think, been underestimated by the critics of the hypothesis. Some of this evidence may here be briefly reviewed. In some cases, through a miscarriage of the mitotic mechanism, one or both of the chromosomes destined for the second polar body are accidentally left in the egg. These chromosomes give rise in the egg to a reticular nucleus, indistinguishable from the egg-nucleus. At a later period this nucleus gives rise to the same number of chromosomes as those that entered into its formation; *i.e.* either one or two. These are drawn into the equatorial plate along with those derived from the germ-nuclei, and mitosis proceeds as usual, the number of chromosomes being, however, abnormally increased from four to five or six (Fig. 103 *C, D*). Again, the two chromosomes left in the egg after removal of the

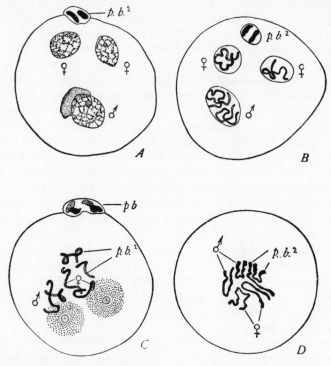

Fig. 103.— Evidence of the individuality of the chromosomes. Abnormalities in the fertilization of *Ascaris*. [BOVERI.]

A. The two chromosomes of the egg-nucleus, accidentally separated, have given rise each to a reticular nucleus (♀, ♀); the sperm-nucleus below (♂). *B.* Later stage of the same, a single chromosome in each egg-nucleus, two in the sperm-nucleus. *C.* An egg in which the second polar body has been retained; *p. b.*² the two chromosomes arising from it, ♀ the egg-chromosomes, ♂ the sperm-chromosomes. *D.* Resulting equatorial plate with six chromosomes.

second polar body may accidentally become separated. In this case each chromosome gives rise to a reticular nucleus of half the usual size, and from each of these a *single* chromosome is afterwards formed (Fig. 103, *A, B*). Finally, it sometimes happens that the two germ-nuclei completely fuse while in the reticular state, as is normally the case in sea-urchins and some other animals (p. 153). From the cleavage-nucleus thus formed arise four chromosomes.

These remarkable observations show that *whatever be the number of chromosomes entering into the formation of a reticular nucleus, the same number afterwards issue from it* — a result which demonstrates that the number of chromosomes is not due merely to the chemical composition of the chromatin-substance, but to a morphological organization of the nucleus. A beautiful confirmation of this conclusion was afterwards made by Boveri ('93, '95, 1) and Morgan ('95, 4) in the case of echinoderms, by rearing larvæ from enucleated egg-

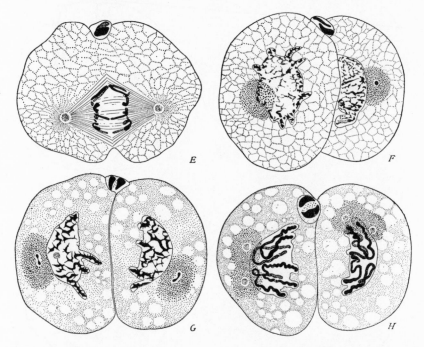

Fig. 104. — Evidence of the individuality of the chromosomes in the egg of *Ascaris*. [BOVERI.]

E. Anaphase of the first cleavage. *F.* Two-cell stage with lobed nuclei, the lobes formed by the ends of the chromosomes. *G.* Early prophase of the ensuing division; chromosomes re-forming, centrosomes dividing. *H.* Later prophase, the chromosomes lying with their ends in the same position as before; centrosomes divided.

fragments, fertilized by a single spermatozoön (p. 258). All the nuclei of such larvæ contain but half the typical number of chromosomes, — *i.e.* nine instead of eighteen, — since all are descended from one germ-nucleus instead of two!

Van Beneden and Boveri were able, furthermore, to demonstrate in *Ascaris* that in the formation of the spireme the chromosomes reappear in the same position as those which entered into the formation of the reticulum, precisely as Rabl maintained. As the long chromosomes diverge, their free ends are always turned towards the middle plane (Fig. 69), and upon the reconstruction of the daughter-nuclei these ends give rise to corresponding lobes of the nucleus, as in Fig. 104, which persist throughout the resting state. At the succeeding division the chromosomes reappear exactly in the same posi-

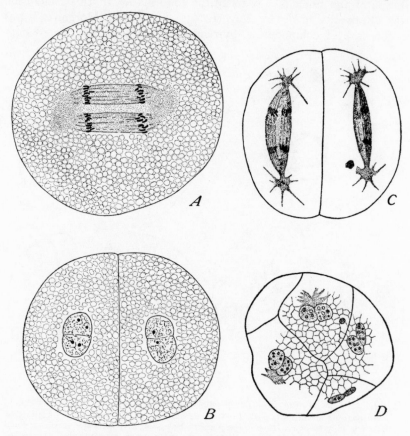

Fig. 105. — Independence of paternal and maternal chromatin in the segmenting eggs of *Cyclops*. [*A–C.* from RÜCKERT; *D.* from HÄCKER.]

    A. First cleavage-figure in *C. strenuus;* complete independence of paternal and maternal chromosomes. *B.* Resulting 2-cell stage with double nuclei. *C.* Second cleavage; chromosomes still in double groups. *D.* Blastomeres with double nuclei from the 8-cell stage of *C. brevicornis.*

tion, *their ends lying in the nuclear lobes as before* (Fig. 104, *G, H*). On the strength of these facts Boveri concluded that the chromosomes must be regarded as "individuals" or "elementary organisms," that have an independent existence in the cell. During the reconstruction of the nucleus they send forth pseudopodia which anastomose to form a network in which their identity is lost to view. As the cell prepares for division, however, the chromosomes contract, withdraw their processes, and return to their "resting state," in which fission takes place. Applying this conclusion to the fertilization of the egg, Boveri expressed his belief that "we may identify every chromatic element arising from a resting nucleus with a definite element that entered into the formation of that nucleus, from which the remarkable conclusion follows *that in all cells derived in the regular course of division from the fertilized egg, one-half of the chromosomes are of strictly paternal origin, the other half of maternal.*" [1]

Boveri's hypothesis has been criticised by many writers, especially by Hertwig, Guignard, and Brauer, and I myself have urged some objections to it. Recently, however, it has received a support so strong as to amount almost to a demonstration, through the remarkable observations of Rückert, Häcker, Herla, and Zoja on the independence of the paternal and maternal chromosomes. These observations, already referred to at p. 156, may be more fully reviewed at this point. Häcker ('92, 2) first showed that in *Cyclops strenuus*, as in *Ascaris* and other forms, the germ-nuclei do not fuse, but give rise to two separate groups of chromosomes that lie side by side near the equator of the cleavage-spindle. In the two-cell stage (of *Cyclops tenuicornis*) each nucleus consists of two distinct though closely united halves, which Häcker believed to be the derivatives of the two respective germ-nuclei. The truth of this surmise was demonstrated three years later by Rückert ('95, 3) in a species of *Cyclops*, likewise identified as *C. strenuus* (Fig. 105). The number of chromosomes in each germ-nucleus is here twelve. Rückert was able to trace the paternal and maternal groups of daughter-chromosomes not only into the respective halves of the daughter-nuclei of the two-cell stage, but into *later cleavage-stages*. From the bilobed nuclei of the two-cell stage arises, in each cell, a double spireme, and a double group of chromosomes, from which are formed bilobed or double nuclei in the four-cell stage. This process is repeated at the next cleavage, and the double character of the nuclei was in many cases distinctly recognizable at a late stage when the germ-layers were being formed.

Finally Victor Herla's remarkable observations on *Ascaris* ('93) showed that in *Ascaris* not only the chromatin of the germ-nuclei, but also the paternal and maternal *chromosomes*, remain perfectly distinct as far as the twelve-cell stage — certainly a brilliant confirmation of Boveri's conclusion. Just how far the distinction is maintained is still uncertain, but Häcker's and Rückert's observations give some ground to believe that it may persist throughout the entire life of the embryo. Both these observers have shown that

[1] '9I, p. 410.

the chromosomes of the germinal vesicle appear *in two distinct groups*, and Rückert suggests that these may represent the paternal and maternal elements that have remained distinct throughout the entire cycle of development, even down to the formation of the egg! When to these facts is added the evidence afforded by Brauer's beautiful observations on *Artemia*, no escape is left from the hypothesis of the individuality of the chromosomes in one form or

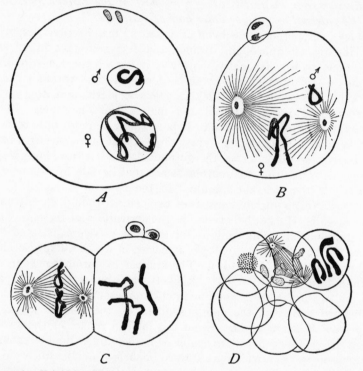

Fig. 106. — Hybrid fertilization of the egg of *Ascaris megalocephala*, var. *bivalens*, by the sper-matozoön of var. *univalens*. [HERLA.]

A. The germ-nuclei shortly before union. *B.* The cleavage-figure forming; the sperm-nucleus has given rise to one chromosome (♂), the egg-nucleus to two (♀). *C.* Two-cell stage dividing, showing the three chromosomes in each cell. *D.* Twelve-cell stage, with the three distinct chromosomes still shown in the primordial germ-cell or stem-cell.

another, even though we admit that Boveri's statement may have gone somewhat too far. The only question is how to state the facts without introducing obscure conceptions as to what constitutes an "individual." It is almost certain, as pointed out beyond (p. 221), that the chromosomes are not the ultimate units of nuclear structure, for they arise as aggregations of chromatin-grains that have likewise the power of growth and division. The fact remains — and it is one of the highest significance — that these more elementary units group themselves into definite aggregates of a higher order that show a certain degree of persistent individual existence. It may be said that the tendency to assume such a grouping is merely a question of nuclear dynamics, and is due to a "formative force" innate in the chromatin-substance. This is undoubtedly true; but it is only another form of expression for the facts, though one that avoids the use of the quasi-metaphysical term "individual." Whether a chromosome that emerges from the resting nucleus is individually the same as one that entered into it can only be determined when we know whether it consists of the same group of chromatin-granules or other elementary bodies. It must not be forgotten, however, that in the case of the egg the chromosomes may persist without loss of their boundaries from one division to another, since no reticulum is formed (cf. p. 193).

(*b*) *Composition of the Chromosomes.* — We owe to Roux[1] the first clear formulation of the view that the chromosomes, or the chromatin-thread, consist of successive regions or elements that are qualitatively different (p. 183). This hypothesis, which has been accepted by Weismann, Strasburger, and a number of others, lends a peculiar interest to the morphological composition of the chromatic substance. The facts are now well established (1) that in a large number of cases the chromatin-thread consists of a series of granules (chromomeres) embedded in and held together by the linin-substance, (2) that the splitting of the chromosomes is caused by the division of these more elementary bodies, (3) that the chromatin-grains may divide at a time when the spireme is only just beginning to emerge from the reticulum of the resting nucleus. These facts point unmistakably to the conclusion that these granules are perhaps to be regarded as independent morphological elements of a lower grade than the chromosomes. That they are not artefacts or coagulation-products is proved by their uniform size and regular arrangement in the thread, especially when the thread is split. A decisive test of their morphological nature is, however, even more difficult than in the case of the chromosomes; for the chromatin-grains often become apparently fused together so that the chromatin-thread appears perfectly homogeneous, and whether they lose their individuality in this close union is undetermined. Observations on their number are still very scanty, but they point to some very interesting conclusions. In Boveri's figures of the egg-maturation of *Ascaris* each element of the tetrad consists of six chromatin-disks arranged in a linear series (Van Beneden's figures of the same object show at most five) which finally fuse to

[1] *Bedeutung der Kerntheilungsfiguren*, 1883, p. 15.

form an apparently homogeneous body.   In the chromosomes of the germ-nuclei the number is at least double this (Van Beneden). Their number has been more carefully followed out in the sperma-togenesis of the same animal (variety *bivalens*) by Brauer.   At the time the chromatin-grains divide, in the reticulum of the spermato-cyte-nucleus, they are very numerous.   His figures of the spireme-thread show at first nearly forty granules in linear series (Fig. 92, *A*). Just before the breaking of the thread into two the number is reduced to ten or twelve (Fig. 92, *C*).   Just after the division to form the two tetrads the number is four or five (Fig. 92, *D*), which finally fuse into a homogeneous body.

It is certain, therefore, that the number of chromomeres is not con-stant in a given species, but it is a significant fact that in *Ascaris* the final number, before fusion, appears to be nearly the same (four to six) both in the oögenesis and the spermatogenesis.   The facts re-garding bivalent and plurivalent chromosomes (p. 61) at once sug-gest themselves, and one cannot avoid the thought that the smallest chromatin-grains may successively group themselves in larger and larger combinations of which the final term is the chromosome. Whether these combinations are to be regarded as "individuals" is a question which can only lead to a barren play of words.   The fact that cannot be escaped is that the history of the chromatin-substance reveals to us, not a homogeneous substance, but a definite morpho-logical organization in which, as through an inverted telescope, we behold a series of more and more elementary groups, the last visi-ble term of which is the smallest chromatin-granule, or nuclear microsome beyond which our present optical appliances do not allow us to see.   Are these the ultimate dividing units, as Brauer suggests (p. 79)?   Here again we may well recall Strasburger's warning, and hesitate to identify the end of the series with the limits reached by our best lenses.   Somewhere, however, the series must end in final chromatic units which cannot be further subdivided without the decomposition of chromatin into simpler chemical substances.   These units must be capable of assimilation, growth, and division without loss of their specific character.   This I believe is an absolute logical necessity.   It is in these ultimate units that we must seek the "qualities," if they exist, postulated in Roux's hypothesis; but the existence of such qualitative differences is a physiological assump-tion that in no manner prejudices our conclusion regarding the ultimate *morphological* composition of the chromatin.

D. CHROMATIN, LININ, AND THE CYTORETICULUM

What, now, is the relation of the smallest visible chromatin-grains to the linin-network and the cytoreticulum? Van Beneden long ago maintained[1] that the achromatic network, the nuclear membrane, and the cytoreticulum have essentially the same structure, all consisting of microsomes united by connective substance, and being only "parts of one and the same structure." But, more than this, he asserted that *the chromatic and achromatic microsomes might be transformed into one another, and were therefore of essentially the same morphological nature.* "They pass successively, in the course of the nuclear evolution, through a chromatic or an achromatic stage, according as they imbibe or give off the chromophilous substance."[2] Both these conclusions are borne out by recent researches. Heidenhain ('93, '94), confirmed by Reinke and Schloter, finds that the nuclear network contains granules of two kinds differing in their staining-capacity. The first are the basichromatin granules, which stain with the true nuclear dyes (basic anilines, etc.), and are identical with the "chromatin-granules" of other authors. The second are the oxychromatin-granules of the linin-network, which stain with the plasma-stains (acid anilines, etc.), and are closely similar to those of the cytoreticulum. *These two forms graduate into one another, and are conjectured to be different phases of the same elements.* This conception is furthermore supported by many observations on the behaviour of the nuclear network as a whole. The chromatic substance is known to undergo very great changes in staining-capacity at different periods in the life of the nucleus (p. 244), and is known to vary greatly in bulk. In certain cases a very large amount of the original chromatic network is cast out of the nucleus at the time of the division, and is converted into cytoplasm. And, finally, in studying mitosis in seaurchin eggs I was forced to the conclusion ('95, 2) that a considerable part of the linin-network, from which the spindle-fibres are formed, is actually derived from the chromatin.

When all these facts are placed in connection, we find it difficult to escape the conclusion that no definite line can be drawn between the cytoplasmic microsomes at one extreme and the chromatin-granules at the other. And inasmuch as the latter are certainly capable of growth and division, we cannot deny the possibility that the former may have like powers. It may well be that our present reagents do not give us a true picture of these elementary units — that "microsomes" are but a rude semblance of reality. That they are never-

[1] '83, p, 580, 583.   [2] *l.c.*, p. 583.

theless an expression of the morphological aggregation of the proto-plasmic network out of more elementary units, must, I think, be accepted as a working hypothesis. Whether they are elementary organisms in Altmann's sense, whether they have a persistent mor-phological identity, whether they arise solely by the division of pre-existing microsomes, or may undergo dissolution and reformation, whether, in short, they are the self-propagating elementary bodies postulated by so many eminent naturalists as the essential basis of the cell, — all these are entirely open questions which the cytology of the future has to solve.

E. The Centrosome

When we turn to the centrosome, we find clear evidence of the existence of a cell-organ which, though scarcely larger than a cyto-microsome, possesses specific physiological powers, assimilates, grows, divides, and may persist from cell to cell, without loss of identity. It is far easier to define the centrosome in physiological than in mor-phological terms.   In the former sense Boveri ('95, 2) defines it as *a single permanent cell-organ which forms the dynamic centre of the cell and multiplies by division to form the centres of the daughter-cells.*[1] A centrosome is necessarily present in all cells at the time of mitosis. Whether, however, it persists in the resting state of all cells is un-known.   The most careful search has thus far failed to reveal its presence in many tissue-cells, *e.g.* in muscle-cells and many gland-cells; but these same cells may, under certain conditions, divide by mitosis, as in regeneration or tumour-formation, and the centrosome may be hidden in the nucleus, or so minute as to escape observation. We must, however, remember that the centrosome often disappears in the mature egg, and the same may be true of some tissue-cells.

Van Beneden's and Boveri's independent identification of centrosome in *Ascaris* as a permanent cell-organ ('87) was quickly supported by numerous observations on other animals and on plants.   In rapid succession the centrosome and attraction-sphere were found to be present in pigment-cells of fishes (Solger, '89, '90), in the spermatocytes of Amphibia (Hermann, '90), in the leucocytes, endothelial cells, con-nective tissue-cells and lung-epithelium of salamanders (Flemming, '91), in various plant-cells (Guignard, '91), in the one-celled diatoms (Bütschli, '91), in the giant-cells and other cells of bone-marrow (Heidenhain, Van Bambeke, Van der Stricht, '91), in the flagellate *Noctiluca* (Ishikawa, '91), in the cells of marine algæ (Stras-burger, '92), in cartilage-cells (Van der Stricht, '92), in the cells of cancerous growths (epithelioma, Lustig and Galeotti, '92), in the young germ-cells as already described, and finally, in gland-cells (vom Rath, '95), and in nerve-cells (Lenhossék, '95). They have not yet been found in resting muscle-cells.

[1] The fact that the centrosome is double in many cells does not conflict with this defini-tion, for the doubling is obviously a precocious preparation for the ensuing division.

The earlier observers of the centrosome always found it lying in the cytoplasm, outside the nucleus. Almost simultaneously, in 1893, three investigators independently discovered it inside the nucleus of the resting cell, — Wasielewsky, in the young ovarian eggs (oögonia) of *Ascaris* ; Brauer, in the spermatocytes of the same animal ; and Karsten, in the cells of a plant, *Psilotum* (Humphrey states, however, that Karsten's observations were erroneous). Several later observers have described a similar intra-nuclear origin of the centrosome, and several of these (Zimmermann, Lavdovsky, Kruten) have followed Wasielewsky in locating it in the nucleolus. Evidence against this latter view has been brought forward, especially by Humphrey and Brauer. The latter observer found both nucleoli and centrosome as separate bodies within the nucleus. He made further the interesting discovery that *in*

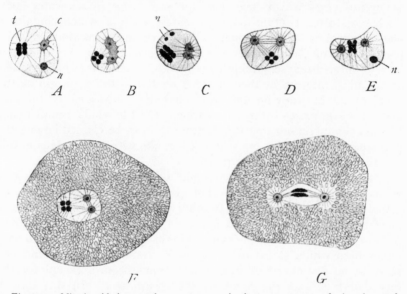

Fig. 107. — Mitosis with intra-nuclear centrosome, in the spermatocytes of *Ascaris megalocephala*, var. *univalens*. [BRAUER.]

A. Nucleus containing a quadruple group or tetrad of chromosomes (*t*), nucleolus (*n*), and centrosome (*c*). *B. C.* Division of the centrosome. *D. E. F. G.* Formation of the mitotic figure, centrosomes escaping from the nucleus in *G*.

Ascaris the centrosome lies, in one variety (univalens) inside the nucleus, in the other variety (bivalens) outside — a fact which proves that its position is non-essential (cf. Figs. 92 and 107). Oscar and Richard Hertwig maintain that the intra-nuclear position of the centrosome is the more primitive, the centrosome having been originally differentiated from a part of the nuclear substance. This view is based in the main on the facts of mitosis in the Infusoria, where the whole mitotic figure appears to arise within the nuclear membrane (cf. p. 62).

Whether a true centrosome may ever arise *de novo* is likewise undetermined. The possibility of such an origin has been conceded by a number of recent writers, among them Bürger, Watasé, Richard Hertwig, Heidenhain, and Reinke. The latter author ('94) would

Q

distinguish in the cell, besides the " primary centres " or centrosomes, secondary and tertiary centres, the latter being single microsomes formed at the nodes of the network. By the successive aggregations of the latter may arise the secondary and primary centres as new formations. Watasé ('94) advocates a somewhat similar view, and states that he has observed numerous gradations between a true aster and such "tertiary asters" as Reinke describes. Further evidence in the same direction is afforded by Morgan's remarkable observations on the formation of "artificial asters" in unfertilized sea-urchin eggs which have lain for some time in sea-water ('96). Such eggs often contain numerous asters, each of which contains a body resembling a centrosome.[1] Beside these observations must be placed those of Richard Hertwig, on the formation of an amphiaster in ripe unfertilized sea-urchin eggs (p. 159). All these observations are of high interest in their bearing on the historical origin of the centrosome; but they do not prove that the centrosome of the normal aster ever arises by free formation. On the whole, the evidence has steadily increased that the centrosome is to be classed among the permanent cell-organs; but whether it ranks with the nucleus in this regard must be left an open question.

The known facts are still too scanty to enable us to state precisely what a centrosome is in a morphological sense, either as regards its actual structure or its relation to other parts of the cell. In its simplest form (Fig. 108, *A*) the centrosome appears under the highest powers as nothing more than a single granule of extraordinary minuteness which stains intensely with iron-hæmatoxylin, and can scarcely be distinguished from the cyto-microsomes except for the fact that it lies at the focus of the astral rays. In this form it appears at the centre of the young sperm-aster in various animals — for example in the sea-urchin (Boveri), in *Chætopterus* (Mead), and in *Nereis*.[2] In almost all cases, however, the centrosome afterwards assumes a more complex structure and becomes surrounded by certain envelopes, the relation of which, on the one hand, to the centrosome and, on the other hand, to the astral rays have not yet been fully cleared up.

Boveri, whose observations have been confirmed by Brauer, Häcker, and others, described the centrosome in the cleavage-asters of *Ascaris* as a small sphere containing a minute central granule; and Brauer's careful studies on the spermatogenesis of the same animal showed

---

[1] I have had the privilege of examining Professor Morgan's preparations, and can confirm his statement that these eggs contain but a single nucleus and hence are not polyspermic.

[2] This appearance is not due to the shrinkage of a larger and more complex structure, as some authors have suggested; for in *Nereis* such a structure — *i.e.* the centrosphere — is afterwards developed around the centrosome.

that both these structures are persistent and that division of the sphere is preceded by division of the granule (Fig. 107). The central granule is exactly like the simple centrosome of the sperm-aster as described above, but we do not yet know with certainty the genesis of the sphere surrounding it, and hence cannot state whether this is part of the centrosome proper or a part of the centrosphere surrounding it. The former view is adopted by Boveri, who suggests the word "centriole" for the central granule; and, according to his observations on *Ascaris* and on sea-urchins, the simple centrosome of the original sperm-aster enlarges to form the sphere, while the centriole afterwards appears within it. In the case of *Thalassema*, however, Griffin's observations leave no doubt that the central granule persists in its original form from its first appearance in the sperm-aster through every stage of the cleavage-amphiaster, dividing during the early anaphase in each aster and giving rise to the centrosomes of the daughter-asters in which it again appears as a simple granule at the focus of the rays without a trace of surrounding envelopes (Fig. 73). In the cleavage-amphiaster it is surrounded by a somewhat vague, rounded mass (apparently representing the entire "centrosome" of Boveri and Brauer), which in turn lies in a reticulated centrosphere, from which the rays radiate. Both these structures disappear during the late anaphase, leaving only the central granule. Here, therefore, the true centrosome certainly corresponds to the central granule or centriole; and all the surrounding structures belong to the centrosphere.

As soon as we look further we find apparent departures from this simple type of centrosome. In leucocytes Heidenhain finds at the centre of the centrosphere not one or two, but always three, and sometimes four, granules, which he conceives as centrosomes forming a central group or microcentrum. In the giant-cells of bone-marrow the central group consists of a very large number (a hundred or more) of such granules, each of which is again conceived as a "centrosome" (Fig. 11, *D*). In the sea-urchin (*Echinus*) Boveri states that the original simple centrosome of the sperm-aster enlarges greatly to form a relatively large, well-defined sphere in which appear numerous granules (centrioles), which he would compare individually with the elements of Heidenhain's "central group." I have given a somewhat similar account of the facts in *Toxopneustes*, describing the centrosphere as a reticulated mass derived from an original granule or centrosome at the focus of the rays,[1] and many

---

[1] Professor Boveri informs me that I was in error in attributing to him the view that the entire central mass of the aster — *i.e.* the centrosphere — here represents the centrosome. The large spherical centrosome of *Echinus* is surrounded by a clear area which he regards as the centrosphere.

other investigators have been unable to find a distinct body to be identified as a centrosome within the centrosphere. As far as the sea-urchins are concerned, there is, I think, good reason to doubt not only my own former conclusions, but also those of Boveri. Both vom Rath ('95, 2) and Hill ('95) find at the centre of the centrosphere in sea-urchins a distinct black granule ("centrosome"), which becomes double in the early anaphase precisely as in *Thalassema*. More-over, Griffin's studies under my direction show that the minute single centrosome of *Thalassema* entirely loses its staining-power after certain reagents and only comes into view after other treatment.[1] I am now, therefore, inclined to believe that many if not all of the accounts asserting the absence of a minute central centrosome in the centro-sphere are based on unsuitable methods, and that in most of such cases, if not in all, it is really present.

However this may be, it is now certainly known that the centro-some is in some cases a granule so small as to be almost indistin-guishable from the microsomes; that in this form it is able to organize the surrounding cytoplasm into the astral system; and that in this form it may be handed on by division from cell to cell. It may well be that in some cases such a centrosome may multiply to form a cen-tral group, as in leucocytes and giant-cells; that it may enlarge to form a granular or reticular sphere, as Boveri describes; and that the individual granules within such a sphere do not have the value of centrosomes. Such secondary morphological modifications do not affect the physiological significance of the centrosome as a perma-nent cell-organ, but they have an important bearing on the question of its relation to the other constituents of the cell.

The latter question has not been definitely answered. Bütschli, who has been followed by Erlanger, regards the centrosome as a small differentiated area in the general alveolar structure; and he describes it in the sea-urchin as actually made up of a number of minute vesicles (Fig. 8, *B*). Bürger ('92) suggested that the entire attraction-sphere and aster arise by a centripetal movement of micro-somes to form a radiating group the centre of which (centrosome) is represented by a condensed mass of the ground-substance. Watasé ('93, '94) added the very interesting suggestion that *the centrosome is itself nothing other than a microsome* of the same morphological nature as those of the astral rays and the general thread-work, differ-ing from them only in size and in its peculiar powers.[2] Despite the

---

[1] The centrosome disappears after fixation with sublimate-acetic, but is perfectly shown after pure sublimate or picro-acetic. See *Science*, Jan. 10, 1896.

[2] The microsome is conceived, if I understand Watasé rightly, not as a permanent mor-phological body, but as a temporary varicosity of the thread, which may lose its identity in the thread and reappear when the thread contracts. The centrosome is in like manner not a permanent organ like the nucleus, but a temporary body formed at the focus of the astral

ambiguity of the word "microsome" Watasé's suggestion is full of interest, indicating as it does that the centrosome is morphologically comparable to other elementary bodies existing in the cytoplasmic structure, and which, minute though they are, may have specific chemical and physiological properties.

F. THE ARCHOPLASMIC STRUCTURES

1. *Asters and Spindle*

The asters and attraction-spheres have a special interest for the study of cell-organs; for these are structures that may divide and persist from cell to cell or may lose their identity and reform in successive cell-generations, and we may here trace with the greatest clearness the origin of a cell-organ by differentiation out of the structural basis. Two sharply opposing views of these structures are now held. Boveri ('88, 2), who has been followed in a measure by Strasburger, maintains that the attraction-sphere of the resting cell is composed of a distinct substance, "*archoplasm*," consisting of granules or microsomes aggregated about the centrosome as the result of an attractive force exerted by the latter. From the material of the attraction-sphere arises the entire achromatic figure, including both the spindle-fibres and the astral rays, and these have nothing to do with the general reticulum of the cell. They grow out from the attraction-sphere into the reticulum as the roots of a plant grow into the soil, and at the close of mitosis are again withdrawn into the central mass, breaking up into granules meanwhile, so that each daughter-cell receives one-half of the entire archoplasmic material of the parent-cell. This material is, however, wholly distinct from that of the general reticulum, not, as many earlier observers have maintained, identical with it. Boveri was further inclined to believe that the individual granules or archoplasmic microsomes were "independent structures, not the nodal points of a general network," and that the archoplasmic rays arose by the arrangement of these granules in

rays. Once formed, however, it may long persist even after disappearance of the aster and serve as a centre of formation for a new aster. In the latter case the astral rays are conceived as actual derivatives of the centrosome which, as it were, spins them out in the cytoplasm. "The aster, from this point of view, may be considered as a physiological device for concentrating the cytoplasmic substance in a form which can be spun out again into filaments in the direction which will produce a definite physiological effect" ('94, p. 284). This part of Watasé's conception is, on the whole, I think, opposed to the facts, though it certainly explains the inpushing of the nuclear membrane during the prophases of mitosis. It is impossible to believe that the rays of the enormous sperm-aster are developed out of the minute granule at their centre or that they flow back into it at the close of division. The centrosome increases in size during the formation of the aster, decreases during its disappearance, which is the reverse of what the hypothesis demands. Many other arguments in the same direction might be urged.

rows without loss of their individuality.[1] In a later paper on the sea-urchin ('95) this view is somewhat modified by the admission that in this case the archoplasm may not pre-exist as formed material, but that the rays and fibres may be a new formation, crystallizing, as it were, out of the protoplasm about the centrosome as a centre,[2] but having no organic relation with the general reticulum.

Strong evidence against the archoplasm-theory has been brought forward by many investigators, and I believe it to be in principle untenable. Nearly all recent workers have accepted in one form or another the early view of Bütschli, Klein, and Van Beneden that the astral rays and spindle-fibres, and hence the attraction-sphere, arise through a morphological rearrangement of the pre-existing protoplasmic network, under the influence of the centrosome. Although this view may be traced back to the early work of Fol ('73) and Auerbach ('74), it was first clearly formulated by Bütschli ('76), who regarded the aster as the optical expression of a peculiar physico-chemical alteration of the protoplasm primarily caused by diffusion-currents converging to the central area of the aster.[3] An essentially similar view is maintained in Bütschli's recent great work on protoplasm,[4] the astral "rays" being regarded as nothing more than the meshes of an alveolar structure arranged radially about the centrosome (Fig. 8, B). The fibrous appearance of the astral rays is an optical delusion, for they are not fibres, but flat lamellæ forming the walls of elongated closed chambers. This view has more recently been urged by Reinke and Eismond.

The same general conception of the aster is adopted by most of those who accept the fibrillar or reticular theory of protoplasm, the astral rays and spindle-fibres being regarded as actual fibres forming part of the general network. One of the first to frame such a conception was Klein ('78), who regarded the aster as due to "a radiar arrangement of what corresponds to the cell-substance," the latter being described as having a fibrillar character.[5] The same view is advocated by Van Beneden in 1883. With Klein, Heitzman, and Frommann he accepted the view that the intra-nuclear and extra-nuclear networks were organically connected, and maintained that the spindle-fibres arose from both.[6] "The star-like rays of the asters are nothing but local differentiations of the protoplasmic network.[7] . . . In my opinion the appearance of the attraction-spheres, the

[1] '88, 2, p. 80.   [2] l.c., p. 40.
[3] For a very careful review of the early views on this subject, see Mark, *Limax*, 1881.
[4] '92, 2, pp. 158–169.
[5] It is interesting to note that in the same place Klein anticipated the theory of fibrillar contractility, both the nuclear and the cytoplasmic reticulum being regarded as contractile (*l.c.*, p. 417).
[6] '83, p. 592.   [7] '83, p. 576.

polar corpuscle (centrosome) and the rays extending from it, including the achromatic fibrils of the spindle, are the result of the appearance in the egg-protoplasm of two centres of attraction comparable to two magnetic poles. This appearance leads to a regular arrangement of the reticulated protoplasmic fibrils and of the achromatic nuclear substance with relation to the centres, in the same way that a magnet produces the stellate arrangement of iron filings." [1]

This view is further developed in Van Beneden's second paper, published jointly with Neyt ('87). "The spindle is nothing but a differentiated portion of the asters." [2] The aster is a "radial structure of the cell-protoplasm, whence results the image designated by the name of aster." [3] The operations of cell-division are carried out through the "contractility of the fibrillæ of the cell-protoplasm and their arrangement in a kind of radial muscular system composed of antagonizing groups." [4]

An essentially similar view of the achromatic figure has been advocated by many later workers. Numerous observers, such as Rabl, Flemming, Carnoy, Watasé, Eismond, Reinke, etc., have observed that the astral fibres branch out peripherally into the general reticulum and become perfectly continuous with its meshes. This is very clearly shown in the formation of the sperm-aster about the middle-piece of the spermatozoön. In the sea-urchin (*Toxopneustes*) the formation of the rays from the cytoplasmic reticulum can be followed step by step, and there can, I think, be no doubt that the astral rays arise by a direct transformation or morphological rearrangement of the pre-existing structure, and that they extend themselves at their outer ends, as the sperm-aster moves through the egg-substance, by progressive differentiation out of this reticulum. [5] Once formed, however, the rays may possess a considerable degree of persistence and may actively elongate by growth. Only thus can we explain the pushing in of the nuclear membrane by the ingrowing spindle-fibres during the prophases of mitosis in certain forms (p. 50) and the bending of the rays when two asters collide, as recently described by Kostanecki and Wierzejski ('96). It seems certain, furthermore, that during the rotation of the amphiaster in the formation of the polar bodies (Fig. 71) and in similar cases, the spindle, at least, moves bodily. The substance of the spindle or of the asters may, moreover, persist in the resting cell, after the close of mitosis, as the attraction-sphere or paranucleus (Nebenkern), and in such cases the term "archoplasm" may conveniently be retained for descriptive purposes. To regard the archoplasm as a primary and independent constituent of the cell would, however, as I believe, be an error.

[1] '83, p. 550.   [2] *l.c.*, p. 263.   [3] *l.c.*, p. 275.   [4] *l.c.*, p. 280.   [5] '95, 2, p. 446.

2. *The Attraction-sphere*

The foregoing conception of the asters receives a strong support
from the study of the attraction-sphere in resting cells. It is agreed
by all observers that this structure is derived from the aster of the
dividing cell; but there is still no general agreement regarding its
precise mode of origin from the aster, and the subject is confused by
differences in the terminology of different authors. There are some
cases in which the entire aster persists throughout the resting cell
(leucocytes, connective tissue-cells) and the term "attraction-sphere"
has by some authors been applied to the whole structure. As originally used by Van Beneden, however,[1] the word was applied (in
Ascaris) not to the entire aster but only to its central portion — a
spherical mass bounded by a circle of microsomes from which the
astral rays proceed. At the close of division the rays fade away in
the general network, leaving only the central sphere containing the
centrosome. Boveri's account of the same object was entirely different; for he conceived the attraction-sphere ("archoplasm-sphere")
of the resting cell as representing the entire aster, the rays being
withdrawn towards the centrosome and breaking up into a mass of
granules. Later workers have proposed different terminologies, which
are at present in a state of complete confusion. Fol ('91) proposed
to call the centrosome the *astrocentre*, and the spherical mass surrounding it (attraction-sphere of Van Beneden) the *astrosphere*.
Strasburger accepted the latter term and proposed the new word
"centrosphere" for the astrosphere and the centrosome taken together.[2] This terminology has been accepted by most botanists and by
some zoölogists. A new complication was introduced by Boveri ('95),
who applied the word "astrosphere" to the *entire aster* exclusive
of the centrosome, in which sense the phrase "astral sphere" had
been employed by Mark in 1881. The word "astrosphere" has
therefore a double meaning and would better be abandoned in favour
of Strasburger's convenient term "centrosphere," which may be
understood as equivalent to the "astrosphere" of Fol.

As regards the structure of the centrosphere, two well-marked types
have been described. In one of these, described by Van Beneden in
Ascaris, by Heidenhain in leucocytes, by Drüner and Braus in dividing cells of amphibia, the centrosphere has a radiate structure, being
traversed by rays which stretch between the centrosome and the
peripheral microsome-circle (Figs. 34, 108, *G*). In the other form,
described by Vejdovský in the eggs of *Rhynchelmis*, by Solger and
Zimmermann in pigment-cells, by myself in sea-urchin eggs and in

[1] '83, p. 548.   [2] '92, p. 51.

Nereis, by Rückert in *Cyclops*, and in a number of other cases, the centrosphere has a non-radiate reticular structure (Figs. 71, 108, *E*). In some cases no centrosome has been found in this sphere; but for reasons already stated (p. 228) I incline to believe that a centrosome is really present.

In many, if not in all cases of both types, the sphere consists of an outer and an inner zone, the latter enclosing the centrosome; but the relation of the inner zone to the centrosome still remains, in a meas-

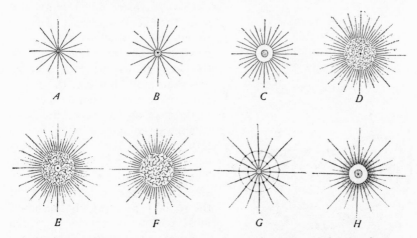

Fig. 108.— Diagrams illustrating various descriptions of centrosome and centrosphere.

A. Simplest type; only a minute centrosome at the focus of the rays (sperm-aster in many forms). *B.* Rays proceeding directly from a centrosome of considerable size within which is a central granule. Example, Brauer's description of the spermatocytes of *Ascaris*. *C.* Rays proceeding from a clear centrosphere (astrosphere of Strasburger), enclosing a centrosome like the last but with no central granule (in flowering plants according to Guignard, Strasburger, and others). *D.* An extremely minute centrosome lying in the middle of a large reticulated centrosphere (*e.g.* Hill's description of the sperm-aster in sea-urchins and tunicates). *E.* Like the last, but with a small spherical body surrounding the centrosome (examples, the eggs of *Thalassema* and *Nereis*). *F.* No centrosome as distinguished from the reticulated centrosphere. Examples in the pigment-cells of fishes according to Zimmerman, in the eggs of echinoderms according to Wilson; many similar accounts have been given, but all are open to question. *G.* In *Ascaris*, according to Van Beneden, outside the centrosome lie the cortical and medullary zones of the attraction-sphere. *H.* The same according to Boveri. The centrosome contains a central granule or centriole (cf. *B.*); outside this is a clear zone (medullary zone of Van Beneden), and outside this a vaguely defined granular zone, probably corresponding to Van Beneden's cortical zone.

ure, in doubt. Van Beneden described the centrosphere in *Ascaris* as consisting of an outer *cortical* and an inner *medullary* zone, both of which were conceived as only a modification of the inner region of the aster. Boveri's account is somewhat different. The centrosome is described as surrounded by a clear zone (" heller Hof "), — probably corresponding with Van Beneden's "medullary zone," — while the " cortical zone " of the latter author is not recognized as distinct from the aster (or archoplasm-sphere). The centrosome itself contains a

minute central granule or *centriole*. This discrepancy between Boveri
and Van Beneden was cleared up in a measure by Heidenhain's
beautiful studies on the asters in leucocytes, and the still more
thorough later work of Drüner on the spermatocyte-divisions of the
salamander. In leucocytes (Fig. 35) the large persistent aster has at its
centre a well-marked radial sphere bounded by a circle of microsomes,
as described by Van Beneden, but without division into cortical and
medullary zones. The astral rays, however, show indications of other

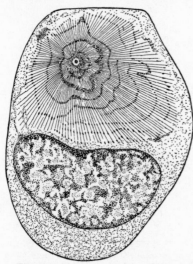

circles of microsomes lying outside the centrosphere.   Drüner
found that a whole series of such
concentric circles might exist (in
the cell shown in Fig. 109 no
less than nine), but that the innermost two are often especially
distinct, so as to mark off a centrosphere composed of a medullary and a cortical zone precisely
as described by Van Beneden.
These observations show conclusively that the centrosphere of
the radial type is merely the innermost portion of the aster, which
acquires an apparent boundary
through the especial development

Fig. 109. — Spermatogonium of salamander. [DRÜNER.]
The nucleus lies below.   Above is the
enormous aster, the centrosome at its centre,
its rays showing indications of nine concentric
circles of microsomes.   The area within the
second circle probably represents the "attraction-sphere" of Van Beneden.

of a ring of microsomes.   And
thus Van Beneden's original view
is confirmed, that not only the
aster as a whole, but also the centrosphere, is but a modified area of the
general cytoplasmic thread-work.

Heidenhain points out that there are many cases — for instance,
the young sperm-aster — in which there is at first no clearly marked
central sphere, and the rays proceed outward directly from the centrosome.   The sphere, in such cases, seems to arise secondarily through
a modification of the inner ends of the astral rays.   Heidenhain therefore concludes that the centrosome is the only constant element in the
sphere, the latter being a secondary formation and not entitled to rank
as a persistent cell-organ, though it may in certain cases persist and
divide like the centrosome. Vom Rath, who has made a very careful
study of the attraction-spheres in a large number of cells among both
vertebrata and invertebrata, arrives at a nearly similar view, though
he lays greater stress on the differentiation and independence of the
sphere.   In asters of dividing cells he could find in many cases no

limit between sphere and aster, though in other cases it is distinctly present. In the resting cell, on the other hand, the boundary of the sphere is often very sharply marked, so that the sphere appears as a well-defined spherical body. The origin of such a definite sphere from the aster has not been very definitely determined, but Drüner's observations indicate that it arises in the manner described by Van Beneden, through the disappearance of the more peripheral portions of the astral rays. It is, in other words, the persistent centrosphere.[1]

The genesis of the reticular type of centrosphere is not so well determined. In *Nereis* the aster (maturation-asters, sperm-aster) has at first nothing more than a minute centrosome at its centre. This becomes surrounded at a later period by a large reticulated centrosphere, showing no sign of radial arrangement, that appears to arise by a transformation of the inner ends of the astral rays. A nearly similar account is given by Hill in the case of the sperm-aster in *Strongylocentrotus* and *Phallusia*. In these latter cases the centrosphere shows no differentiation into cortical and medullary zones. In *Thalassema* and *Nereis*, on the other hand, the minute centrosome becomes surrounded by a somewhat vague body distinctly different from the reticulum of the outer centrosphere, and this body perhaps represents a "medullary zone." This body, with the centrosome, corresponds very nearly to the "centrosome" of *Ascaris* with its "centriole" or central granule as described by Boveri and Brauer; but in *Thalassema* Griffin's observations show conclusively that the minute central granule alone is the centrosome, and that the surrounding body does not persist after division. I cannot avoid the suspicion that the body described by Boveri as the "centrosome" in *Echinus* may represent this medullary region of the centrosphere, and that he, like myself, may have overlooked the centrosome. Nor does it seem impossible that the "centriole" or central granule of *Ascaris* (Boveri, Brauer) may likewise represent the true centrosome. These questions can only be cleared up by further investigation.

To sum up: The history of the "archoplasmic" structures gives strong ground for the conclusion that *attraction-spheres, asters, and spindle are, like the nucleus, differentiations of the general cell-network, which is, as it were, moulded by the centrosome into a specific form.* If this be well founded, the word "archoplasm" has no significance save in a topographical or descriptive sense. In this light it is an interesting fact that the aster or attraction-sphere may either persist and divide, like a permanent cell-organ, or may disappear and re-form in successive cell-generations.

---

[1] The same general result is indicated in the case of plants, though the phenomena have here been less carefully examined.

G. Summary and Conclusion

A minute analysis of the various parts of the cell leads to the conclusion that all cell-organs, whether temporary or "permanent," are local differentiations of a common structural basis. Temporary organs, such as cilia or pseudopodia, are formed out of this basis, persist for a time, and finally merge their identity in the common basis again. Permanent organs, such as the nucleus or centrosome, are constant areas in the same basis, which never are formed *de novo*, but arise by the division of pre-existing areas of the same kind. These two extremes are, however, connected by various intermediate gradations, examples of which are the contractile vacuoles of Protozoa, which belong to the category of temporary organs, yet in many cases are handed on from one cell to another by fission, and the attraction-spheres and asters, which may either persist from cell to cell or disappear and re-form about the centrosome.

The facts point strongly to the conclusion, which has been especially urged by De Vries and Wiesner, that in many if not in all cases the division of cell-organs is in the last analysis brought about by the division of more elementary masses of which they are made up; and furthermore that *the degree of permanence depends on the degree of cohesion manifested by these masses*. The clearest evidence in this direction is afforded by the chromatic substance of the nucleus, the division of which does not take place as a single mass-division, but through the fission of more elementary discrete bodies of which it consists or into which it is resolved before division. Several orders of such bodies are visible in the dividing nucleus, forming a series of which the highest term is the plurivalent chromosome, the lowest the smallest visible dividing basichromatin-grains, while the intermediate terms are formed by the successive aggregation of these to form the chromomeres of which the dividing chromosomes consist. Whether any or all of these bodies are "individuals" is a question of words. The facts point, however, to the conclusion that at the bottom of the series there must be masses that cannot be further split up without loss of their characteristic properties, and which form the elementary morphological units of the nucleus.

There is reason to believe that the linin-network is likewise composed of minute bodies, the oxychromatin-granules, which are closely similar in appearance to the smallest chromatin-grains, and differ from them only in chemical nature as shown by the difference of staining-power. Whether the oxychromatin-granules have also the power of growth and division is unknown; but if, as Van Beneden and Heidenhain maintain, the basichromatin- and oxychromatin-granules be only different modifications of the same element, a presumption certainly exists that they have such powers. When we extend this comparison to the cytoplasm, the ground becomes more uncertain. It seems well established that the cytoreticulum is of the same nature as the linin-network. If this be admitted, we are led to accept on *a priori* grounds that some at least of the cytomicrosomes are not artefacts, but morphological bodies comparable with those of the linin and chromatin networks, and like them capable of growth and division. This conclusion is, as yet, no more than a somewhat doubtful inference. In the centrosome, however, we have a body, no larger in many cases than a "microsome," which is positively known to be a persistent morphological element, having the power of growth, division, and persistence in the daughter-cells. Probably these powers of the centrosome would never have been discovered were it not that its staining-capacity renders it conspicuous and its position at the focus of the astral rays isolates it for observation. When we consider the analogy between the centrosome and the basichromatin-grains, when we recall the evidence that the latter graduate into the oxychromatin-granules, and these in turn into the cytomicrosomes, we must admit that Brücke's cautious suggestion that the whole cell might be a congeries of self-propagating units of a lower order is to-day not entirely without the support of facts.

LITERATURE. VI

Van Beneden, E. — (See List IV.)

Van Beneden and Julin. — La segmentation chez les Ascidiens et ses rapports avec l'organisation de la larve : *Arch. Biol.*, V. 1884.

Boveri, Th. — Zellenstudien. (See List IV.)

Brücke, C. — Die Elementarorganismen : *Wiener Sitz.-Ber.*, XLIV. 1861.

Bütschli, O. — Protoplasma. (See List I.)

Häcker, V. — Über den heutigen Stand der Centrosomenfrage : *Verh. d. deutsch. Zoöl. Ges.* 1894.

Heidenhain, M. — (See List I.)

Herla, V. — Etude des variations de la mitose chez l'ascaride megalocéphale : *Arch. Biol.*, XIII. 1893.

Nussbaum, M. — Über die Teilbarkeit der lebendigen Materie : *Arch. mik. Anat.*, XXVI. 1886.

Rabl, C. — Über Zellteilung : *Morph. Jahrb.*, X. 1885.

Rückert, J. — (See List IV.)

De Vries, H. — Intracelluläre Pangenesis : *Jena*, 1889.

Watasé, S. — Homology of the Centrosome : *Journ. Morph.*, VIII. 2. 1893.

Id. — On the Nature of Cell-organization : *Woods Holl Biol. Lectures.* 1893.

Wiesner, J. — Die Elementarstruktur und das Wachstum der lebenden Substanz : *Wien*, 1892.

Wilson, Edm. B. — Archoplasm, Centrosome, and Chromatin in the Sea-urchin Egg : *Journ. Morph.*, Vol. XI. 1895.

CHAPTER VII

SOME ASPECTS OF CELL-CHEMISTRY AND CELL-PHYSIOLOGY

"Les phénomènes fonctionnels ou de dépense vitale *auraient donc leur siège dans le protoplasme cellulaire.*

" Le noyau est un appareil de *synthèse organique, l'instrument de la production, le germe de la cellule.*" CLAUDE BERNARD.[1]

I

A. CHEMICAL RELATIONS OF NUCLEUS AND CYTOPLASM

It is no part of the purpose of this work to give even a sketch of general cell-chemistry. I shall only attempt to consider certain questions that bear directly upon the functional relations of nucleus and cytoplasm and are of especial interest in relation to the process of nutrition and through it to the problems of development. It has often been pointed out that we know little or nothing of the chemical conditions existing in living protoplasm, since every attempt to examine them by precise methods necessarily kills the protoplasm. We must, therefore, in the main rest content with inferences based upon the chemical behaviour of dead cells. But even here investigation is beset with difficulties, since it is in most cases impossible to isolate the various parts of the cell for accurate chemical analysis, and we are obliged to rely largely on the less precise method of observing with the microscope the visible effects of dyes and other reagents. This difficulty is increased by the fact that both cytoplasm and karyoplasm are not simple chemical compounds, but mixtures of many complex substances; and both, moreover, undergo periodic changes of a complicated character which differ very widely in different kinds of cells. Our knowledge is, therefore, still fragmentary, and we have as yet scarcely passed the threshold of a subject which belongs largely to the cytology of the future.

It has been shown in the foregoing chapter that all the parts of the cell arise as local differentiations of an all-pervading substratum which in the greater number of cases, perhaps in all, has the form of

[1] *Leçons sur les phénomènes de la vie,* I., 1878, p. 198.

a sponge-like network. Cell-organs, such as the nucleus, the spindle and asters, the centrosome, are to be regarded as specialized areas in this network, just as the visible organs of the multicellular body are specialized regions in the all-pervading cellular tissue. And precisely as the various organs and tissues are the seat of special chemical activities leading to the formation and characteristic transformation of specific substances, — as for instance hæmoglobin is characteristic of the red blood-corpuscles, or chlorophyll of the assimilating tissues of plants, — so in the cell the various morphological regions are areas of specific chemical activities and are characterized by the presence of corresponding substances. The morphological differentiation of cell-organs is therefore in a way the visible expression of underlying chemical specializations; and these are in the last analysis reducible to differences of metabolic action.

1. *The Proteids and their Allies*

The most important chemical compounds found in the cell are the group of *protein substances;* and there is every reason to believe that these form the principal basis of living protoplasm in all of its forms. These substances are complex compounds of carbon, hydrogen, nitrogen, and oxygen, often containing a small percentage of sulphur, and in some cases also phosphorus and iron. They form a very extensive group of which the different members differ considerably in physical and chemical properties, though all have certain common traits and are closely related. They are variously classified even by the latest writers. Halliburton ('93) employs the word "proteids" as synonymous with *albuminous substances*, including under them the various forms of *albumin* (egg-albumin, cell-albumin, muscle-albumin, vegetable-albumins), *globulin* (fibrinogen, vitellin, etc.), and the *peptones* (diffusible hydrated proteids). This author places in a separate class of *albuminoids* another series of nearly related substances (reckoned by some chemists among the "proteids"), examples of which are gelatine, mucin, and especially *nuclein*, and the *nucleo-albumins*. The three last-named bodies are characterized by the presence of phosphorus, in which respect they show a very definite contrast to the "proteids," many of which, such as egg-albumin, contain no phosphorus, and others only a trace. By Hammarsten and some others the word "proteid" is, however, employed in a more restricted sense, being applied to substances such as the nucleins and nucleo-proteids, of greater complexity than the albumins and globulins. The latter, together with the nucleo-albumins, are classed as albuminous bodies (Eiweisskörper).[1]

[1] See Hammersten, '95, p. 16.

The distribution of these substances throughout the cell varies greatly not only in different cells, but at different periods in the life of the same cell. The cardinal fact always, however, remains, that *there is a definite and constant contrast between nucleus and cytoplasm.* The latter always contains large quantities of nucleo-albumins, certain globulins, and sometimes small quantities of albumins and peptones; the former contains, in addition to these, *nuclein* and *nucleo-proteids*, which as the names indicate, forms its main bulk and its most constant and characteristic feature. It is the remarkable substance, nuclein, — which is almost certainly identical with chromatin, — that chiefly claims our attention here on account of the physiological *rôle* of the nucleus.

2. *The Nuclein Series*

Nuclein was first isolated and named by Miescher in 1871, by subjecting cells to artificial gastric digestion. The cytoplasm is thus digested, leaving only the nuclei; and in some cases, for instance pus-cells and spermatozoa, it is possible by this method to procure large quantities of nuclear substance for accurate quantitative analysis. The results of analysis show it to be a complex albuminoid substance, rich in phosphorus, for which Miescher gave the chemical formula $C_{29}H_{49}N_9P_3O_{22}$. Later analyses gave somewhat discordant results, as appears in the following table of percentage-compositions : [1] —

	PUS-CELLS. (HOPPE-SEYLER.)	SPERMATOZOA OF SALMON. (MIESCHER.)	HUMAN BRAIN. (V. JAKSCH.)
C	49.58	36.11	50.6
H	7.10	5.15	7.6
N	15.02	13.09	13.18
P	2.28	5.59	1.89

These differences led to the opinion, first expressed by Hoppe-Seyler, and confirmed by later investigations, that there are several varieties of nuclein which form a group having certain characters in common. Altmann ('89) opened the way to an understanding of the matter by showing that "nuclein" may be split up into two substances; namely, (1) an organic acid rich in phosphorus, to which he gave the name *nucleic acid*, and (2) a form of albumin. Moreover,

[1] From Halliburton, '91, p. 203. [The oxygen-percentage is omitted in this table.]

the nuclein may be synthetically formed by the re-combination of these two substances. Pure nucleic acid contains no sulphur, a high percentage of phosphorus (above 9 %), and no albumin. By adding it to a solution of albumin a precipitate is formed which contains sulphur, a lower percentage of phosphorus, and has the chemical characters of nuclein. This indicates that the discordant results in the analyses of nuclein, referred to above, were probably due to varying proportions of the two constituents; and Altmann suggested that the "nuclein" of spermatozoa, which contains no sulphur and a maximum of phosphorus (over 9.5 %), might be uncombined nucleic acid itself. Kossel accordingly drew the conclusion, based on his own work as well as that of Liebermann, Altmann, Malfatti, and others, that "what the histologists designate as *chromatin* consists essentially of combinations of nucleic acid with more or less albumin, and in some cases may even be free nucleic acid. The less the percentage of albumin in these compounds, the nearer do their properties approach those of pure nucleic acid, and we may assume that the percentage of albumin in the chromatin of the same nucleus may vary according to physiological conditions."[1] In the same year Halliburton, following in part Hoppe-Seyler, stated the same view as follows. The so-called "nucleins" form a series leading downward from nucleic acid thus : —

(1) Those containing no albumin and a maximum (9–10 %) of phosphorus (pure nucleic acid). Nuclei of spermatozoa.

(2) Those containing little albumin and rich in phosphorus. Chromatin of ordinary nuclei.

(3) Those with a greater proportion of albumin — a series of substances in which may probably be included *pyrenin* (nucleoli) and *plastin* (linin). These graduate into

(4) Those containing a minimum (0.5 to 1 %) of phosphorus — the nucleo-albumins, which occur both in the nucleus and in the cytoplasm (vitellin, caseinogin, etc.).

Finally, we reach the globulins and albumins, especially characteristic of the cell-substance, and containing no nucleic acid. "We thus pass by a gradual transition (from the nucleo-albumins) to the other proteid constituents of the cell, the cell-globulins, which contain no phosphorus whatever, and to the products of cell-activity, such as the proteids of serum and of egg-white, which are also principally phosphorus-free."[2] Further, "in the processes of vital activity there are changing relations between the phosphorized constituents of the nucleus, just as in all metabolic processes there is a continual inter-

[1] '93, p. 158.   [2] '93, p. 574.

R

change, some constituents being elaborated, others breaking down into simpler products." [1]   These conclusions established a probability that the chemical differences between chromatin and cytoplasm, striking and constant as they are, are differences of degree only; and they opened the way to a more precise investigation of the physiological *rôle* of nucleus and cytoplasm in metabolism.

3. *Staining-reactions of the Nuclein-series*

We may now bring these facts into relation with the staining-reactions of chromatin and cytoplasm when treated with the aniline dyes.   These dyes are divided into two main classes,[2] viz. the " basic " anilines and the " acid " anilines, the colouring-matter playing the part of a base in the former and of an acid in the latter.   The basic anilines (*e.g.* methyl-green, Bismarck brown, saffranin) are in general "nuclear stains," having a strong affinity for chromatin, while the acid anilines (acid fuchsin, Congo red, eosin, etc.) are "plasma-stains," colouring more especially the cytoplasmic elements. We owe to Malfatti and Lilienfeld the very interesting discovery that *the various members of the nuclein series show an affinity for the basic dyes in direct proportion to the amount of nucleic acid* (*as measured by the amount of phosphorus*) *they contain.*   Thus the nuclei of spermatozoa, known to consist of nearly pure nucleic acid, stain most intensely with basic dyes, those of ordinary tissue-cells, which contain less phosphorus, less intensely.   Malfatti ('91) tested various members of the nuclein-series, synthetically produced as combinations of egg-albumin and nucleic acid from yeast, with a mixture of red acid fuchsin and basic methyl-green.   With this combination free nucleic acid was coloured pure green, nucleins containing less phosphorus became bluish-violet, those with little or no phosphorus pure red.   Lilienfeld's more precise experiments in this direction ('92, '93) led to similar results.   His starting-point was given by the results of Kossel's researches on the relations of the nuclein group, which are expressed as follows : [3] —

---

[1] It has long been known that a form of " nuclein " may also be obtained from the nucleo-albumins of the cytoplasm, *e.g.* from the yolk of hens' eggs (vitellin). Such nucleins differ, however, from those of nuclear origin in not yielding as cleavage-products the nuclein bases (adenin, xanthin, etc.). The term " paranuclein " (Kossel) or " pseudo-nuclein " (Hammarsten) has therefore been suggested for this substance. True nucleins containing a large percentage of albumin are distinguished as *nucleo-proteids.* They may be split into albumin and nucleic acid, the latter yielding as cleavage-products the nuclein bases.   Pseudo-nucleins containing a large percentage of albumin are designated as *nucleo-albumins,* which in like manner split into albumin and paranucleic or pseudo-nucleic acid, which yields no nuclein bases.   (See Hammarsten, '94.)

[2] See Ehrlich, '79.

[3] From Lilienfeld, after Kossel, '92, p. 129.

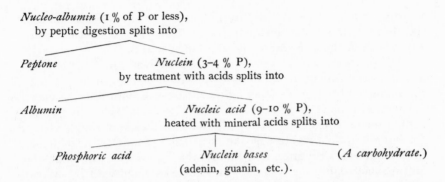

Nucleo-albumin (1 % of P or less),
   by peptic digestion splits into

Peptone   *Nuclein* (3–4 % P),
                    by treatment with acids splits into

Albumin   *Nucleic acid* (9–10 % P),
                        heated with mineral acids splits into

   Phosphoric acid   *Nuclein bases*   (*A carbohydrate.*)
                          (adenin, guanin, etc.).

Now, according to Kossel and Lilienfeld, the principal nucleo-albumin (nucleo-proteid) in the nucleus of leucocytes is *nucleo-histon*, containing about 3 % of phosphorus, which may be split into a form of *nuclein* playing the part of an acid, and an albuminoid base, the *histon* of Kossel; the nuclein may in turn be split into albumin and nucleic acid. These four substances — albumin, nucleo-histon, nuclein, nucleic acid — thus form a series in which the proportion of phosphorus, *i.e.* of nucleic acid, successively increases from zero to 9–10 %. If the members of this series be treated with the same mixture of red acid fuchsin and basic methyl-green, the result is as follows. Albumin (egg-albumin) is stained red, nucleo-histon greenish-blue, nuclein bluish-green, nucleic acid intense green. "We see, therefore, that the principle that determines the staining of the nuclear substances is always the nucleic acid. All the nuclear substances, from those richest in albumin to those poorest in it, or containing none, assume the tone of the nuclear (*i.e.* basic) stain, but the combined albumin modifies the green more or less towards blue." [1] Lilienfeld explains the fact that chromatin in the cell-nucleus seldom appears pure green on the assumption, supported by many facts, that the proportion of nucleic acid and albumin vary with different physiological conditions, and he suggests further that the intense staining-power of the chromosomes during mitosis is probably due to the fact that they consist, like the chromatin of spermatozoa, of pure or nearly pure nucleic acid. Very interesting and convincing is a comparison of the foregoing staining-reactions with those given by a mixture of a *red basic* dye (saffranin) and a *green acid* one ("light green"). With this combination an effect is given which reverses that of the Biondi-Ehrlich mixture; *i.e.* the nuclein is coloured red, the albumin green. This is a beautiful demonstration of the fact that staining-reagents cannot be logically classified according to colour, but only according to their chemical

[1] *l.c.*, p. 394.

nature. Such terms as "erythrophilous," "cyanophilous," and the like have therefore no meaning apart from the chemical composition both of the dye and of the substance stained.[1]

The constancy and accuracy of these reactions await further test, and until this has been carried out we should be careful not to place too implicit a trust in the staining-reactions as an indication of chemical nature, especially as they are known to be affected by the preceding mode of fixation. They afford, nevertheless, a rough method for the micro-chemical test of the proportion of nucleic acid present in the nuclear structures, and this in the hands of Heidenhain has led to some suggestive results. Leucocytes stained with the Biondi-Ehrlich mixture of acid fuchsin and methyl-green show the following reactions. Cytoplasm, centrosome, attraction-sphere, astral rays, and spindle-fibres are stained pure red. The nuclear substance shows a very sharp differentiation. The chromatic network and the chromosomes of the mitotic figure are green. The linin-substance and the true nucleoli or plasmosomes appear red, like the cytoplasm. The linin-network of leucocytes is stated by Heidenhain to consist of two elements, namely, of red granules or microsomes suspended in a colourless network. The latter alone is called "linin" by Heidenhain. To the red granules is applied the term "oxychromatin," while the green substance of the ordinary chromatic network, forming the "chromatin" of Flemming, is called "basichromatin."[2] Morphologically, the granules of both kinds are exactly alike,[3] and in many cases the oxychromatin-granules are found not only in the "achromatic" nuclear network, but also intermingled with the basichromatin-granules of the chromatic network. Collating these results with those of the physiological chemists, Heidenhain concludes that basichromatin is a substance rich in phosphorus (i.e. nucleic acid), oxychromatin a substance poor in phosphorus, and that, further, "basichromatin and oxychromatin are by no means to be regarded as permanent unchangeable bodies, but may change their colour-reactions by combining with or giving off phosphorus." In other words, "the affinity of the chromatophilous microsomes of the nuclear network for basic and acid aniline dyes are regulated by certain physiological conditions of the nucleus or of the cell."[4]

This conclusion, which is entirely in harmony with the statements of Kossel and Halliburton quoted above, opens up the most interesting questions regarding the periodic changes in the nucleus. The staining-power of chromatin is at a maximum when in the preparatory stages of mitosis (spireme-thread, chromosomes). During the ensuing growth of the nucleus it always diminishes, suggesting that a com-

---

[1] Cf. p. 127.　　[2] '94, p. 543.　　[3] l.c., p. 547.　　[4] l.c., p. 548.

bination with albumin has taken place. This is illustrated in a very striking way by the history of the egg-nucleus or germinal vesicle, which exhibits the nuclear changes on a large scale. It has long been known that the chromatin of this nucleus undergoes great changes during the growth of the egg, and several observers have maintained its entire disappearance at one period. Rückert first carefully traced out the history of the chromatin in detail in the

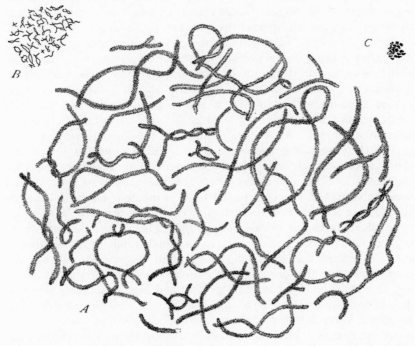

Fig. 110.— Chromosomes of the germinal vesicle in the shark *Pristiurus*, at different periods, drawn to the same scale. [RÜCKERT.]

A. At the period of maximal size and minimal staining-capacity (egg 3 mm. in diameter). *B.* Later period (egg 13 mm. in diameter). *C.* At the close of ovarian life, of minimal size and maximal staining-power.

eggs of sharks, and his general results have since been confirmed by Born in the eggs of *Triton*. In the shark *Pristiurus* Rückert ('92, 1) finds that the chromosomes, which persist throughout the entire growth-period of the egg, undergo the following changes (Fig. 110): At a very early stage they are small, and stain intensely with nuclear dyes. During the growth of the egg they undergo a great increase in size, and progressively *lose their staining-capacity*. At the same time their surface is enormously increased by the development of long threads which grow out in every direction from the central axis

(Fig. 110, A).   As the egg approaches its full size, the chromosomes rapidly diminish in size, the radiating threads disappear, and the staining-capacity increases (Fig. 110, B).   They are finally again reduced to minute intensely staining bodies which enter into the equatorial plate of the first polar mitotic figure (Fig. 110, C).   How great the change of volume is may be seen from the following figures.   At the beginning the chromosomes measure, at most, 12 μ (about $\frac{1}{2000}$ in.) in length and $\frac{1}{2}\mu$ in diameter.   At the height of their development they are almost eight times their original length and twenty times their original diameter.   In the final period they are but 2 μ in length and 1 μ in diameter.   These measurements show a change of volume so enormous, even after making due allowance for the loose structure of the large chromosomes, that it cannot be accounted for by mere swelling or shrinkage.   The chromosomes evidently absorb a large amount of matter, combine with it to form a substance of diminished staining-capacity, and finally give off matter, leaving an intensely staining substance behind.   As Rückert points out, the great increase of surface in the chromosomes is adapted to facilitate an exchange of material between the chromatin and the surrounding substance; and he concludes that the coincidence between the growth of the chromosomes and that of the egg, points to an intimate connection between the nuclear activity and the formative energy of the cytoplasm.

If these facts are considered in the light of the known staining-reaction of the nuclein series, we must admit that the following conclusions are something more than mere possibilities.   We may infer that the original chromosomes contain a high percentage of nucleic acid; that their growth and loss of staining-power is due to a combination with a large amount of albuminous substance to form a lower member of the nuclein series, perhaps even a nucleo-albumin; that their final diminution in size and resumption of staining-power is caused by a giving up of the albumin constituent, restoring the nuclein to its original state as a preparation for division.   The growth and diminished staining-capacity of the chromatin occurs during a period of intense constructive activity in the cytoplasm; its diminution in bulk and resumption of staining-capacity coincides with the cessation of this activity.   This result is in harmony with the observations of Schwarz and Zacharias on growing plant-cells, the percentage of nuclein in the nuclei of embryonic cells (meristem) being at first relatively large and diminishing as the cells increase in size.   It agrees further with the fact that of all forms of nuclei those of the spermatozoa, in which growth is suspended, are richest in nucleic acid, and in this respect stand at the opposite extreme from the nuclei of the rapidly growing egg-cell.

Accurately determined facts in this direction are still too scanty to

admit of a safe generalization.   They are, however, enough to indicate the probability that chromatin may pass through a certain cycle
in the life of the cell, the percentage of albumin increasing during
the vegetative activity of the nucleus, decreasing in its reproductive
phase.   In other words, a combination of albumin with nuclein or
nucleic acid is an accompaniment of constructive metabolism.   As
the cell prepares for division, the combination is dissolved and the
nuclein-radicle or nucleic acid is handed on by division to the daughter-cells.   It is a tempting hypothesis, suggested to me by Mr. A. P.
Mathews on the basis of Kossel's work, that the nuclein is in a chemical sense the formative centre of the cell, attracting to it the food-
matters, entering into loose combination with them, and giving them
off to the cytoplasm in an elaborated form.   Could this be established, we should have a clue to the nuclear control of the cell
through the process of synthetic metabolism.   Claude Bernard
advanced a nearly similar hypothesis two score years ago ('78), maintaining that the cytoplasm is the seat of destructive metabolism, the
nucleus the organ of constructive metabolism and organic synthesis,
and insisting that the *rôle* of the nucleus in nutrition gives the key
to its significance as the organ of development, regeneration, and
inheritance.[1]

That the nucleus is especially concerned in synthetic metabolism
is now becoming more and more clearly recognized by physiological
chemists.   Kossel concludes that the formation of new organic matter
is dependent on the nucleus,[2] and that nuclein in some manner plays
a leading *rôle* in this process ; and he makes some interesting suggestions regarding the synthesis of complex organic matters in the living
cell with nuclein as a starting-point.   Chittenden, too, in a review of
recent chemico-physiological discoveries regarding the cell, concludes :
"The cell-nucleus may be looked upon as in some manner standing in
close relation to those processes which have to do with the formation
of organic substances.   Whatever other functions it may possess, it
evidently, through the inherent qualities of the bodies entering into
its composition, has a controlling power over the metabolic processes
in the cell, modifying and regulating the nutritional changes" ('94).

[1] " Il semble donc que la cellule qui a perdu son *noyau* soit stérilisée au point de vue de
la génération, c'est à dire de la synthèse morphologique, et qu'elle le soit aussi au point de
vue de la synthèse chimique, car elle cesse de produire des principes immediats, et ne peut
guère qu'oxyder et détruire ceux qui s'y étaient accumulés par une élaboration antérieure du
noyau.   Il semble donc que le *noyau* soit le *germe* de nutrition.de la cellule; il attire autour
de lui et élabore les matériaux nutritifs " ('78, p. 523).

[2] Schiefferdecker und Kossel, *Gewebelehre*, p. 57.

B.   Physiological Relations of Nucleus and Cytoplasm

How nearly the foregoing facts bear on the problem of the formative power of the cell in a morphological sense is obvious, and they
have in a measure anticipated certain conclusions regarding the *rôle* of
nucleus and cytoplasm which we may now examine from a somewhat
different point of view.

Brücke long ago drew a clear distinction between the chemical and
molecular composition of organic substances, on the one hand, and,
on the other hand, their definite grouping in the cell by which arises
organization in a morphological sense.   Claude Bernard, in like manner, distinguished between *chemical synthesis*, through which organic
matters are formed, and *morphological synthesis*, by which they are
built into a specifically organized fabric ; but he insisted that these two
processes are but different phases or degrees of the same phenomenon, and that both are expressions of the nuclear activity.   We have
now to consider some of the evidence that the formative power of the
cell, in a morphological sense, centres in the nucleus, and that this is
therefore to be regarded as the especial organ of inheritance.   This
evidence is mainly derived from the comparison of nucleated and
non-nucleated masses of protoplasm ; from the form, position and
movements of the nucleus in actively growing or metabolizing cells ;
and from the history of the nucleus in mitotic cell-division, in fertilization, and in maturation.

1.   *Experiments on Unicellular Organisms*

Brandt ('77) long since observed that enucleated fragments of
Actinosphærium soon die, while nucleated fragments heal their wounds
and continue to live.   The first decisive comparison between nucleated and non-nucleated masses of protoplasm was, however, made by
Moritz Nussbaum in 1884 in the case of an infusorian, *Oxytricha*.
If one of these animals be cut into two pieces, the subsequent
behaviour of the two fragments depends on the presence or absence
of the nucleus or a nuclear fragment.   The nucleated fragments
quickly heal the wound, regenerate the missing portions, and thus
produce a perfect animal.   On the other hand, enucleated fragments,
consisting of cytoplasm only, quickly perish.   Nussbaum therefore
drew the conclusion that the nucleus is indispensable for the formative energy of the cell.   The experiment was soon after repeated by
Gruber ('85) in the case of *Stentor*, another infusorian, and with the
same result (Fig. 112).   Fragments possessing a large fragment of the
nucleus completely regenerated within twenty-four hours.   If the nu-

clear fragment were smaller, the regeneration proceeded more slowly. If no nuclear substance were present, no regeneration took place, though the wound closed and the fragment lived for a considerable time. The only exception—but it is a very significant one—was the case of individuals in which the process of normal fission had begun; in these a non-nucleated fragment in which the formation of a new peristome had already been initiated healed the wound and completed the formation of the peristome. Lillie ('96) has recently

found that *Stentor* may by shaking be broken into fragments of all sizes, and that nucleated fragments as small as $\frac{1}{27}$ the volume of the entire animal are still capable of complete regeneration. All non-nucleated fragments perish.

These studies of Nussbaum and Gruber formed a prelude to more extended investigations in the same direction by Gruber, Balbiani, Hofer, and especially Verworn. Verworn ('88) proved that in *Polystomella*, one of the Foraminifera, nucleated fragments are able to repair the shell, while non-nucleated fragments lack this power. Balbiani ('89) showed that although non-nucleated fragments of infusoria had no power of regeneration, they might nevertheless continue to live and

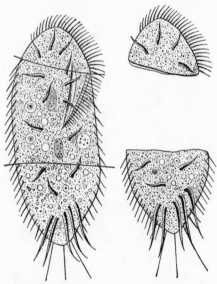

Fig. 111.— *Stylonychia*, and enucleated fragments. [VERWORN.]

At the left an entire animal, showing planes of section. The middle-piece, containing two nuclei, regenerates a perfect animal. The enucleated pieces, shown at the right, swim about for a time, but finally perish.

swim actively about for many days after the operation, the contractile vacuole pulsating as usual. Hofer ('89), experimenting on *Amœba*, found that non-nucleated fragments might live as long as fourteen days after the operation (Fig. 113). Their movements continued, but were somewhat modified, and little by little ceased, but the pulsations of the contractile vacuole were but slightly affected; they lost more or less completely the capacity to digest food, and the power of adhering to the substratum. Nearly at the same time Verworn ('89) published the results of an extended comparative investigation of various Protozoa that placed the whole matter in a very clear light. His experiments, while fully confirming the accounts of his predecessors in regard to regeneration, added many extremely important and significant results. Non-nucleated fragments both of infusoria (*e.g.*, *Lachrymaria*) and rhizopods (*Polystomella, Thalassicolla*) not only live for a considerable period, but perform perfectly normal and characteristic movements, show the same susceptibility to stimulus, and have the same power of ingulfing food, as the nucleated fragments. *They lack, however, the power of digestion and secretion.* Ingested food-matters may be slightly

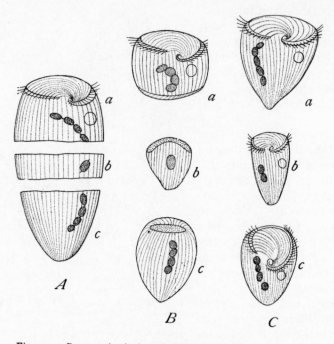

Fig. 112. — Regeneration in the unicellular animal *Stentor*. [GRUBER.]

A. Animal divided into three pieces, each containing a fragment of the nucleus. *B.* The three fragments shortly afterwards. *C.* The three fragments after twenty-four hours, each regenerated to a perfect animal.

altered, but are never completely digested. The non-nucleated fragments are unable to secrete the material for a new shell (*Polystomella*) or the slime by which the animals adhere to the substratum (*Amœba, Difflugia, Polystomella*). Beside these results should be placed the well-known fact that dissevered nerve-fibres in the higher animals are only regenerated from that end which remains in connection with the nerve-cell, while the remaining portion invariably degenerates.

These beautiful observations prove that destructive metabolism, as manifested by co-ordinated forms of protoplasmic contractility, may go on for some time undisturbed in a mass of cytoplasm deprived of a nucleus. On the other hand, the formation of new chemical or morphological products by the cytoplasm only takes place in the presence of a nucleus. These facts form a complete demonstration that the nucleus plays an essential part not only in the operations of synthetic metabolism or chemical synthesis, but also in the *morphological*

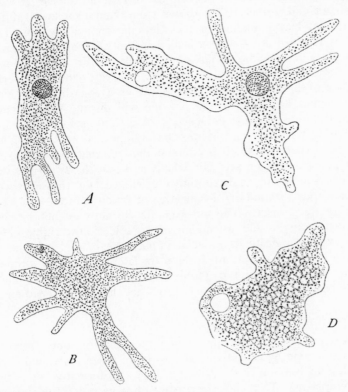

Fig. 113. — Nucleated and non-nucleated fragments of *Amœba*. [HOFER.]

A. B. An *Amœba* divided into nucleated and non-nucleated halves, five minutes after the operation. *C. D.* The two halves after eight days, each containing a contractile vacuole.

determination of these operations, i.e. the morphological synthesis of Bernard — a point of capital importance for the theory of inheritance, as will appear beyond.

Convincing experiments of the same character and leading to the same result have been made on the unicellular plants. Klebs observed as long ago as 1879 that naked protoplasmic fragments of *Vaucheria* and other algæ were incapable of forming a new cellulose membrane if devoid of a nucleus; and he afterwards showed ('87) that the same is true of *Zygnema* and *Œdigonium*. By plasmolysis the cells of these forms may be broken up into fragments, both nucleated and non-nucleated. The former surround themselves with a new wall, grow, and develop into complete plants; the latter, while able to form starch by means of the chlorophyll they contain, are incapable of utilizing it, and are devoid of the power of forming a new membrane, and of growth and regeneration.[1]

Although Verworn's results confirm and extend the earlier work of Nussbaum and Gruber, he has drawn from them a somewhat different conclusion, based mainly on the fact, determined by him, that a nucleus deprived of cytoplasm is as devoid of the power to regenerate the whole as an enucleated mass of cytoplasm. From this he argues, with perfect justice, that the formative energy cannot properly be ascribed to the nucleus alone, but is rather a co-ordinate activity of both nucleus and cytoplasm. No one will dispute this conclusion; yet in the light of other evidence it is, I think, stated in somewhat misleading terms which obscure the significance of Verworn's own beautiful experiments. It is undoubtedly true that the cell, like any other living organism, acts as a whole, and that the integrity of all of its parts is necessary to its continued existence; but this no more precludes a specialization and localization of function in the cell than in the higher organism. The experiments certainly do not prove that the nucleus is the sole instrument of organic synthesis, but they no less certainly indicate its especial importance in this process. The sperm-nucleus is unable to develop its latent capacities without becoming associated with the cytoplasm of an ovum, but its significance as the bearer of the paternal heritage is not thereby lessened one iota.

2. *Position and Movements of the Nucleus*

Many observers have approached the same problem from a different direction by considering the position, movements, and changes of form in the nucleus with regard to the formative activities in the cytoplasm. To review these researches in full would be impossible, and we must be content to consider only the well-known researches of Haberlandt ('77) and Korschelt ('89), both of whom have given extensive reviews of the entire subject in this regard. Haberlandt's studies related to the position of the nucleus in plant-cells with especial regard to the growth of the cellulose membrane. He determined the very significant fact that local growth of the cell-wall is always preceded by a movement of the nucleus to the

---

[1] Palla ('90) has disputed this result, maintaining that enucleated masses of protoplasm pressed out from pollen-tubes might surround themselves with membranes and grow out into long tubes.   Later observations, however, by Acqua ('91), throw doubt on Palla's conclusion.

point of growth. Thus, in the formation of epidermal cells the nucleus lies at first near the centre, but as the outer wall thickens, the nucleus moves towards it, and remains closely applied to it throughout its growth, after which the nucleus often moves into another part of the cell (Fig. 114, *A, B*). That this is not due simply to a movement of the nucleus towards the air and light is beautifully shown in the coats of certain seeds, where the nucleus

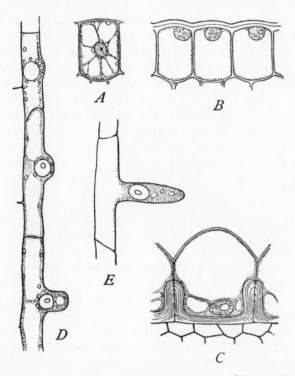

Fig. 114. — Position of the nuclei in growing plant-cells. [HABERLANDT.]

A. Young epidermal cell of *Luzula* with central nucleus, before thickening of the membrane. *B.* Three epidermal cells of *Monstera*, during the thickening of the outer wall. *C.* Cell from the seed-coat of *Scopulina* during the thickening of the inner wall. *D. E.* Position of the nuclei during the formation of branches in the root-hairs of the pea.

moves not to the outer, but to the inner wall of the cell, and here the thickening takes place (Fig. 114, *C*). The same position of the nucleus is shown in the thickening of the walls of the guard-cells of stomata, in the formation of the peristome of mosses, and in many other cases. In the formation of root-hairs in the pea, the primary outgrowth always takes place from the immediate neighbourhood of the nucleus, which is carried outward and remains near the tip of the growing hair (Fig. 114, *D, E*). The same is true of the rhizoids of fern-prothallia and liverworts. In the hairs of aërial plants this rule is reversed, the nucleus lying near the base of the hair; but this apparent exception proves the rule, for both Hunter and Haberlandt show that in this case growth of the hair is not apical, but proceeds from the base! Very interesting is Haberlandt's observation that in the regeneration of fragments of *Vaucheria* the growing region, where a new membrane is formed, contains no chlorophyll, but numerous nuclei. The general result, based on the study of a. large number of cases, is in Haberlandt's words that "the nucleus is in most cases placed in the neighbourhood, more or less immediate, of the points at which growth is most active and continues longest." This fact points to the conclusion that "its function is especially connected with the developmental processes of the cell,"[1] and that "in the growth of the cell, more especially in the growth of the cell-wall, the nucleus plays a definite part."

Korschelt's work deals especially with the correlation between form and position of the nucleus and the nutrition of the cell; and since it bears more directly on chemical than on morphological synthesis, may be only briefly reviewed at this point. His general conclusion is that there is a definite correlation, on the one hand between the position of the nucleus and the source of food-supply, on the other hand between the size of the nucleus and the extent of its surface and the elaboration of material by the cell. In support of the latter conclusion many cases are brought forward of secreting cells in which the nucleus is of enormous size and has a complex branching form. Such nuclei occur, for example, in the silk-glands of various lepidopterous larvæ (Meckel, Zaddach, etc.), which are characterized by an intense secretory activity concentrated into a very short period. Here the nucleus forms a labyrinthine network (Fig. 11, *E*), by which its surface is brought to a maximum, pointing to an active exchange of material between nucleus and cytoplasm. The same type of nucleus occurs in the Malpighian tubules of insects (Leydig, R. Hertwig), in the spinning-glands of amphipods (Mayer), and especially in the nutritive cells of the insect ovary already referred to at p. 114. Here the developing ovum is accompanied and surrounded by cells, which there is good reason to believe are concerned with the elaboration of food for the egg-cell. In the earwig *Forficula* each egg is accompanied by a single large nutritive cell (Fig. 115), which has a very large nucleus rich in chromatin (Korschelt). This cell increases in size as the ovum grows, and its nucleus assumes the complex branching form shown in the figure. In the butterfly *Vanessa* there is a group

[1] *l.c.*, p. 99.

of such cells at one pole of the egg from which the latter is believed to draw its nutriment (Fig. 58). A very interesting case is that of the annelid *Ophryotrocha*, referred to at p. 114. Here, as described by Korschelt, the egg floats in the perivisceral fluid, accompanied by a nurse-cell having a very large chromatic nucleus, while that of the egg is smaller and poorer in chromatin. As the egg completes its growth, the nurse-cell dwindles away and finally perishes (Fig. 57). In all these cases it is scarcely possible to doubt that the egg is in a measure relieved of the task of elaborating cytoplasmic products by the nurse-cell, and that the great development of the nucleus in the latter is correlated with this function.

Regarding the position and movements of the nucleus, Korschelt reviews many facts pointing towards the same conclusion. Perhaps the most suggestive of these relate to the nucleus of the egg during its ovarian history. In many of the insects, as in both the cases referred to above,

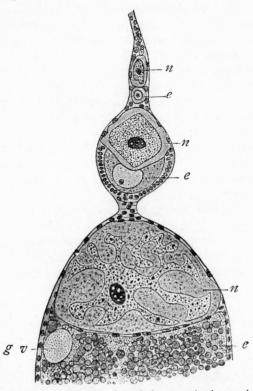

Fig. 115. — Upper portion of the ovary in the earwig *Forficula*, showing eggs and nurse-cells. [KORSCHELT.]

Below, a portion of the nearly ripe egg (*e*), showing deuto-plasm-spheres and germinal vesicle (*g v*). Above it lies the nurse-cell (*n*) with its enormous branching nucleus. Two successively younger stages of egg and nurse are shown above.

the egg-nucleus at first occupies a central position, but as the egg begins to grow, it moves to the periphery on the side turned towards the nutritive cells. The same is true in the ovarian eggs of some other animals, good examples of which are afforded by various cœlenterates, *e.g.* in medusæ (Claus, Hertwig) and actinians (Korschelt, Hertwig), where the germinal vesicle is always near the point of attachment of the egg. Most suggestive of all is the case of the water-beetle *Dytiscus*, in which Korschelt was able to observe the movements and changes of form in the living object. The eggs here lie in a single series alternating with chambers of nutritive cells. The latter contain granules which are believed by Korschelt to pass into the egg, perhaps bodily, perhaps by dissolving and entering in a liquid form.   At all events, the egg contains accumulations of similar granules, which extend inwards in dense masses from the nutritive cells to the germinal vesicle, which they may more or less completely surround.   The latter meanwhile becomes amœboid, sending out long pseudopodia, which are always directed towards the principal mass of granules (Fig. 58).   The granules could not be traced into the nucleus, but the latter grows rapidly during these changes, proving that matter must be absorbed by it, probably in a liquid form.[1]

All of these and a large number of other observations in the same direction lead to the conclusion that the cell-nucleus plays an active part in nutrition, and that it is especially active during its constructive phase.   On the whole, therefore, the behaviour of the nucleus in this regard is in harmony with the result reached by experiment on the one-celled forms, though it gives in itself a far less certain and convincing result.

We now turn to evidence which, though less direct than the experimental proof, is scarcely less convincing.   This evidence, which has been exhaustively discussed by Hertwig, Weismann, and Strasburger, is drawn from the history of the nucleus in mitosis, fertilization, and maturation.   It calls for only a brief review here, since the facts have been fully described in earlier chapters.

3. *The Nucleus in Mitosis*

To Wilhelm Roux ('83) we owe the first clear recognition of the fact that the transformation of the chromatic substance during mitotic division is manifestly designed to effect a precise division of all its parts, — *i.e.* a panmeristic division as opposed to a mere mass-division, — and their definite distribution to the daughter-cells.   "The essential operation of nuclear division is the division of the mother-granules" (*i.e.* the individual chromatin-grains); "all the other phenomena are for the purpose of transporting the daughter-granules derived from the division of a mother-granule, one to the centre of one of the daughter-cells, the other to the centre of the other."   In this respect the nucleus stands in marked contrast to the cytoplasm, which undergoes on the whole a mass-division, although certain of its elements, such as the plastids and the centrosome, may separately divide, like the elements of the nucleus.   From this fact Roux argued, first, that different regions of the nuclear substance

---

[1] Some observers have maintained that the nucleus may take in as well as give off solid matters.   This statement rests, however, on a very insecure foundation.

must represent different qualities, and second, that the apparatus of mitosis is designed to distribute these qualities, according to a definite law, to the daughter-cells. The particular form in which Roux and Weismann developed this conception has now been generally rejected, and in any form it has some serious difficulties in its way. We cannot assume a precise localization of chromatin-elements in all parts of the nucleus; for on the one hand a large part of the chromatin may degenerate or be cast out (as in the maturation of the egg), and on the other hand in the Protozoa a small fragment of the nucleus is able to regenerate the whole. Nevertheless, the essential fact remains, as Hertwig, Kölliker, Strasburger, De Vries, and many others have insisted, that in mitotic cell-division the chromatin of the mother-cell is distributed with the most scrupulous equality to the nuclei of the daughter-cells, and that in this regard there is a most remarkable contrast between nucleus and cytoplasm. This holds true with such wonderful constancy throughout the series of living forms, from the lowest to the highest, that it must have a deep significance. And while we are not yet in a position to grasp its full meaning, this contrast points unmistakably to the conclusion that the most essential material handed on by the mother-cell to its progeny is the chromatin, and that this substance therefore has a special significance in inheritance.

4. *The Nucleus in Fertilization*

The foregoing argument receives an overwhelming reinforcement from the facts of fertilization. Although the ovum supplies nearly all the cytoplasm for the embryonic body, and the spermatozoön at most only a trace, the latter is nevertheless as potent in its effect on the offspring as the former. On the other hand, the nuclei contributed by the two germ-cells, though apparently different, become in the end exactly equivalent in every visible respect — in structure, in staining-reactions, and in the number and form of the chromosomes to which each gives rise. But furthermore the substance of the two germ-nuclei is distributed with absolute equality, certainly to the first two cells of the embryo, and probably to all later-formed cells. The latter conclusion, which long remained a mere surmise, has been rendered nearly a certainty by the remarkable observations of Rückert, Zoja, and Häcker, described in Chapters IV. and VI. The conclusion is irresistible that the specific character of the cell is in the last analysis determined by that of the nucleus, that is by the chromatin, and that in the equal distribution of paternal and maternal chromatin to all the cells of the offspring we find the physiological explanation of the fact that every part of the latter may show the characteristics of either or both parents.

Boveri ('89, '95, 1) has attempted to test this conclusion by a most ingenious and beautiful experiment; and although his conclusions do not rest on absolutely certain ground, they at least open the way to a decisive test. The Hertwig brothers showed that the eggs of sea-urchins might be enucleated by shaking, and that spermatozoa would enter the enucleated fragments and cause them to segment. Boveri proved that such fragments would even give rise to dwarf larvæ, indistinguishable from the normal in general appearance and differing from the latter only in size and in the very significant fact that their nuclei contain only half the normal number of chromosomes. Now, by fertilizing enucleated egg-fragments of one species (*Sphærechinus granularis*) with the spermatozoa of another (*Echinus microtuberculatus*), Boveri obtained in a few instances dwarf Plutei *showing purely paternal characteristics* (Fig. 116). From this he concluded that the maternal cytoplasm has no determining effect on the offspring, but supplies only material in which the sperm-nucleus operates. Inheritance is, therefore, effected by the nucleus alone.[1] Boveri's result

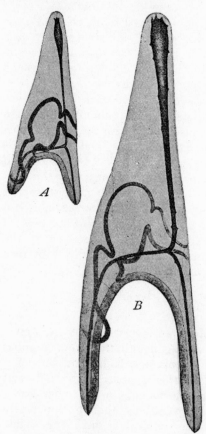

Fig. 116.—Normal and dwarf larvæ of the sea-urchin. [BOVERI.]

A. Dwarf Pluteus arising from an enucleated egg-fragment of *Sphærechinus granularis*, fertilized with spermatozoön of *Echinus microtuberculatus*, and showing *purely paternal characters*. *B*. Normal Pluteus of *Echinus microtuberculatus*.

is unfortunately not quite conclusive, as has been pointed out by Seeliger and Morgan, yet his extensive experiments establish, I think, a strong presumption in its favour. Should they be positively confirmed, they would furnish a practical demonstration of inheritance through the nucleus.

---

[1] The centrosome is left out of account, since it is frequently derived from one sex only.

5. *The Nucleus in Maturation*

Scarcely less convincing, finally, is the contrast between nucleus and cytoplasm in the maturation of the germ-cells. It is scarcely an exaggeration to say that the whole process of maturation, in its broadest sense, renders the cytoplasm of the germ-cells as unlike, the nuclei as like, as possible. The latter undergo a series of complicated changes which are expressly designed to establish a perfect equivalence between them at the time of their union, and, more remotely, a perfect equality of distribution to the embryonic cells. The cytoplasm, on the other hand, undergoes a special and persistent differentiation in each to effect a secondary division of labour between the germ-cells. When this is correlated with the fact that the germ-cells, on the whole, have an equal effect on the specific character of the embryo, we are again forced to the conclusion that this effect must primarily be sought in the nucleus, and that the cytoplasm is in a sense only its agent.

C. The Centrosome

Nearly all investigators have now accepted Van Beneden's and Boveri's conclusion that *the centrosome is an organ for cell-division*, and that in this sense it represents the dynamic centre of the cell (cf. p. 56). This is most clearly shown in the ordinary fertilization of the ovum, in which process, as Boveri has insisted, it is the centrosome that is the fertilizing element *par excellence*, since its introduction into the egg confers upon the latter the power of division, and hence of development. Boveri's interesting observations on "partial fertilization" in the sea-urchin referred to at p. 140 afford a beautiful illustration of this point. In certain exceptional cases the egg may divide before conjugation of the germ-nuclei has occurred, the sperm-nucleus lying passive in the cytoplasm until after the first cleavage and then conjugating with one of the nuclei of the two-celled stage. The egg is here *fertilized — i.e.* rendered capable of division — by the centrosome, which separates from the sperm-nucleus, approaches the egg-nucleus, and gives rise to the cleavage-amphiaster as usual.

Again, Boveri has observed that the segmenting ovum of *Ascaris* sometimes contains a supernumerary centrosome that does not enter into connection with the chromosomes, but lies alone in the cytoplasm (Fig. 117). Such a centrosome forms an independent centre of division, the cell dividing into three parts, two of which are normal blastomeres, while the third contains only the centrosome and attraction-sphere. The fate of such eggs was not determined, but they form a complete demonstration that it is the centrosome and not the nucleus that is the active centre of cell-division in the cell-body. Scarcely less conclusive is the case of dispermic eggs in sea-urchins. In such eggs both sperm-nuclei conjugate with the egg-nucleus, and both sperm-centrosomes divide (Fig. 118). The cleavage-nucleus, therefore, arises by the union of *three* nuclei and *four* centrosomes. Such eggs invariably divide at the first cleavage into four equal blastomeres, each of which receives one of the centrosomes. The latter must, therefore, be the centres of division.[1]

The statement that the centrosome is an organ for cell-division does not, however, express the whole truth; for in leucocytes and pigment-cells the astral system formed about it is devoted, as there is good reason to believe, not to cell-division, but to movements of the

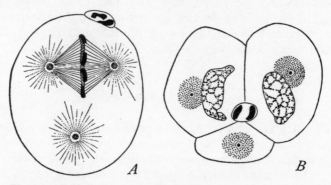

Fig. 117.—Eggs of *Ascaris* with supernumerary centrosome. [BOVERI.]
A. First cleavage-spindle above, isolated centrosome below. *B.* Result of the ensuing division.

cell-body as a whole; and, moreover, amitotic division may apparently take place independently of the centrosome. The *rôle* of the centrosome and attraction-sphere in gland-cells (where they are sometimes very large) and in the nerve-cells is still wholly problematical. It would seem, therefore, that the primary function of the centrosome is to organize an astral system, of which it forms the focus, that is primarily an apparatus for mitotic division, but may secondarily become devoted to other functions. The nature of the energy by which this organization takes place is almost wholly in the dark. The extraordinary resemblance of the amphiaster to the lines of force in a magnetic field has impressed many observers, but Roux has proved that the axis of the mitotic figure is not affected, during its formation, by a powerful electro-magnet. The molecules or micro-

[1] This phenomenon was first observed by Hertwig, and afterwards by Driesch. I have repeatedly observed the internal changes in the living eggs of *Toxopneustes*.

somes of the fibres must be in some manner polarized by an influence emanating from the centrosome, but in the present state of knowledge it would be useless to speculate on the nature of this influence. One fact, however, should be borne in mind, namely, that the centrosome differs chemically from the substance of the fibres as shown by its staining-reactions; and this may form a clue to the further investigation of this most interesting problem.

The principal point in connection with our present theme is that the centrosome cannot be regarded as taking any important part in

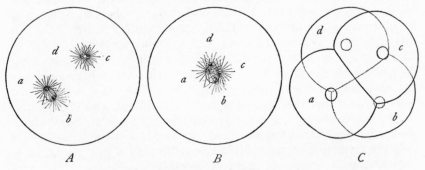

Fig. 118. — Cleavage of dispermic egg of *Toxopneustes*.

A. One sperm-nucleus has united with the egg-nucleus, shown at *a*, *b*; the other lies above. Both sperm-asters have divided to form amphiasters (*a*, *b* and *c*, *d*). *B.* The cleavage-nucleus formed by union of the three germ-nuclei, is surrounded by the four asters. *C.* Result of the first cleavage, the four blastomeres lettered to correspond with the four asters.

the general metabolism of the cell, nor can it be an organ of inheritance; for on the one hand it is absent or so small as to be indistinguishable in many actively metabolizing cells, such as those of the pancreas or kidney, or the older ovarian eggs, and, on the other hand, in fertilization it may be derived from one sex only. The conclusion regarding inheritance would not be invalidated, even if it could be positively shown that in some cases both germ-cells might contribute a centrosome; for a single case of its one-sided origin would be conclusive, and many such are actually known.

D. SUMMARY AND CONCLUSION

All of the facts reviewed in the foregoing pages converge, I think, to the conclusion drawn by Claude Bernard, that the nucleus is the formative centre of the cell in a chemical sense, and through this is the especial seat of the formative energy in a morphological sense. That the nucleus has such a significance in synthetic metabolism is proved by the fact that digestion and absorption of food, growth, and secretion cease with its removal from the cytoplasm, while destructive metabolism may long continue as manifested by the phenomena of irritability and contractility. It is indicated by the position and movements of the nucleus in relation to the food-supply and to the formation of specific cytoplasmic products. It harmonizes with the fact, now universally admitted, that active exchanges of material go on between nucleus and cytoplasm. The periodic changes of staining-capacity undergone by the chromatin during the cycle of cell-life, taken in connection with the researches of physiological chemists on the chemical composition and staining-reactions of the nuclein-series, indicate that the substance known as *nucleic acid* plays a leading part in the constructive process. During the vegetative phase of the cell this substance appears to enter into combination with proteid or albuminous substance to form a nuclein. During its mitotic or reproductive phase the albumin is split off, leaving the substance of the chromosomes as nearly pure nucleic acid. When this is correlated with the fact that the sperm-nucleus, which brings with it the paternal heritage, likewise consists of nearly pure nucleic acid, the possibility is opened that this substance may be in a chemical sense not only the formative centre of the nucleus but also a primary factor in the constructive processes of the cytoplasm.

The *rôle* of the nucleus in constructive metabolism is intimately related with its *rôle* in morphological synthesis and thus in inheritance; for the recurrence of similar morphological characters must in the last analysis be due to the recurrence of corresponding forms of metabolic action of which they are the outward expression. That the nucleus is in fact a primary factor in morphological as well as chemical synthesis is demonstrated by experiments on unicellular plants and animals, which prove that the power of regenerating lost parts disappears with its removal, though the enucleated fragment may continue to live and move for a considerable period.

This fact establishes the presumption that the nucleus is, if not the actual seat of the formative energy, at least the controlling factor in that energy, and hence the controlling factor in inheritance. This presumption becomes a practical certainty when we turn to the facts of maturation, fertilization, and cell-division. All of these converge to the conclusion that the chromatin is the most essential element in development. In maturation the germ-nuclei are by an elaborate process prepared for the subsequent union of equivalent chromatic elements from the two sexes. By fertilization these elements are brought together and by mitotic division distributed with exact equality to the embryonic cells. The result proves that the spermatozoön is as potent in inheritance as the ovum, though the latter contributes an amount of cytoplasm which is but an infinitesimal fraction of that supplied by the ovum. The centrosome, finally, is excluded from the process of inheritance, since it may be derived from one sex only.

LITERATURE. VII

Bernard, Claude. — Leçons sur les Phénomènes de la Vie: 1st ed. 1878; 2d ed. 1885. *Paris.*

Chittenden, R. H. — Some Recent Chemico-physiological Discoveries regarding the Cell: *Am. Nat.*, XXVIII., Feb., 1894.

Haberlandt, G. — Über die Beziehungen zwischen Funktion und Lage des Zellkerns. *Fischer*, 1887.

Halliburton, W. D. — A Text-book of Chemical Physiology and Pathology. *London*, 1891.

Id. — The Chemical Physiology of the Cell (*Gouldstonian Lectures*): *Brit. Med. Journ.* 1893.

Hammarsten, O. — Lehrbuch der physiologische Chemie. 3d ed. *Wiesbaden*, 1895.

Hertwig, O. & R. — Über den Befruchtungs- und Teilungsvorgang des tierischen Eies unter dem Einfluss äusserer Agentien. *Jena*, 1887.

Kölliker, A. — Das Karyoplasma und die Vererbung, eine Kritik der Weismann'schen Theorie von der Kontinuität des Keimplasmas: *Zeitschr. wiss. Zoöl.*, XLIV. 1886.

Korschelt, E. — Beiträge sur Morphologie und Physiologie des Zell-kernes: *Zoöl. Jahrb. Anat. u. Ontog.*, IV. 1889.

Kossel, A. — Über die chemische Zusammensetzung der Zelle: *Arch. Anat. u. Phys.* 1891.

Lilienfeld, L. — Über die Wahlverwandtschaft der Zellelemente zu Farbstoffen: *Arch. Anat. u. Phys.* 1893.

Malfatti, H. — Beiträge zur Kenntniss der Nucleine: *Zeitschr. Phys. Chem.*, XVI. 1891.

Rückert, J. — Zur Entwicklungsgeschichte des Ovarialeies bei Selachiern: *An. Anz.*, VII. 1892.

Sachs, J. — Vorlesungen über Pflanzen-physiologie. *Leipzig*, 1882.

Id. — Stoff und Form der Pflanzen-organe: *Gesammelte Abhandlungen*, II. 1893.

Verworn, M. — Die Physiologische Bedeutung des Zellkerns: *Arch. für die Ges. Phys.*, XLI. 1892.

Id. — Allgemeine Physiologie. *Jena*, 1895.

Zacharias, E. — Über Chromatophilie: *Ber. d. deutsch. Bot. Ges.* 1893.

Id. — Über des Verhalten des Zellkerns in wachsenden Zellen: *Flora*, 81. 1895.

Whitman, C. O. — The Seat of Formative and Regenerative Energy: *Journ. Morph.*, II. 1888.

CHAPTER VIII

CELL–DIVISION AND DEVELOPMENT

"Wir können demnach endlich den Satz aufstellen, dass sämmtliche im entwickelten Zustande vorhandenen Zellen oder Aequivalente von Zellen durch eine fortschreitende Gliederung der Eizelle in morphologisch ähnliche Elemente entstehen, und dass die in einer embryonischen Organ-Anlage enthaltenden Zellen, so gering auch ihre Zahl sein mag, dennoch die ausschliessliche ungegliederte Anlage für sämmtliche Formbestandtheile der späteren Organe enthalten."   REMAK.[1]

SINCE the early work of Kölliker and Remak it has been recognized that the cleavage or segmentation of the ovum, with which the development of all higher animals begins, is nothing other than a rapid series of mitotic cell-divisions by which the egg splits up into the elements of the tissues. This process is merely a continuation of that by which the germ-cell arose in the parental body. A long pause, however, intervenes during the latter period of its ovarian life, during which no divisions take place. Throughout this period the egg leads, on the whole, a somewhat passive existence, devoting itself especially to the storage of potential energy to be used during the intense activity that is to come. Its power of division remains dormant until the period of full maturity approaches. The entrance of the spermatozoön, bringing with it a new centrosome, arouses in the egg a new phase of activity. Its power of division, which may have lain dormant for months or years, is suddenly raised to the highest pitch of intensity, and in a very short time it gives rise by division to a myriad of descendants which are ultimately differentiated into the elements of the tissues.

The divisions of the egg during cleavage are exactly comparable with those of tissue-cells, and all of the essential phenomena of mitosis are of the same general character in both. But for two reasons the cleavage of the egg possesses a higher interest than any other case of cell-division. First, the egg-cell gives rise by division not only to cells like itself, as is the case with most tissue-cells, but also to many other kinds of cells. The operation of cleavage is therefore immediately connected with the process of differentiation,

[1] *Untersuchungen*, 1855, p. 140.

which is the most fundamental phenomenon in development. Second, definite relations may often be traced between the planes of division and the structural axes of the adult body, and these relations are sometimes so clearly marked and appear so early that with the very first cleavage the position in which the embryo will finally appear in the egg may be exactly predicted. Such " promorphological " relations of the segmenting egg possess a very high interest in their bearing on the theory of germinal localization and on account of the light which they throw on the conditions of the formative process.

The present chapter is in the main a prelude to that which follows, its purpose being to sketch some of the external features of early development regarded as particular expressions of the general laws of cell-division. For this purpose we may consider the cleavage of the ovum under two heads, namely: —

1. *The Geometrical Relations of Cleavage-forms*, with reference to the general laws of cell-division.

2. *The Promorphological Relations* of the blastomeres and cleavage-planes to the parts of the adult body to which they give rise.

I

A. GEOMETRICAL RELATIONS OF CLEAVAGE-FORMS

The geometrical relations of the cleavage-planes and the relative size and position of the cells vary endlessly in detail, being modified by innumerable mechanical and other conditions, such as the amount and distribution of the inert yolk or deutoplasm, the shape of the ovum as a whole, and the like. Yet all the forms of cleavage are variants of a single type which has been moulded this way or that by special conditions, and which is itself an expression of two general laws of cell-division, first formulated by Sachs in the case of plant-cells. These are:

1. *The cell typically tends to divide into equal parts.*

2. *Each new plane of division tends to intersect the preceding plane at a right angle.*

In the simplest and least modified forms the direction of the cleavage-planes, and hence the general configuration of the cell-system, depends on the general form of the dividing mass; for, as Sachs has shown, the cleavage-planes tend to be either vertical to the surface (*anticlines*) or parallel to it (*periclines*). Ideal schemes of division may thus be constructed for various geometrical figures. In a flat circular disc, for example, the anticlinal planes pass through the radii; the periclines are circles concentric with the periphery. If the disc be elongated to form an ellipse, the periclines also become ellipses, while the anticlines are converted into hyperbolas confocal with the periclines.   If it have the form of a parabola, the periclines and anticlines form two systems of confocal parabolas intersecting at

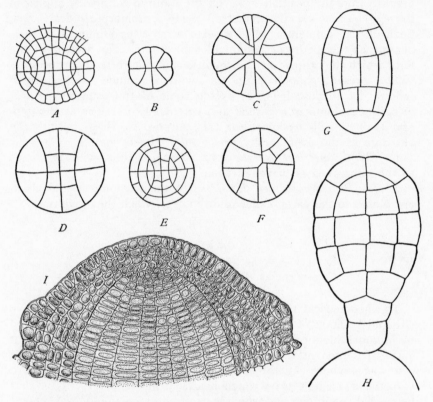

Fig. 119. — Geometrical relations of cleavage-planes in growing plant-tissues.   [From SACHS, after various authors.]

A. Flat ellipsoidal germ-disc of *Melobesia* (Rosanoff) ;   nearly typical relation of elliptic periclines and hyperbolic anticlines.   *B. C.* Apical view of terminal knob on epidermal hair of *Pinguicola*.   *B.* shows the ellipsoid type, *C.* the circular (spherical type), somewhat modified (only anticlines present).   *D.* Growing point of *Salvinia* (Pringsheim) ;   typical ellipsoid type, the single pericline is however incomplete.   *E.* Growing point of *Azolla* (Strasburger) ;   circular or spheroidal type transitional to ellipsoidal.   *F.* Root-cap of *Equisetum* (Nägeli and Leitgeb) ; modified circular type.   *G.* Cross-section of leaf-vein, *Trichomanes* (Prantl) ;   ellipsoidal type with incomplete periclines.   *H.* Embryo of *Alisma ;* typical ellipsoid type, pericline incomplete only at lower side.   *I.* Growing point of bud of the pine (*Abies*) ;   typical paraboloid type, both anticlines and periclines having the form of parabolas (Sachs).

right angles.   All these schemes are, *mutatis mutandis*, directly convertible into the corresponding solid forms in three dimensions.

Sachs has shown in the most beautiful manner that all the above ideal types are closely approximated in nature, and Rauber has applied the same principle to the cleavage of animal cells. The discoid or spheroid form is more or less nearly realized in the thalloid growths of various lower plants, in the embryos of flowering plants, and elsewhere (Fig. 119). The paraboloid form is according to Sachs characteristic of the growing points of many higher plants; and here too the actual form is remarkably similar to the ideal scheme (Fig. 119, *I*).

For our purpose the most important form is the sphere, which is the typical shape of the egg-cell; and all forms of cleavage are derivatives of the typical division of a sphere in accordance with Sachs's laws. The ideal form of cleavage would here be a succession of rectangular cleavages in the three dimensions of space, the anticlines passing through the centre so as to split the egg in the initial stages successively into halves, quadrants, and octants, the periclines being parallel to the surface so as to separate the inner ends of these cells from the outer. No case is known in which this order is accurately followed throughout, and the periclinal cleavages are of comparatively rare occurrence, being found as a regular feature of the early cleavage only in those cases where the primary germ-layers are separated by delamination. The simplest and most typical form of egg-cleavage occurs in eggs like those of echinoderms, which are of spherical form, and in which the deutoplasm is small in amount and equally distributed through its substance. Such a cleavage is beautifully displayed in the egg of the holothurian *Synapta*, as shown in the diagrams, Fig. 120, constructed from Selenka's drawings.[1] The first cleavage is vertical, or *meridional*, passing through the egg-axis and dividing the egg into equal halves. The second, which is also meridional, cuts the first plane at right angles and divides the egg into quadrants. The third is horizontal, or *equatorial*, dividing the egg into equal octants. The order of division is thus far exactly that demanded by Sachs's law and agrees precisely with the cleavage of various kinds of spherical plant-cells. The later cleavages depart from the ideal type in the absence of periclinal divisions, the embryo becoming hollow, and its wall consisting of a single layer of cells in which anticlinal cleavages occur in regular rectangular succession. The fourth cleavage is again meridional, giving two tiers of eight cells each; the fifth is horizontal, dividing each tier into an upper and a lower layer. The regular alternation is continued up to the ninth division (giving 512 cells), when the divisions pause while the gastrulation begins. In later stages the regularity is lost.

This simple and regular mode of division forms a type to which nearly all forms of cleavage may be referred; but the order and form

[1] Cf. also Fig. 3.

of the divisions is endlessly varied by special conditions. These modifications are all referable to the three following causes : —

1. Disturbances in the rhythm of division.
2. Displacement of the cells.
3. Unequal division of the cells.

The first of these requires little comment. Nothing is more common than a departure from the mathematical regularity of division. The variations are sometimes quite irregular, sometimes follow a definite law, as, for instance, in the annelid *Nereis* (Fig. 122), where the typical succession in the number of cells is with great constancy

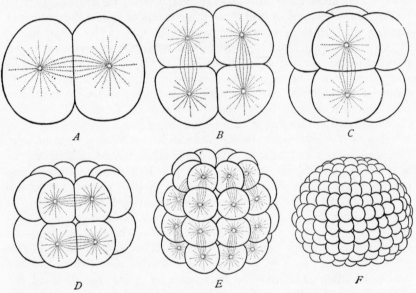

Fig. 120. — Cleavage of the ovum in the holothurian *Synapta* (slightly schematized). [After Selenka.]

A–E. Successive cleavages to the 32-cell stage. *F.* Blastula of 128 cells.

2, 4, 8, 16, 20, 23, 29, 32, 37, 38, 41, 42, after which the order is more or less variable. The meaning of such variations in particular cases is not very clear. They are certainly due in part to variations in the amount of deutoplasm ; for, as Balfour long since pointed out ('75), the rapidity of division in any part of the ovum is in general inversely proportional to the amount of deutoplasm it contains. Exceptions to this law are, however, known.

The second series of modifications, due to displacements of the cells, are probably due to mutual pressure, however caused,[1] which

[1] The pressure is probably due primarily to an attraction between the cells (*cytotropism* of Roux), but may be increased by the presence of membranes, by turgor, or by special processes of growth.

leads them to take up the position of least resistance or greatest economy of space. In this regard the behaviour of tissue-cells in general has been shown to conform on the whole to that of elastic spheres, such as soap-bubbles when massed together and free to move. Such bodies, as Plateau and Lamarle have shown, assume a polyhedral form and tend towards such an arrangement that *the area*

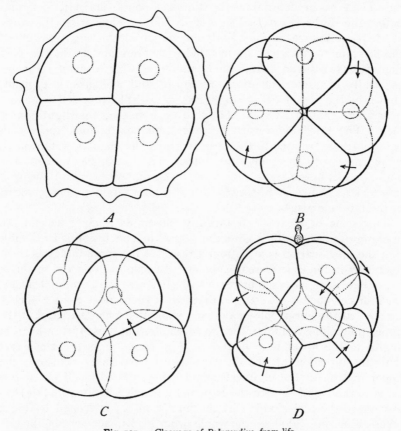

Fig. 121. — Cleavage of *Polygordius*, from life.

A. Four-cell stage, from above. *B.* Corresponding view of 8-cell stage. *C.* Side view of the same (contrast Fig. 120, *C*). *D.* Sixteen-cell stage from the side.

of surface-contact between them is a minimum. Spheres in a mass thus tend to assume the form of interlocking polyhedrons so arranged that three planes intersect in a line, while four lines and six planes meet at a point. If arranged in a single layer on an extended surface they assume the form of hexagonal prisms, three planes meeting along a line as before. Both these forms are commonly shown in the arrangement of the cells of plant and animal tissues; and Berthold

('86) and Errara ('86, '87) have pointed out that in almost all cases the cells tend to alternate or interlock so as to reduce the contact-area to a minimum. Thus arise many of the most frequent modifications of cleavage. Sometimes, as in *Synapta*, the alternation of the cells is effected through displacement of the blastomeres after their formation. More commonly it arises during the division of the cells and may even be predetermined by the position of the mitotic figures before the slightest external sign of division. Thus arises that form of cleavage known as the spiral, oblique, or alternating type, where the blastomeres interlock during their formation and lie in the position of least resistance from the beginning. This form of cleavage, especially characteristic of many worms and mollusks, is typically shown by the egg of *Polygordius* (Fig. 121). The four-celled stage is nearly like that of *Synapta*, though even here the cells slightly interlock. The third division is, however, oblique, the four upper cells being virtually rotated to the right (with the hands of a watch) so as to alternate with the four lower ones. The fourth cleavage is likewise oblique, but at right angles to the third, so that all of the cells interlock as shown in Fig. 121, *D*. This alternation regularly recurs in the later cleavages.

This form of cleavage beautifully illustrates Sachs's second law operating under modified conditions, and the conclusion is irresistible that the modification is at bottom a result of the same forces as those operating in the case of soap-bubbles. In many worms and mollusks the obliquity of cleavage appears still earlier, at the second cleavage, the four cells being so arranged that two of them meet along a "cross-furrow" at the lower pole of the egg, while the other two meet at the upper pole along a similar, though often shorter, cross-furrow at right angles to the lower (*e.g.* in *Nereis*, Fig. 122). It is a curious fact that the direction of the displacement is extremely constant, the upper quartet in the eight-cell stage being rotated in all but a few cases to the right, or with the hands of a watch. Crampton ('94) has discovered the remarkable fact that in *Physa*, a gasteropod having a reversed or sinistral shell, the whole order of displacement is likewise reversed.

The third class of modifications, due to unequal division of the cells, leads to the most extreme types of cleavage. Such divisions appear sooner or later in all forms of cleavage, the perfect equality so long maintained in *Synapta* being a rare phenomenon. The period at which the inequality first appears varies greatly in different forms. In *Polygordius* (Fig. 121) the first marked inequality appears at the fifth cleavage; in sea-urchins it appears at the fourth (Fig. 3); in *Amphioxus* at the third (Fig. 123); in the tunicate *Clavelina* at the second (Fig. 126); in *Nereis* at the first division (Figs. 43, 122). The extent of the inequality varies in like manner. Taking the third cleavage as a type, we may trace every transition from an equal division (echinoderms, *Polygordius*), through forms in which it is but slightly marked (*Amphioxus*, frog), those in which it is conspicuous (*Nereis, Lymnæa, Polyclades, Petromyzon*, etc.), to forms such as *Clepsine*, where the cells of the upper quartet are so minute as to appear like mere buds from the four large lower cells (Fig. 123). At the

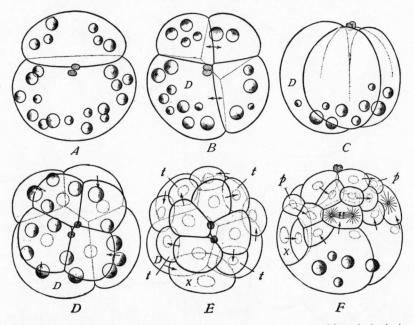

Fig. 122. — Cleavage of *Nereis*. An example of a spiral cleavage, unequal from the beginning and of a marked mosaic-like character.

A. Two-cell stage (the circles are oil-drops). *B*. Four-cell stage; the second cleavage-plane passes through the future median plane. *C*. The same from the right side. *D*. Eight-cell stage. *E*. Sixteen cells; from the cells marked *t* arises the prototroch or larval ciliated belt, from *X* the ventral nerve-cord and other structures, from *D* the mesoblast-bands, the germ-cells, and a part of the alimentary canal. *F*. Twenty-nine-cell stage, from the right side; *p*. girdle of prototrochal cells which give rise to the ciliated belt.

extreme of the series we reach the partial or meroblastic cleavage, such as occurs in the cephalopods, in many fishes, and in birds and reptiles. Here the lower hemisphere of the egg does not divide at all, or only at a late period, segmentation being confined to a disc-like region or blastoderm at one pole of the egg (Fig. 124).

Very interesting is the case of the *teloblasts* or *pole-cells* characteristic of the development of many annelids and mollusks and found in some arthropods. These remarkable cells are large blastomeres, set aside early in the development, which bud forth smaller cells in regular succession at a fixed point, thus giving rise to long cords of cells (Fig. 125). The teloblasts are especially characteristic of apical growth, such as occurs in the elongation of the body in annelids, and they are closely analogous to the apical cells situated at the growing point in many plants, such as the ferns and stoneworts.

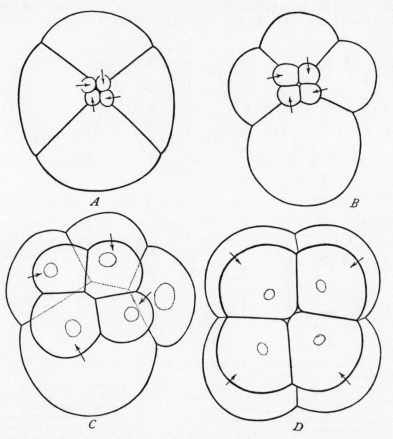

Fig. 123.—The 8-cell stage of four different animals showing gradations in the inequality of the third cleavage.

A. The leech *Clepsine* (Whitman). *B.* The chætopod *Rhynchelmis* (Vejdovský). *C.* The lamellibranch *Unio* (Lillie). *D. Amphioxus.*

Unequal division still awaits an explanation. The fact has already been pointed out (p. 51) that the inequality of the daughter-cells is preceded, if not caused, by an inequality of the asters; but we are still almost entirely ignorant of the ultimate cause of this inequality. In the cleavage of the animal egg unequal division is closely connected with the distribution of yolk—a fact generalized by Balfour in the statement ('80) that the size of the cells formed in cleavage varies inversely to the relative amount of protoplasm in the region of the egg from which they arise. Thus, in all telolecithal ova, where the deutoplasm is mainly stored in the lower or vegetative hemisphere, as in many worms, mollusks, and vertebrates, the cells of the upper or protoplasmic hemisphere are smaller than those of the lower, and may be distinguished as *micromeres* from the larger *macromeres* of the lower hemisphere. The size-ratio between micromeres and macromeres is on the whole directly proportional to the ratio between protoplasm and deutoplasm. Partial or discoidal cleavage occurs when the mass of deutoplasm is so great as entirely to prevent cleavage in the lower hemisphere.

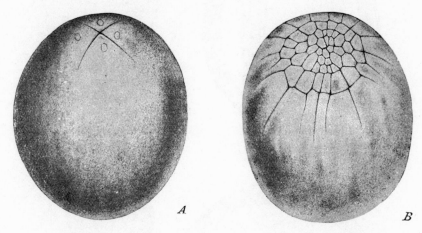

Fig. 124. — Partial or meroblastic cleavage in the squid *Loligo*. [WATASÉ.]

Balfour's law undoubtedly explains a large number of cases, but by no means all; for innumerable cases are known in which no correlation can be made out between the distribution of inert substance and the inequality of division. This is the case, for example, with the teloblasts mentioned above, which contain no deutoplasm, yet regularly divide unequally. It seems to be inapplicable to the inequalities of the first two divisions in annelids and gasteropods. It is conspicuously inadequate in the history of individual blastomeres, where the history of division has been accurately determined. In *Nereis*, for example, a large cell known as the first somatoblast, formed at the fourth cleavage (*X*, Fig. 122, *E*), undergoes an invariable order of division, three unequal divisions being followed by an equal one, then by three other unequal divisions, and again by an equal. This cell contains no deutoplasm and undergoes no percepti-

T

ble changes of substance. The cause of the definite succession of equal and unequal divisions is here wholly unexplained.

Such cases prove that Balfour's law is only a partial explanation, and is probably the expression of a more deeply lying cause, and there is reason to believe that this cause lies outside the immediate mechanism of mitosis. Conklin ('94) has called attention to the

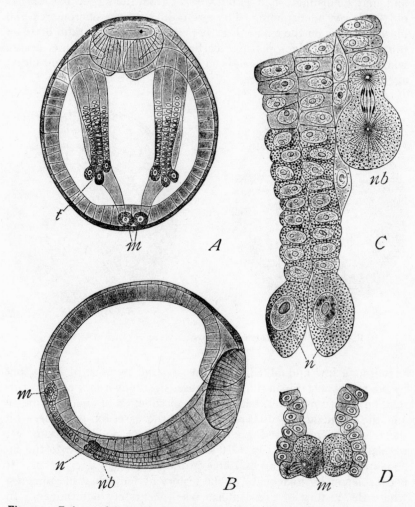

Fig. 125. — Embryos of the earthworm *Allolobophora fœtida*, showing teloblasts or apical cells.

A. Gastrula from the ventral side. B. The same from the right side; *m*, the terminal teloblasts or *primary mesoblasts*, which bud forth the mesoblast-bands, cell by cell; *t*, lateral teloblasts, comprising a *neuroblast*, *nb*, from which the ventral nerve-cord arises, and two *nephroblasts*, *n*, of somewhat doubtful nature but probably concerned in the formation of the nephridia. C. Lateral group of teloblasts, more enlarged, the neuroblast, *nb*, in division; *n*, the nephroblasts. D. The primary mesoblasts enlarged; one in division.

fact [1] that the immediate cause of the inequality probably does not lie either in the nucleus or in the amphiaster; for not only the chromatin-halves, *but also the asters*, are exactly equal in the early prophases, and the inequality of the asters only appears as the division proceeds. Probably, therefore, the cause lies in some relation between the mitotic figure and the cell-body in which it lies. I believe there is reason to accept the conclusion that this relation is one of position, however caused. A central position of the mitotic figure results in an equal division; an eccentric position caused by a radial movement of the mitotic figure, in the direction of its axis towards the periphery, leads to unequal division, and the greater the eccentricity, the greater the inequality, an extreme form being beautifully shown in the formation of the polar bodies. Here the original amphiaster is perfectly symmetrical, with the asters of equal size (Fig. 71, *A*). As the spindle rotates into its radial position and approaches the periphery, the development of the outer aster becomes, as it were, suppressed, while the central aster becomes enormously large. *The size of the aster, in other words, depends upon the extent of the cytoplasmic area that falls within the sphere of influence of the centrosome;* and this area depends upon the position of the centrosome. If, therefore, the polar amphiaster could be artificially prevented from moving to its peripheral position, the egg would probably divide equally.

The causes that determine the position of the amphiaster are scarcely known. It has been proved by experiment that *in some cases* this position may be determined by mechanical causes. Thus, Driesch has shown that when the eggs of sea-urchins are flattened by pressure, the amphiasters all assume the position of least resistance, *i.e.* parallel to the flattened sides, so that the cleavages are all vertical, and the egg segments as a flat plate of eight, sixteen, or thirty-two cells (Fig. 135). This is totally different from the normal form of cleavage; yet such eggs, when released from pressure, are capable of development and give rise to normal embryos. This interesting experiment makes it highly probable that the disc-like cleavage of meroblastic eggs, like that of the squid or bird, is a mechanical result of the accumulation of yolk by which the formative protoplasmic region of the ovum is reduced to a thin layer at the upper pole; and it indicates, further, that the unequal cleavage of less modified telolecithal eggs, like those of the frog or snail, are in like manner due to the displacement of the mitotic figures towards the upper pole. Even here, however, the hypothesis of a merely mechanical displacement probably does not touch the root of the

---

[1] In the cleavage of gasteropod eggs.

matter; for it will not account for the eccentric position of the
spindle in the formation of the polar bodies or in teloblasts.   Neither
will it explain the eccentric position of the horizontal spindle in such
cases as the first cleavage of the annelid egg.   In *Nereis*, for example (Figs. 43, 122), the inequality of the first cleavage is predetermined long before actual division both by an eccentric position of
the spindle and an inequality in the asters, neither of which can be
referred to an unequal horizontal distribution of the yolk.[1]   In this
and many similar cases we must assume more subtle causes lying
in the organization of the cytoplasmic mass, or rather of the egg
as a whole; but these deeper causes still lie beyond our grasp.
Unequal division, which plays so important a part in development,
still therefore awaits a final explanation, and until this is forthcoming we have but a vague comprehension of the primary factors of
growth.

Hertwig's Development of Sachs's Law.—We have now to consider
two additional laws of cell-division formulated by Oscar Hertwig in
1884, which bear directly on the facts just outlined and which lie
behind Sachs's principle of the rectangular intersection of successive
division-planes.   These are:—

1. *The nucleus tends to take up a position at the centre of its sphere
of influence, i.e. of the protoplasmic mass in which it lies.*

2. *The axis of the mitotic figures typically lies in the longest axis
of the protoplasmic mass, and division therefore tends to cut this axis
at a right angle.*

The second law explains not only the mode of division in flattened
eggs, but also the normal succession of the division-planes according
to Sachs's second law.   The first division of a homogeneous spherical
egg, for example, is followed by a second division at right angles to it,
since each hemisphere is twice as long in the plane of division as in
any plane vertical to it.   The mitotic figure of the second division
lies therefore parallel to the first plane, which forms the base of the
hemisphere, and the ensuing division is vertical to it.   The same
applies to the third division, since each quadrant is as long as the
entire egg while at most only half its diameter.   Division is therefore transverse to the long axis and vertical to the first two planes.

Hertwig's second law has caused much discussion and has been
shown to have many exceptions, as for instance in the cambium-cells
of plants and in columnar epithelium.   While undoubtedly one of
the most important laws of cell-division thus far determined, it only
pushes the analysis a stage further back, and leaves unexplained

---

[1] In an earlier paper I made the erroneous statement that the first cleavage-spindle of
Nereis lies centrally in the egg.   Later and more careful studies by means of sections prove
that this was incorrect.

the nature of the forces that determine the position of the spindle-axis. Pflüger[1] assumed that this position must be that of least resistance to the elongation of the spindle, which is obviously in the long axis of the protoplasmic mass; and the same view has been advocated by Braem and Driesch. Now, there can of course be no doubt that the final direction of the spindle, like that of any body, is the position of least resistance, *i.e.* the position of equilibrium determined by the resultant of all the forces operating upon it. The undetermined point is whether these forces are of a simple mechanical nature, such as pressure and the like, or of a more subtle physiological character. Roux seeks them in the "tractive forces" of the protoplasmic mass modified by an innate predisposition to a particular form and succession of divisions that has its seat in the nucleus. Heidenhain identifies them with conditions of intra-cellular tension determined by the astral rays.

It cannot be doubted that all these forces may play a part in determining the position of the spindle, but it must be confessed that the problem is still very far from a solution. In some cases Hertwig's law is directly opposed to the facts, the spindle lying transversely to the axis of the protoplasmic mass. In other cases, as for instance in the division of some Protozoa (*Euglypha*, t. Schewiakoff) and in segmenting ova (*Crepidula*, t. Conklin), the protoplasmic elongation leads the way, and may be fully determined before the spindle is formed. In still other cases the reverse is true, as in the formation of the polar bodies, where the spindle forms and rotates into position before the egg shows any corresponding change of form. In many ova we can assign no mechanical cause for the rotation, such as the pressure of deutoplasm and the like; and even when deutoplasm is present, its position is such that we should expect a horizontal rather than a vertical position of the polar spindles were it a mechanical result of the presence of deutoplasm.

The ultimate determination of the planes of division is probably to be sought in those influences that determine the movements of the centrosomes. Sachs's law of rectangular succession is primarily a result of the fact that the daughter-centrosomes typically diverge, and so determine the spindle-axis, in a line which is at right angles to the axis of the mother-spindle; hence the ensuing cleavage is vertical to the last.[2] What we do not really understand is the principle by which this typical succession is modified. The pressure-experiments prove that the modifications *may* be produced by simple

[1] '84, p. 613.
[2] In this we find also an explanation of the fact first observed by Roux in the frog's egg, and confirmed by me in the sea-urchin egg, that the first plane of cleavage passes through the sperm-track and hence approximately through the entrance-point of the spermatozoön.

mechanical means.   The history of division in the cambium-cells
and columnar epithelium seems to show that neither direct pressure
nor the shape of the cells caused by it can be the ultimate cause.
The succession of divisions, always in the same plane, in apical cells
and in teloblasts, is directly related with a deeply lying law of growth
that affects the whole developing organism, and we cannot at present distinguish in such cases between cause and effect; for whether
the apical growth of the body as a whole is caused by local conditions within the apical cells, or the reverse, is undetermined.   This
unsatisfactory result shows how far we still are from an understanding of the fundamental laws of growth and their relation to cell-
division, and how vast a field for experimental research lies open in
this direction.

B.   Promorphological Relations of Cleavage

The cleavage of the ovum has thus far been considered merely as
a problem of cell-division.   We have now to regard it in a far more
interesting and suggestive aspect; namely, in its morphological relations to the body to which it gives rise.   From what has been said
thus far it might be supposed that the egg simply splits up into indifferent cells which, to use the phrase of Pflüger, have no more definite
relation to the structure of the adult body than have snow-flakes to the
avalanche to which they contribute.   Such a conclusion would be
totally erroneous.   It is a remarkable fact that in a very large number of cases a precise relation exists between the cleavage-products
and the adult parts to which they give rise; and this relation may
often be traced back to the beginning of development, so that from
the first division onwards we are able to predict the exact future of
every individual cell.   In this regard the cleavage of the ovum often
goes forward with a wonderful clock-like precision, giving the impres-
sion of a strictly ordered series in which every division plays a definite *rôle* and has a fixed relation to all that precedes and follows it.

But more than this, the apparent predetermination of the embryo
may often be traced still further back to the regions of the undivided
and even unfertilized ovum.   The egg, therefore, may exhibit a distinct promorphology; and the morphological aspect of cleavage
must be considered in relation to the promorphology of the ovum
of which it is an expression.

1. *Promorphology of the Ovum*

(*a*) *Polarity and the Egg-axis.* — It was long ago recognized by
von Baer ('34) that the unsegmented egg of the frog has a definite
egg-axis connecting two differentiated poles, and that the position of

the embryo is definitely related to it.   The great embryologist
pointed out, further, that the early cleavage-planes also are definitely related to it, the first two passing through it in two meridians
intersecting each other at a right angle, while the third is transverse
to it, and is hence equatorial.[1]   Remak afterwards recognized the
fact[2] that the larger cells of the lower hemisphere represent, broadly
speaking, the "vegetative layer" of von Baer, *i.e.* the inner germ-
layer or entoblast, from which the alimentary organs arise; while
the smaller cells of the upper hemisphere represent the "animal
layer," outer germ-layer or ectoblast from which arise the epidermis,
the nervous system, and the sense-organs.   This fact, afterwards
confirmed in a very large number of animals, led to the designation
of the two poles as *animal* and *vegetative, formative* and *nutritive,* or
protoplasmic and *deutoplasmic,* the latter terms referring to the fact
that the nutritive deutoplasm is mainly stored in the lower hemisphere, and that development is therefore more active in the upper.
The polarity of the ovum is accentuated by other correlated phenomena.   In every case where an egg-axis can be determined by the
accumulation of deutoplasm in the lower hemisphere the egg-nucleus
sooner or later lies eccentrically in the upper hemisphere, and the
polar bodies are formed at the upper pole.   Even in cases where
the deutoplasm is equally distributed or is wanting — if there really
be such cases — an egg-axis is still determined by the eccentricity
of the nucleus and the corresponding point at which the polar bodies
are formed.

   In vastly the greater number of cases the polarity of the ovum has
a definite promorphological significance; for the egg-axis shows a
definite and constant relation to the axes of the adult body.   This
relation is, it is true, somewhat variable in different animals, yet the
evidence indicates that as a rule it is constant in a given species.   It
is a very general rule that the upper pole, as marked by the position of the polar bodies, lies in the median plane at a point which is
afterwards found to lie at or near the anterior end.   Throughout
the annelids and mollusks, for example, the upper pole is the point
at which the cerebral ganglia are afterwards formed; and these
organs lie in the adult on the dorsal side near the anterior extremity.
This relation holds true for many of the Bilateralia, though the
primitive relation is often disguised by asymmetrical growth in the
later stages, such as occur in echinoderms.   It is not, however, a
universal rule.   The recent observations of Castle ('96), which are
in accordance with the earlier work of Seeliger, show that in the

---

[1] The third plane is in this case not precisely at the equator, but considerably above it,
forming a "parallel" cleavage.

[2] '55, p. 130.

tunicate *Ciona* the usual relation is reversed, the polar bodies being formed at the vegetative (*i.e.* deutoplasmic) pole, which afterwards becomes the ventral side of the larva. In *Ascaris* Boveri's observations seem to show that the position of the polar bodies has no constant relation to the adult axes, and Häcker describes a similar variability in the copepods (Fig. 130). My own observations on the echinoderm-egg indicate that here also the primitive egg-axis has an entirely inconstant and casual relation to the gastrula-axis. It may perhaps still be possible to show that these exceptions are only apparent, and the principle involved is too important to be accepted without further proof. As the facts now stand, however, they seem to admit of no other conclusion than that the relation of the primitive egg-axis to the adult axes is not absolutely constant, and may in particular cases be variable. To admit this is to grant that this relation is not of a fundamental character, and that the axes of the adult are not predetermined from the beginning, but are established in the egg in the course of development.

(*b*) *Axial Relations of the Primary Cleavage-planes.* — Since the egg-axis is definitely related to the embryonic axes, and since the first two cleavage-planes pass through it, we may naturally look for a definite relation between these planes and the embryonic axes; and if such a relation exists, then the first two or four blastomeres must likewise have a definite prospective value in the development. Such relations have, in fact, been accurately determined in a large number of cases. The first to call attention to such a relation seems to have been Newport ('54), who discovered the remarkable fact that *the first cleavage-plane in the frog's egg coincides with the median plane of the adult body;* that, in other words, one of the first two blastomeres gives rise to the left side of the body, the other to the right. This discovery, though long overlooked and, indeed, forgotten, was confirmed more than thirty years later by Pflüger and Roux ('87). It was placed beyond all question by a remarkable experiment by Roux ('88), who succeeded in killing one of the blastomeres by puncture with a heated needle, whereupon the uninjured cell gave rise to a half-body as if the embryo had been bisected down the middle line (Fig. 131).

A similar result has been reached in a number of other animals by following out the cell-lineage; *e.g.* by Van Beneden and Julin ('84) in the egg of the tunicate *Clavelina* (Fig. 126), and by Watasé ('91) in the eggs of cephalopods (Fig. 127). In both these cases all the early stages of cleavage show a beautiful bilateral symmetry, and not only can the right and left halves of the segmenting egg be distinguished with the greatest clearness, but also the anterior and posterior regions, and the dorsal and ventral aspects. These discoveries seemed, at first, to justify the hope that a fundamental law of development had been discovered, and Van Beneden was thus led, as early as 1883, to express the view that the development of all bilateral animals would probably be found to agree with the frog and ascidian in respect to the relations of the first cleavage.

This conclusion was soon proved to have been premature. In one series of forms, not the first but the second cleavage-plane was found

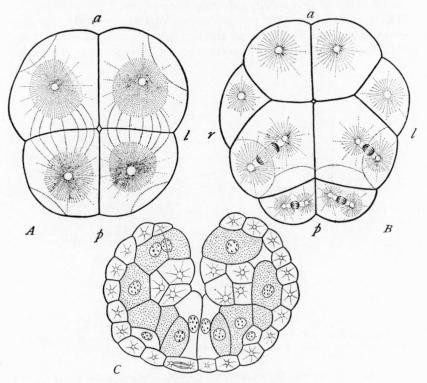

Fig. 126. — Bilateral cleavage of the tunicate egg.

A. Four-celled stage of *Clavelina*, viewed from the ventral side. *B.* Sixteen-cell stage (VAN BENEDEN and JULIN). *C.* Cross-section through the gastrula stage (CASTLE); *a*, anterior; *p*, posterior end; *l*, left, *r*, right side. [Orientation according to CASTLE.]

to coincide with the future long axis (*Nereis*, and some other annelids; *Crepidula, Umbrella,* and other gasteropods). In another series of forms neither of the first cleavages passes through the median plane, but both form an angle of about 45° to it (*Clepsine* and other leeches; *Rhynchelmis* and other annelids; *Planorbis, Nassa, Unio,* and other mollusks; *Discocœlis* and other platodes). In a few cases the first cleavage departs entirely from the rule, and is equatorial, as in *Ascaris* and some other nematodes. The whole subject was finally thrown into apparent confusion, first by the discovery of Clapp ('91), Jordan, and Eycleshymer ('94) that in some cases there seems to be no constant relation whatever between the early cleavage-planes and the adult axes, even in the same species (teleosts, urodeles); and even in the frog Hertwig showed that the relation described by Newport and Roux is not invariable. Driesch finally demonstrated that the direction of the early cleavage-planes might be artificially modified by pressure without perceptibly affecting the end-result (cf. p. 309).

These facts prove that the promorphology of the early cleavage-forms can have no fundamental significance. Nevertheless, they are of the highest interest and importance; for the fact that the forma-

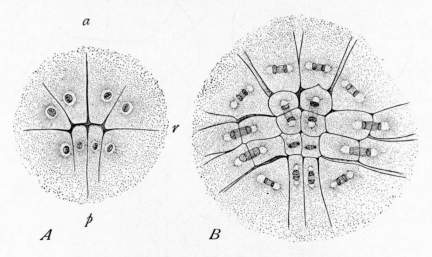

Fig. 127. — Bilateral cleavage of the squid's egg. [WATASÉ.]

A. Eight-cell stage. *B*. The fifth cleavage in progress. The first cleavage (*a-p*) coincides with the future median plane; the second (*l-r*) is transverse.

tive forces by which development is determined may or may not coincide with those controlling the cleavage, gives us some hope of disentangling the complicated factors of development through a comparative study of the different forms.

(*c*) *Other Promorphological Characters of the Ovum*. — Besides the polarity of the ovum, which is the most constant and clearly marked of its promorphological features, we are often able to discover other characters that more or less clearly foreshadow the later development. One of the most interesting and clearly marked of these is the bilateral symmetry of the ovum in bilateral animals, which is sometimes so clearly marked that the exact position of the embryo may be predicted in the unfertilized egg, sometimes even before it is laid. This is the case, for example, in the cephalopod egg, as shown by Watasé (Fig. 128). Here the form of the new-laid egg, before cleavage begins, distinctly foreshadows that of the embryonic body, and forms as it were a mould in which the whole development is cast. Its general shape is that of a hen's egg slightly flattened on one side, the narrow end, according to Watasé, representing the dorsal aspect, the broad end the ventral aspect, the flattened side the posterior region, and the more convex side the anterior region. *All the early cleavage-furrows are bilaterally arranged with respect to the plane of symmetry in the undivided egg;* and the same is true of the later development of all the bilateral parts.

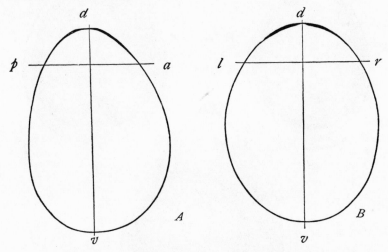

Fig. 128. — Outline of unsegmented squid's egg, to show bilaterality. [WATASE.]
A. From right side. *B*. From the posterior aspect.
a-p, antero-posterior axis; *d-v*, dorso-ventral axis; *l*, left side; *r*, right side.

Scarcely less striking is the case of the insect egg, as has been pointed out especially by Hallez, Blochmann, and Wheeler (Figs. 44, 129). In a large number of cases the egg is elongated and bilaterally symmetrical, and, according to Blochmann and Wheeler, may even show a bilateral distribution of the yolk corresponding with the bilaterality of the ovum. Hallez asserts as the result of a study of the cockroach (*Periplaneta*), the water-beetle (*Hydrophilus*), and the locust (*Locusta*) that "the egg-cell possesses the same orientation as the maternal organism that produces it; it has a cephalic pole and a caudal pole, a right side and a left, a dorsal aspect and a ventral; and these different aspects of the egg-cell coincide with the corresponding aspects of the embryo." [1] Wheeler ('93), after examining some thirty different species of insects, reached the same

[1] See Wheeler, '93, p. 67.

result, and concluded that even when the egg approaches the spherical form the symmetry still exists, though obscured. Moreover, according to Hallez ('86) and later writers, the egg always lies in the same position in the oviduct, its cephalic end being turned

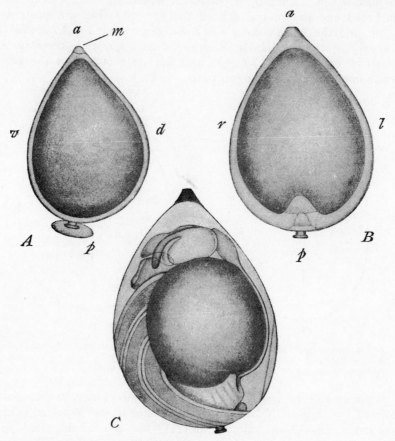

Fig. 129. — Eggs of the insect *Corixa*. [METSCHNIKOFF.]

A. Early stage before formation of the embryo, from one side. *B.* The same viewed in the plane of symmetry. *C.* The embryo in its final position.

a, anterior end; *p*, posterior; *l*, left side, *r*, right; *v*, ventral, *d*, dorsal aspect. (These letters refer to the *final* position of the embryo, which is nearly diametrically opposite to that in which it first develops) ; *m*, micropyle; near *p* is the pedicle by which the egg is attached.

forwards towards the upper end of the oviduct, and hence towards the head-end of the mother.[1]

[1] The micropyle usually lies at or near the anterior end, but may be at the posterior. It is a very important fact that the position of the polar bodies varies, being sometimes at the anterior end, sometimes on the side, either dorsal or lateral (Heider, Blochmann).

2. *Meaning of the Promorphology of the Ovum*

The interpretation of the promorphology of the ovum cannot be adequately treated apart from the general discussion of development given in the following chapter; nevertheless it may conveniently be considered at this point. Two fundamentally different interpretations of the facts have been given. On the one hand, it has been suggested by Flemming and Van Beneden,[1] and urged especially by Whitman,[2] that the cytoplasm of the ovum possesses a definite primordial organization which exists from the beginning of its existence even though invisible, and is revealed to observation through polar differentiation, bilateral symmetry, and other obvious characters in the unsegmented egg. On the other hand, it has been maintained by Pflüger, Mark, Oscar Hertwig, Driesch, Watasé, and the writer that all the promorphological features of the ovum are of secondary origin; that the egg-cytoplasm is at the beginning isotropous — *i.e.* indifferent or homaxial — and gradually acquires its promorphological features during its pre-embryonic history. Thus the egg of a bilateral animal is not at the beginning actually, but only potentially, bilateral. Bilaterality once established, however, it forms as it were the mould in which the cleavage and other operations of development are cast.

I believe that the evidence at our command weighs heavily on the side of the second view, and that the first hypothesis fails to take sufficient account of the fact that development does not necessarily begin with fertilization or cleavage, but may begin at a far earlier period during ovarian life. As far as the *visible* promorphological features of the ovum are concerned, this conclusion is beyond question. The only question that has any meaning is whether these visible characters are merely the expression of a more subtle pre-existing invisible organization of the same kind. I do not believe that this question can be answered in the affirmative save by the trite and, from this point of view, barren statement that every effect must have its pre-existing cause. That the egg possesses no fixed and predetermined cytoplasmic localization with reference to the adult parts, has, I think, been demonstrated through the remarkable experiments of Driesch, Roux, and Boveri, which show that a fragment of the egg may give rise to a complete larva (p. 308). There is strong evidence, moreover, that the egg-axis is not primordial, but is established at a particular period; and even after its establishment it may be entirely altered by new conditions. This is proved, for example, by the case of the frog's egg, in which, as Pflüger ('84), Born ('85), and Schultze ('94) have shown, the cytoplasmic materials

[1] See p. 298.   [2] Cf. pp. 299, 300.

may be entirely re-arranged under the influence of gravity, and a new axis established. In sea-urchins, my own observations ('95) render it probable that the egg-axis is not finally established until after fertilization. Finally, it is becoming more and more doubtful whether the relation of the egg-axis to the adult axis has so deep a significance as was at first assumed. This relation has been found

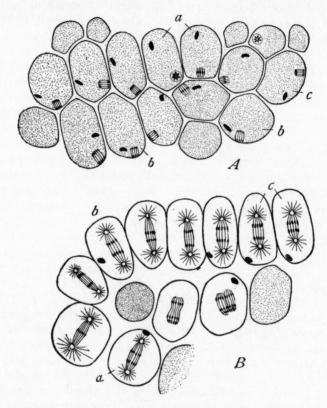

Fig. 130. — Variations in the axial relations of the eggs of *Cyclops*. From sections of the eggs as they lie in the oviduct. [HÄCKER.]

A. Group of eggs showing variations in relative position of the polar spindles and the sperm-nucleus (the latter black); in *a* the sperm-nucleus is opposite to the polar spindle, in *b*, near it or at the side. *B*. Group showing variations in the axis of first cleavage with reference to the polar bodies (the latter black); *a*, *b*, and *c*, show three different positions.

to vary not only in nearly related forms (insects), but even in the same species (*Ascaris*, according to Boveri and others; *Toxopneustes*, according to my own observations; copepods, according to Häcker).

All these and many other similar facts force us, I think, to the conclusion that the promorphological features of the egg are as truly a result of development as the characters coming into view at later stages. They are gradually established during the pre-embryonic stages, and the egg, when ready for fertilization, has already accomplished part of its task by laying the basis for what is to come.

Mark, who was one of the first to examine this subject carefully, concluded that the ovum is at first an indifferent or homaxial cell (*i.e.* isotropic), which afterwards *acquires* polarity and other promorphological features.[1] The same view was very precisely formulated by Watasé in 1891, in the following statement, which I believe to express accurately the truth: "It appears to me admissible to say at present that the ovum, which may start out without any definite axis at first, may acquire it later, and at the moment ready for its cleavage the distribution of its protoplasmic substances may be such as to exhibit a perfect symmetry, and the furrows of cleavage may have a certain definite relation to the inherent arrangement of the protoplasmic substances which constitute the ovum. Hence, in a certain case, the plane of the first cleavage-furrow may coincide with the plane of the median axis of the embryo, and the sundering of the protoplasmic material may take place into right and left, according to the pre-existing organization of the egg at the time of cleavage; and in another case the first cleavage may roughly correspond to the differentiation of the ectoderm and the entoderm, also according to the pre-organized constitution of the protoplasmic materials of the ovum.

"It does not appear strange, therefore, that we may detect a certain structural differentiation in the unsegmented ovum, with all the axes foreshadowed in it, and the axial symmetry of the embryonic organism identical with that of the adult."[2]

This passage contains, I believe, the gist of the whole matter, as far as the promorphological relations of the ovum and of cleavage-forms are concerned, though Watasé does not enter into the question as to how the arrangement of protoplasmic materials is effected. In considering this question, we must hold fast to the fundamental fact that the egg is a cell, like other cells, and that from an *a priori* point of view there is every reason to believe that the cytoplasmic differentiations that it undergoes must arise in essentially the same way as in other cells. We know that such differentiations, whether in form or in internal structure, show a definite relation to the environment of the cell — to its fellows, to the source of food, and the like. We know further, as Korschelt especially has pointed out, that *the egg-axis, as expressed by the eccentricity of the germinal vesicle, often shows a definite relation to the ovarian tissues*, the germinal vesicle lying near the point of attachment or of food-supply. Mark made

[1] '81, p. 512.　　　　　[2] '91, p. 280.

the pregnant suggestion, in 1881, that the primary polarity of the egg might be determined by "*the topographical relation of the egg* (when still in an indifferent state) *to the remaining cells of the maternal tissue from which it is differentiated*," and added that this relation might operate through the nutrition of the ovum.   "It would certainly be interesting to know if that phase of polar differentiation which is manifest in the position of the nutritive substance and of the germinal vesicle bears a constant relation to the free surface of the epithelium from which the egg takes its origin.   If, in cases where the egg is directly developed from epithelial cells, this relationship were demonstrable, it would be fair to infer the existence of corresponding, though obscured, relations in those cases where (as, for example, in mammals) the origin of the ovum is less directly traceable to an epithelial surface."[1] The polarity of the egg would therefore be comparable to the polarity of epithelial or gland cells, where, as pointed out at p. 40, the nucleus usually lies towards the base of the cell, near the source of food, while the characteristic cytoplasmic products, such as zymogen granules and other secretions, appear in the outer portion.[2] The exact conditions under which the ovarian egg develops are still too little known to allow of a positive conclusion regarding Mark's suggestion.   Moreover, the force of Korschelt's observation is weakened by the fact that in many eggs of the extreme telolecithal type, where the polarity is very marked, the germinal vesicle occupies a central or sub-central position during the period of yolk-formation and only moves towards the periphery near the time of maturation.

Indeed, in mollusks, annelids, and many other cases, the germinal vesicle remains in a central position, surrounded by yolk on all sides, until the spermatozoön enters.   Only then does the egg-nucleus move to the periphery, the deutoplasm become massed at one pole, and the polarity of the egg come into view (*Nereis*, Figs. 43 and 71).[3]   In such cases the axis of the egg is not improbably predetermined by the position of the centrosome, and we have still to seek the causes by which the position is established in the ovarian history of the egg. These considerations show that the problem is a complex one, involving, as it does, the whole question of cell-polarity; and I know of no more promising field of investigation than the ovarian history of the ovum with reference to this question.   That Mark's view is correct in principle is indicated by a great array of general evidence considered in the following chapter, where its bearing on the general theory of development is more fully dealt with.

---

[1] '81, p. 515.   [2] Hatschek has suggested the same comparison (*Zoölogie*, p. 112).

[3] The immature egg of *Nereis* shows, however, a distinct polarity in the arrangement of the fat-drops, which form a ring in the equatorial region.

C. THE ENERGY OF DIVISION

The causes by which cell-division is incited and by which its cessation is determined are as yet scarcely comprehended, and the questions that they suggest merge into the larger problem of the general control of growth. All animals and plants have a limit of growth, which is, however, much more definite in some forms than in others, and which differs in different tissues. During the individual development the energy of cell-division is most intense in the early stages (cleavage) and diminishes more and more as the limit of growth is approached. When the limit is attained a more or less definite equilibrium is established, some of the cells ceasing to divide and perhaps losing this power altogether (nerve-cells), others dividing only under special conditions (connective tissue-cells, gland-cells, muscle-cells), while others continue to divide throughout life, and thus replace the worn-out cells of the same tissue (Malpighian layer of the epidermis, etc.). The limit of size at which this state of equilibrium is attained is an hereditary character, which in many cases shows an obvious relation to the environment, and has therefore probably been determined and is maintained by natural selection. From the cytological point of view the limit of body-size appears to be correlated with the total *number* of cells formed rather than with their individual size. This relation has been carefully studied by Conklin ('96) in the case of the gasteropod *Crepidula*, an animal which varies greatly in size in the mature condition, the dwarfs having in some cases not more than $\frac{1}{25}$ the volume of the giants. The eggs are, however, of the same size in all, and their *number* is proportional to the size of the adult. The same is true of the tissue-cells. Measurements of cells from the epidermis, the kidney, the liver, the alimentary epithelium, and other tissues show that they are on the whole as large in the dwarfs as in the giants. The body-size therefore depends on the total number of cells rather than on their size individually considered, and the same appears to be the case in plants.[1]

Morgan has examined the same question experimentally through a comparison of normal larvæ of echinoderms and *Amphioxus* with dwarf larvæ of the same species developed from egg-fragments ('95, 1 ; '96). Broadly speaking, his results agree with Conklin's, though they show that the relation is by no means simple or constant. If unsegmented eggs of sea-urchins (*Sphærechinus*) be shaken to pieces, fragments of all sizes are obtained which may segment and produce blastulas and gastrulas ranging down to $\frac{1}{64}$ the volume of the normal size. Dwarfs are also obtained from isolated blastomeres of two-, four-, or eight-cell stages. In both cases the num-

[1] See Amelung ('93) and Strasburger ('93).

U

ber of cells in the blastula just before invagination is approximately proportional to the size of the blastula, though the smaller fragments show a tendency to produce a somewhat larger number, and their cells are, therefore, somewhat smaller than in the larger forms. The same is true in *Amphioxus*. Morgan, therefore, draws the very interesting conclusion that "the ultimate size of the cells produced by repeated division determines when the division shall come to an end for a certain stage of the ontogeny."[1]   This conclusion is, however, subject to exception; for Morgan finds that the dwarf larvæ show a tendency to use the same number of cells in the formation of certain organs as the full-sized individuals. Thus the dwarf blastulas tend to invaginate the same number of cells to form the archenteron as in the normal forms; and in *Amphioxus* the notochord of the dwarfs consists in cross-section of three cells, as in normal individuals, irrespective of the total number of cells. It is clear, therefore, that there is another factor, besides the size of the cells, to be taken into account, and the whole subject awaits further investigation.

The gradual diminution of the energy of division during development by no means proceeds at a uniform pace in all of the cells, and, during the cleavage, the individual blastomeres are often found to exhibit entirely different rhythms of division, periods of active division being succeeded by long pauses, and sometimes by an entire cessation of division even at a very early period. In the echinoderms, for example, it is well established that division suddenly pauses, or changes its rhythm, just before the gastrulation (in *Synapta* at the 512-cell stage, according to Selenka), and the same is said to be the case in *Amphioxus* (Hatschek, Lwoff). In *Nereis*, one of the blastomeres on each side of the body in the forty-two-cell stage suddenly ceases to divide, migrates into the interior of the body, and is converted into a unicellular glandular organ.[2] In the same animal, the four lower cells (macromeres) of the eight-cell stage divide in nearly regular succession up to the thirty-eight-cell stage, when a long pause takes place, and when the divisions are resumed they are of a character totally different from those of the earlier period. The cells of the ciliated belt or prototroch in this and other annelids likewise cease to divide at a certain period, their number remaining fixed thereafter.[3] Again, the number of cells produced for the foundation of particular structures is often definitely fixed, even when their number is afterwards increased by division. In

---

[1] '95, p. 119.

[2] This organ, doubtfully identified by me as the head-kidney, is probably a mucus-gland (Mead).

[3] Cf. Fig. 122.

annelids and gasteropods, for example, the entire ectoblast arises from twelve micromeres segmented off in three successive quartets of micromeres from the blastomeres of the four-cell stage. In *Echinus*, according to Morgan, the number of cells used in the formation of the archenteron is approximately one hundred; in *Sphærechinus* the number is approximately fifty.

Perhaps the most interesting numerical relation of this kind are those recently discovered in the division of teloblasts, where the number of divisions is directly correlated with the number of segments or somites. It is well known that this is the case in certain plants (*Characeæ*), where the alternating nodes and internodes of the stem are derived from corresponding single cells successively segmented off from the apical cell. Vejdovský's observations on the annelid *Dendrobæna* give strong ground to believe that the number of metamerically repeated parts of this animal, and probably of other annelids, corresponds in like manner with that of the number of cells segmented off from the teloblasts. The most remarkable and accurately determined case of this kind is that of the isopod crustacea, where the number of somites is limited and perfectly constant. In the embryos of these animals there are two groups of teloblasts near the hinder end of the embryo, viz. an inner group of mesoblasts, from which arise the mesoblast-bands, and an outer group of ectoblasts, from which arise the neural plates and the ventral ectoblast. McMurrich ('95) has recently demonstrated that the mesoblasts always divide exactly sixteen times, the ectoblasts thirty-two (or thirty-three) times, before relinquishing their teloblastic mode of division and breaking up into smaller cells. Now the sixteen groups of cells thus formed give rise to the sixteen respective somites of the post-naupliar region of the embryo (*i.e.* from the second maxilla backward). In other words, each single division of the mesoblasts and each double division of the ectoblasts splits off the material for a single somite! The number of these divisions, and hence of the corresponding somites, is a fixed inheritance of the species.

The causes that determine the rhythm of division, and thus finally establish the adult equilibrium, are but vaguely comprehended. The ultimate causes must of course lie in the inherited constitution of the organism, and are referable in the last analysis to the structure of the germ-cells. Every division must, however, be the response of the cell to a particular set of conditions or stimuli; and it is through the investigation of these stimuli that we may hope to penetrate further into the nature of development. It must be confessed that the specific causes that incite or inhibit cell-division are scarcely known. The egg-cell is in most cases stimulated to divide by the entrance of the spermatozoön, but in parthenogenesis exactly the same result is produced by a different cause. In the adult, cells may be stimulated to divide by the utmost variety of agencies — by chemical stimulus, as in the formation of galls, or in hyperplasia induced by the injection of foreign substances into the blood; by mechanical pressure, as in the formation of calluses; by injury, as in the healing of wounds and in the regeneration of lost parts; and by a multitude of more complex physiological and pathological conditions, — by any agency, in short, that disturbs the normal equilibrium of the body. In all these cases, however, it is difficult to determine the *immediate stimulus* to division; for a long chain of causes and effects may intervene between the primary disturbance and the ultimate reaction of the dividing cells. Thus there is reason to believe that the formation of a callus is not directly caused by pressure or friction, but through the determination of an increased blood-supply to the part affected and a heightened nutrition of the cells. Cell-division is here probably incited by local chemical changes; and the opinion is gaining ground that the immediate causes of division, whatever their antecedents, are to be sought in this direction. The most promising field for their investigation seems to lie in the direction of cellular pathology through the study of tumours and other abnormal growths. The work of Ziegler and Obolonsky indicates that the cells of the liver and kidney may be directly incited to divide through the action of arsenic and phosphorus; and several others have reached analogous results in the case of other tissues and other poisons. The formation of galls seems to leave no doubt that extremely complex and characteristic abnormal growths may result from specific chemical stimuli, and some pathologists have held a similar view in regard to the origin of abnormal growths in the animal body.

Suggestive as these results are, they scarcely touch the ultimate problem. The unknown factor is that which determines and maintains the normal equilibrium. A very interesting suggestion is the resistance theory of Thiersch and Boll, according to which each tissue continues to grow up to the limit afforded by the resistance of neighbouring tissues or organs. The removal or lessening of this resistance through injury or disease causes a resumption of growth and division, leading either to the regeneration of the lost parts or to the formation of abnormal growths. Thus the removal of a salamander's limb would seem to remove a barrier to the proliferation and growth of the remaining cells. These processes are therefore resumed, and continue until the normal barrier is re-established by the regeneration. To speak of such a "barrier" or "resistance" is, however, to use a highly figurative phrase which is not to be construed in a rude mechanical sense. There is no doubt that hypertrophy, atrophy, or displacement of particular parts often leads to compensatory changes in the neighbouring parts; but it is equally certain that such changes are not a direct mechanical effect of the disturbance, but a highly complex physiological response to it. How complex the problem is, is shown by the fact that even closely related animals may differ widely in this respect. Thus Fraisse has shown that the salamander may completely regenerate an amputated limb, while the frog only heals the wound without further regeneration.[1] Again, in the case of cœlenterates, Loeb and Bickford have shown that the tubularian hydroids are able to regenerate the tentacles at both ends of a segment of the stem, while the polyp *Cerianthus* can regenerate them only at the distal end of a section (Fig. 142). In the latter case, therefore, the body possesses an inherent polarity which cannot be overturned by external conditions.

D. CELL-DIVISION AND GROWTH

The relation between cell-division and growth has already been touched upon at pp. 41 and 265. The direction of the division-planes in the individual cells evidently stands in some causal relation with the axes of growth in the body, as is especially clear in the case of rapidly elongating structures (apical buds, teloblasts, and the like), where the division-planes are predominantly transverse to the axis of elongation. Which of these is the primary factor, the direction of general growth or the direction of the division-planes? This question is a difficult one to answer, for the two phenomena are often too closely related to be disentangled. As far as the plants are concerned, however, it has been conclusively shown by Hofmeister, De Bary, and Sachs that *the growth of the mass is the primary factor;* for the characteristic mode of growth is often shown by the growing mass before it splits up into cells, and the form of cell-division adapts itself to that of the mass: " Die Pflanze bildet Zellen, nicht die Zelle bildet Pflanzen " (De Bary).

The opinion has of late rapidly gained ground that the same is true in principle of animal growth, and this view has been urged by many writers, among whom may be mentioned Rauber, Hertwig, and especially Whitman, whose fine essay on the *Inadequacy of the Cell-theory of Development* ('93) marks a distinct advance in our point of view. It is certain that in the earlier stages of development, and in a less degree in later stages as well, the character of growth and division in the individual cell is but a local manifestation of a formative power pervading the organism as a whole; and

---

[1] In salamanders regeneration only takes place when the bone is cut across, and does not occur if the limb be exarticulated and removed at the joint.

the general truth of this view has been in certain cases conclusively demonstrated by experiment.[1] It has, however, become clear that this conclusion can be accepted only with certain reservations; for as development proceeds, the cells may acquire so high a degree of independence that profound modifications may occur in special regions through injury or disease, without affecting the general equilibrium of the body. The most striking proof of this lies in the fact that grafts or transplanted structures may perfectly retain their specific character, though transferred to a different region of the body, or even to another species. Nevertheless the facts of regeneration prove that even in the adult the formative processes in special parts are in many cases definitely correlated with the organization of the entire mass; and in the following chapter we shall see reason to conclude that such a correlation is a survival, in the adult, of a condition characteristic of the embryonic stages, and that the independence of special parts in the adult is a secondary result of development.

LITERATURE. VIII

Berthold, G. — Studien über Protoplasma-mechanik. *Leipzig*, 1886.

Boll, Fr. — Das Princip des Wachsthums. *Berlin*, 1876.

Bourne, G. C. — A Criticism of the Cell-theory; being an answer to Mr. Sedgwick's article on the Inadequacy of the Cellular Theory of Development: *Quart. Journ. M. S.*, XXXVIII. 1, 1895.

Errara. — Zellformen und Seifenblasm: *Tagebl. der 60 Versammlung deutscher Naturforscher und Aerzte zu Wiesbaden.* 1887.

Hertwig, O. — Das Problem der Befruchtung und der Isotropie des Eies, eine Theorie der Vererbung. *Jena*, 1884.

Hofmeister. — Die Lehre von der Pflanzenzelle. *Leipzig*, 1867.

McMurrich, J. P. — Embryology of the Isopod Crustacea: *Journ. Morph.*, XI. 1. 1895.

Mark, E. L. — Limax. (See List IV.)

Rauber, A. — Neue Grundlegungen zur Kenntniss der Zelle: *Morph. Jahrb.*, VIII. 1883.

Sachs, J. — Pflanzenphysiologie. (See List VII.)

Sedgwick, H. — On the Inadequacy of the Cellular Theory of Development, etc.: *Quart. Journ. Mic. Sci.*, XXXVII. 1. 1894.

Strasburger, E. — Ueber die Wirkungssphäre der Kerne und die Zellgrösse: *Histologische Beiträge*, V. 1893.

Watasé, S. — Studies on Cephalopods; I., Cleavage of the Ovum: *Journ. Morph.*, IV. 3. 1891.

Whitman, C. O. — The Inadequacy of the Cell-theory of Development: *Wood's Holl Biol. Lectures.* 1893.

Wilson, Edm. B. — The Cell-lineage of *Nereis*: *Journ. Morph.*, VI. 3. 1892.

Id. — Amphioxus and the Mosaic Theory of Development: *Journ. Morph.*, VIII. 3. 1893.

---

[1] Cf. p. 312.

CHAPTER IX

THEORIES OF INHERITANCE AND DEVELOPMENT

"It is certain that the germ is not merely a body in which life is dormant or potential, but that it is itself simply a detached portion of the substance of a pre-existing living body."
HUXLEY.[1]

"Inheritance must be looked at as merely a form of growth." DARWIN.[2]

"Ich möchte daher wohl den Versuch wagen, durch eine Darstellung des Beobachteten Sie zu einer tiefern Einsicht in die Zeugungs- und Entwickelungsgeschichte der organischen Körper zu führen und zu zeigen, wie dieselben weder vorgebildet sind, noch auch, wie man sich gewöhnlich denkt, aus ungeformter Masse in einem bestimmten Momente plötzlich ausschiessen." VON BAER.[3]

EVERY discussion of inheritance and development must take as its point of departure the fact that the germ is a single cell similar in its essential nature to any one of the tissue-cells of which the body is composed. That a cell can carry with it the sum total of the heritage of the species, that it can in the course of a few days or weeks give rise to a mollusk or a man, is the greatest marvel of biological science. In attempting to analyze the problems that it involves, we must from the outset hold fast to the fact, on which Huxley insisted, that the wonderful formative energy of the germ is not impressed upon it from without, but is inherent in the egg as a heritage from the parental life of which it was originally a part. The development of the embryo is nothing new. It involves no breach of continuity, and is but a continuation of the vital processes going on in the parental body. What gives development its marvellous character is the rapidity with which it proceeds and the diversity of the results attained in a span so brief.

But when we have grasped this cardinal fact we have but focussed our instruments for a study of the real problem. *How* do the adult characteristics lie latent in the germ-cell; and how do they become patent as development proceeds? This is the final question that looms in the background of every investigation of the cell. In

---

[1] *Evolution, Science and Culture*, p. 291.
[2] *Variation of Animals and Plants*, II. p. 398.
[3] *Entwick. der Thiere*, II., 1837, p. 8.

approaching it we may well make a frank confession of ignorance; for in spite of all that the microscope has revealed, we have not yet penetrated the mystery, and inheritance and development still remain in their fundamental aspects as great a riddle as they were to the Greeks. What we have gained is a tolerably precise acquaintance with the external aspects of development. The gross errors of the early preformationists have been dispelled.[1] We know that the germ-cell contains no predelineated embryo; that development is manifested, on the one hand, by a continued process of cell-division, on the other hand, by a process of differentiation, through which the cells gradually assume diverse forms and functions, and so accomplish a physiological division of labour. But we have not yet fathomed the inmost structure of the germ-cell, and the means by which the latent adult characters that it involves are made actual as development proceeds. And it should be clearly understood that when we attempt to approach these deeper problems we are compelled to advance beyond the solid ground of fact into a region of more or less doubtful and shifting hypothesis, where the point of view continually changes as we proceed. It would, however, be an error to conclude that modern hypotheses of inheritance and development are baseless speculations that attempt a merely formal solution of the problem, like those of the seventeenth and eighteenth centuries. They are a product of the inductive method, a direct outcome of accurately determined fact, and they lend to the study of embryology a point and precision that it would largely lack if limited to a strictly objective description of phenomena.

All discussions of development are now revolving about two central hypotheses, a preliminary examination of which will serve as an introduction to the general subject. These are, first, the theory of *Germinal Localization*[2] of Wilhelm His ('74), and second, the *Idioplasm Hypothesis* of Nägeli ('84). The relation between these two conceptions, close as it is, is not at first sight very apparent; and for the purpose of a preliminary sketch they may best be considered separately.

A. The Theory of Germinal Localization

Although the *naïve* early theory of preformation and evolution was long since abandoned, yet we find an after-image of it in the theory of germinal localization which in one form or another has

---

[1] Cf. Introduction, p. 6.
[2] I venture to suggest this term as an English equivalent for the awkward expression " Organbildende Keimbezirke " of His.

been advocated by some of the foremost students of development. It is maintained that, although the embryo is not pre-*formed* in the germ, it must nevertheless be pre-*determined* in the sense that the egg contains definite areas or definite substances predestined for the formation of corresponding parts of the embryonic body. The first definite statement of this conception is found in the interesting and suggestive work of Wilhelm His ('74) entitled *Unsere Körperform*. Considering the development of the chick, he says : " It is clear, on the one hand, that every point in the embryonic region of the blastoderm must represent a later organ or part of an organ, and on the other hand, that every organ developed from the blastoderm has its preformed germ (" vorgebildete Anlage ") in a definitely located region of the flat germ-disc. . . . The material of the germ is already present in the flat germ-disc, but is not yet morphologically marked off and hence not directly recognizable. But by following the development backwards we may determine the location of every such germ, even at a period when the morphological differentiation is incomplete or before it occurs ; logically, indeed, we must extend this process back to the fertilized or even the unfertilized egg. According to this principle, the germ-disc contains the organ-germs spread out in a flat plate, and, conversely, every point of the germ-disc reappears in a later organ ; I call this the *principle of organ-forming germ-regions*." [1] His thus conceived the embryo, not as pre-*formed*, but as having all of its parts pre-*localized* in the egg-protoplasm (cytoplasm).

A great impulse to this conception was given during the following decade by discoveries relating, on the one hand, to protoplasmic structure, on the other hand, to the promorphological relations of the ovum. Ray Lankester writes, in 1877 : " Though the substance of a cell [2] may appear homogeneous under the most powerful microscope, it is quite possible, indeed certain, that it may contain, *already formed and individualized*, various kinds of physiological molecules. The visible process of segregation is only the sequel of a differentiation already established, and not visible." [3] The egg-cytoplasm has a definite molecular organization directly handed down from the parent ; cleavage sunders the various " physiological molecules " and isolates them in particular cells. Whitman expresses a similar thought in the following year : " While we cannot say that the embryo is predelineated, we can say that it is predetermined. The ' Histogenetic sundering ' of embryonic elements begins with the cleavage,

[1] *l.c.*, p. 19.
[2] It is clear from the context that by " substance" Lankester had in mind the cytoplasm, though this is not specifically stated.
[3] '77, p. 14.

and every step in the process bears a definite and invariable relation to antecedent and subsequent steps. . . . It is, therefore, not surprising to find certain important histological differentiations and fundamental structural relations anticipated in the early phases of cleavage, and foreshadowed even before cleavage begins."[1] It was, however, Flemming who gave the first specific statement of the matter from the cytological point of view : " But if the substance of the egg-cell has a definite *structure* (Bau), and if this structure and the nature of the network varies in different regions of the cell-body, we may seek in it a basis for the predetermination of development wherein one egg differs from another, and it will be possible to look for it *with the microscope*. How far this search can be carried no one can say, but its ultimate aim is nothing less than a true *morphology of inheritance*.[2] In the following year Van Beneden pointed out how nearly this conception approaches to a theory of preformation : " If this were the case (*i.e.* if the egg-axis coincided with the principal axis of the adult body), the old theory of evolution would not be as baseless as we think to-day. The fact that in the ascidians, and probably in other bilateral animals, the median plane of the body of the future animal is marked out from the beginning of cleavage, fully justifies the hypothesis that the materials destined to form the right side of the body are situated in one of the lateral hemispheres of the egg, while the left hemisphere gives rise to all of the organs of the left half."[3]

The hypothesis thus suggested seemed, for a time, to be placed on a secure basis of fact through a remarkable experiment subsequently performed by Roux ('88) on the frog's egg. On killing one of the blastomeres of the two-cell stage by means of a heated needle the uninjured half developed in some cases into a perfectly formed half-larva (Fig. 131), accurately representing the right or left half of the body, containing one medullary fold, one auditory pit, etc.[4] Analogous, though less complete, results were obtained by operating with the four-cell stage. Roux was thus led to the declaration (made with certain subsequent reservations) that " the development of the frog-gastrula and of the embryo formed from it is from the second cleavage onward a mosaic-work consisting of at least four vertical

[1] '78, p. 49.

[2] Zellsubstanz, '82, p. 70; the italics are in the original.

[3] '83, p. 571.

[4] The accuracy of this result was disputed by Oscar Hertwig ('93, 1), who found that the uninjured blastomere gave rise to a defective larva, in which certain parts were missing, but not to a true half-body. Later observers, especially Schultze, Endres, and Morgan, have, however, shown that both Hertwig and Roux were right, proving that the uninjured blastomere may give rise to a perfect half-larva, to a larva with irregular defects, or to a whole larva of half-size, according to circumstances (p. 319).

independently developing pieces." [1] This conclusion seemed to form a very strong support to His's theory of germinal localization, though, as will appear beyond, Roux transferred this theory to the nucleus, and thus developed it in a very different direction from Lankester or Van Beneden.

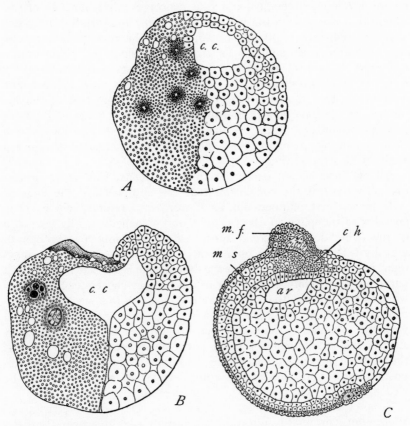

Fig. 131. — Half-embryos of the frog (in transverse section) arising from a blastomere of the 2-cell stage after killing the other blastomere. [ROUX.]

A. Half-blastula (dead blastomere on the left). *B*. Later stage. *C*. Half-tadpole with one medullary fold and one mesoblast plate; regeneration of the missing (right) half in process.

ar., archenteric cavity: *c.c.*, cleavage-cavity; *ch*, notochord; *m.f.*, medullary fold; *ms.*, meso-blast-plate.

In an able series of later works Whitman has followed out the sug-gestion made in his paper of 1878, already cited, pointing out how essential a part is played in development by the cytoplasm and insist-ing that cytoplasmic pre-organization must be regarded as a leading factor in the ontogeny. Whitman's interesting and suggestive views

[1] *l.c.*, p. 30.

are expressed with great caution and with a full recognition of the difficulty and complexity of the problem. From his latest essay, indeed ('94), it is not easy to gather his precise position regarding the theory of cytoplasmic localization. Through all his writings, nevertheless, runs the leading idea that the germ is definitely organized before development begins, and that cleavage only reveals an organization that exists from the beginning. " That organization precedes cell-formation and regulates it, rather than the reverse, is a conclusion that forces itself upon us from many sides." [1] " The organism exists before cleavage sets in, and persists throughout every stage of cell-multiplication." [2] In so far as this view involves the assumption that the organization of the egg-cytoplasm at the beginning of cleavage is a primordial character of the egg, Whitman's conception must, I think, be placed on the side of the localization theory; but his point of view can only be appreciated through a study of his own writings.

All of these views, excepting those of Roux, lean more or less distinctly towards the conclusion that the cytoplasm of the egg-cell is from the first mapped out, as it were, into regions which correspond with the parts of the future embryonic body. The cleavage of the ovum does not create these regions, but only reveals them to view by marking off their boundaries. Their topographical arrangement in the egg does not necessarily coincide with that of the adult parts, but only involves the latter as a necessary consequence — somewhat as a picture in the kaleidoscope gives rise to a succeeding picture composed of the same parts in a different arrangement. The germinal localization may, however, in a greater or less degree, foreshadow the arrangement of adult parts — for instance, in the egg of the tunicate or cephalopod, where the bilateral symmetry and anteroposterior differentiation of the adult is foreshadowed not only in the cleavage stages, but even in the unsegmented egg.

By another set of writers, such as Roux, De Vries, Hertwig, and Weismann, germinal localization is primarily sought not in the cytoplasm, but in the nucleus; but these views can best be considered after a review of the idioplasm hypothesis, to which we now proceed.

B. The Idioplasm Theory

We owe to Nägeli the first systematic attempt to discuss heredity regarded as inherent in a definite physical basis; [3] but it is hardly necessary to point out his great debt to earlier writers, foremost among them Darwin, Herbert Spencer, and Häckel. It was the

[1] '93, p. 115.   [2] *l.c.*, p. 112.   [3] *Theorie der Abstammungslehre*, 1884.

great merit of Nägeli's hypothesis to consider inheritance as effected by the transmission not of a cell, considered as a whole, but of a particular substance, the *idioplasm*, contained within a cell, and forming the physical basis of heredity. The idioplasm is to be sharply distinguished from the other constituents of the cell, which play no direct part in inheritance and form a "nutritive plasma" or *trophoplasm*. Hereditary traits are the outcome of a definite molecular organization of the idioplasm. The hen's egg differs from the frog's because it contains a different idioplasm. The species is as completely contained in the one as in the other, and the hen's egg differs from a frog's as widely as a hen from a frog.

The idioplasm was conceived as an extremely complex substance consisting of elementary complexes of molecules known as *micellæ*. These are variously grouped to form units of higher orders, which, as development proceeds, determine the development of the adult cells, tissues, and organs. The specific peculiarities of the idioplasm are therefore due to the arrangement of the micellæ; and this, in its turn, is owing to dynamic properties of the micellæ themselves. During development the idioplasm undergoes a progressive transformation of its substance, not through any material change, but through dynamic alterations of the conditions of tension and movement of the micellæ. These changes in the idioplasm cause reactions on the part of surrounding structures leading to definite chemical and plastic changes, *i.e.* to differentiation and development.

Nägeli made no attempt to locate the idioplasm precisely or to identify it with any of the known morphological constituents of the cell. It was somewhat vaguely conceived as a network extending through both nucleus and cytoplasm, and from cell to cell throughout the entire organism. Almost immediately after the publication of his theory, however, several of the foremost leaders of biological investigation were led to locate the idioplasm in the nucleus, and succeeding researches have rendered it more and more highly probable that it is to be identified with *chromatin*. The grounds for this conclusion, which have already been stated in Chapter VII., may be here again briefly reviewed. The beautiful experiments of Nussbaum, Gruber, and Verworn proved that the regeneration of differentiated cytoplasmic structures in the Protozoa can only take place when nuclear matter is present (cf. p. 248). The study of fertilization by Hertwig, Strasburger, and Van Beneden proved that in the sexual reproduction of both plants and animals the nucleus of the germ is equally derived from both sexes, while the cytoplasm is derived almost entirely from the female. The two germ-nuclei, which by their union give rise to that of the germ, were shown by Van Beneden to be of exactly the same morphological nature, since each gives rise to chromosomes of the same number, form, and size. Van Beneden and Boveri proved (p. 134) that the paternal and maternal nuclear substances are equally distributed to each of the first two cells, and the more recent work of Häcker, Rückert, Herla, and Zoja establishes a strong probability that this equal distribution continues in the later divisions. Roux pointed out the telling fact that the entire complicated mechanism of mitosis seems designed to effect the most accurate division of the entire nuclear substance in all of its parts, while fission of the cytoplasmic cell-body is in the main a mass-division, and not a meristic division of the individual parts. Again, the complicated processes of maturation show the significant fact that while the greatest pains is taken to prepare the germ-nuclei for their coming union, by rendering them exactly equivalent, the cytoplasm becomes widely different in the two germ-cells and is devoted to entirely different functions.

It was in the main these considerations that led Hertwig, Strasburger, Kölliker, and Weismann independently and almost simultaneously to the conclusion that *the nucleus contains the physical basis of inheritance, and that chromatin, its essential constituent, is the idioplasm postulated in Nägeli's theory.* This conclusion is now widely accepted; and notwithstanding certain facts which at first sight may seem opposed to it, I believe it rests upon a basis so firm that it may be taken as one of the elementary data of heredity. To accept it is, however, to reject the theory of germinal localization in so far as it assumes a pre-localization of the egg-cytoplasm as a fundamental character of the egg. For if the specific character of the organism be determined by an idioplasm contained in the chromatin, then every characteristic of the cytoplasm must in the long run be determined from the same source. A striking illustration of this fact is given by the phenomena of colour-inheritance in plant-hybrids, as De Vries has pointed out. Pigment is developed in the embryonic cytoplasm, which is derived from the mother-cell; yet in hybrids it may be inherited from the male through the nucleus of the germ-cell. The specific form of cytoplasmic metabolism by which the pigment is formed must therefore be determined by the paternal chromatin in the germ-nucleus, and not by a pre-determination of the egg-cytoplasm.

C. Union of the Two Theories

We have now to consider the attempts that have been made to transfer the localization-theory from the cytoplasm to the nucleus, and thus to bring it into harmony with the theory of nuclear idioplasm. These attempts are especially associated with the names of

Roux, De Vries, Weismann, and Hertwig; but all of them may be traced back to Darwin's celebrated hypothesis of pangenesis as a prototype. This hypothesis is so well known as to require but a brief review. Its fundamental postulate assumes that the germ-cells contain innumerable ultra-microscopic organized bodies or *gemmules*, each of which is the germ of a cell and determines the development of a similar cell during the ontogeny. The germ-cell is, therefore, in Darwin's words, a microcosm formed of a host of inconceivably minute self-propagating organisms, every one of which predetermines the formation of one of the adult cells. De Vries ('89) brought this conception into relation with the theory of nuclear idioplasm by assuming that the gemmules of Darwin, which he called *pangens*, are contained in the nucleus, migrating thence into the cytoplasm step by step during ontogeny, and thus determining the successive stages of development. The same view was afterwards accepted by Hertwig and Weismann.[1]

The theory of germinal localization is thus transferred from the cytoplasm to the nucleus. It is not denied that the egg-cytoplasm may be more or less distinctly differentiated into regions that have a constant relation to the parts of the embryo. This differentiation is, however, conceived, not as a primordial characteristic of the egg, but as one secondarily determined through the influence of the nucleus. Both De Vries and Weismann assume, in fact, that the entire cytoplasm is a product of the nucleus, being composed of pangens that migrate out from the latter, and by their active growth and multiplication build up the cytoplasmic substance.[2]

D. THE ROUX-WEISMANN THEORY OF DEVELOPMENT

We now proceed to an examination of two sharply opposing hypotheses of development based on the theory of nuclear idioplasm. One of these originated with Roux ('83) and has been elaborated especially by Weismann. The other was clearly outlined by De Vries ('89), and has been developed in various directions by Oscar Hertwig,

---

[1] The neo-pangenesis of De Vries differs from Darwin's hypothesis in one very important respect. Darwin assumed that the gemmules arose in the body, being thrown off as germs by the individual tissue-cells, transported to the germ-cells, and there accumulated as in a reservoir; and he thus endeavoured to explain the transmission of acquired characters. De Vries, on the other hand, denies such a transportal from cell to cell, maintaining that the pangens arise or pre-exist in the germ-cell, and those of the tissue-cells are derived from this source by cell-division.

[2] This conception obviously harmonizes with the *rôle* of the nucleus in the synthetic process. In accepting the view that the nuclear control of the cell is effected by an emanation of specific substances from the nucleus, we need not, however, necessarily adopt the pangen-hypothesis.

Driesch, and other writers.   In discussing them, it should be borne
in mind that, although both have been especially developed by the
advocates of the pangen-hypothesis, neither necessarily involves that
hypothesis in its strict form, *i.e.* the postulate of discrete self-propagating units in the idioplasm.   This hypothesis may therefore be laid
aside as an open question, and will be considered only in so far as it
is necessary to a presentation of the views of individual writers.

The Roux-Weismann hypothesis has already been touched on at
p. 183.   Roux conceived the idioplasm (*i.e.* the chromatin) not as a
single chemical compound or a homogeneous mass of molecules, but
as a highly complex mixture of different substances, representing
different qualities, and having their seat in the individual chromatin-
granules.   In mitosis these become arranged in a linear series to
form the spireme-thread, and hence may be precisely divided by the
splitting of the thread.   Roux assumes, as a fundamental postulate,
that division of the granules may be either *quantitative* or *qualitative*.
In the first mode the group of qualities represented in the mother-
granule is first doubled and then split into equivalent daughter-groups,
the daughter-cells therefore receiving the same qualities and remaining of the same nature.   In "qualitative division," on the other hand,
the mother-group of qualities is split into dissimilar groups, which,
passing into the respective daughter-nuclei, lead to *a corresponding
differentiation in the daughter-cells*.   By qualitative divisions, occurring in a fixed and predetermined order, the idioplasm is thus split
up during ontogeny into its constituent qualities, which are, as it were,
sifted apart and distributed to the various nuclei of the embryo.
Every cell-nucleus, therefore, receives a specific form of chromatin which
determines the nature of the cell at a.given period and its later history.   Every cell is thus endowed with a power of *self-determination*,
which lies in the specific structure of its nucleus, and its course of
development is only in a minor degree capable of modification through
the relation of the cell to its fellows ("correlative differentiation").

Roux's hypothesis, be it observed, does not commit him to the
theory of pangenesis.   It was reserved for Weismann to develop the
hypothesis of qualitative division in terms of the pangen-hypothesis,
and to elaborate it as a complete theory of development.   In his
first essay ('85), published before De Vries's paper, he went no further than Roux.   "I believe that we must accept the hypothesis that
in indirect nuclear division, the formation of non-equivalent halves
may take place quite as readily as the formation of equivalent halves,
and that the equivalence or non-equivalence of the subsequently produced daughter-cells must depend upon that of the nuclei.   Thus,
during ontogeny a gradual transformation of the nuclear substance
takes place, necessarily imposed upon it, according to certain laws,

by its own nature, and such transformation is accompanied by a gradual change in the character of the cell-bodies." [1] In later writings Weismann advanced far beyond this, building up an elaborate artificial system, which appears in its final form in the remarkable book on the germ-plasm ('92). Accepting De Vries's conception of the pangens, he assumes a definite grouping of these bodies in the germ-plasm or idioplasm (chromatin), somewhat as in Nägeli's conception. The pangens or *biophores* are conceived to be successively aggregated in larger and larger groups; namely, (1) *determinants*, which are still beyond the limits of microscopical vision; (2) *ids*, which are identified with the visible chromatin-granules; and (3) *idants*, or chromosomes. The chromatin has, therefore, a highly complex fixed architecture, which is transmitted from generation to generation, and determines the development of the embryo in a definite and specific manner. Mitotic division is conceived as an apparatus which may distribute the elements of the chromatin to the daughter-nuclei either equally or unequally. In the former case ("*homœokinesis*," *integral* or *quantitative division*), the resulting nuclei remain precisely equivalent. In the second case ("*heterokinesis*," *qualitative* or *differential division*), the daughter-cells receive different groups of chromatin-elements, and hence become differently modified. During ontogeny, through successive qualitative divisions, the elements of the idioplasm or *germ-plasm* (chromatin) are gradually sifted apart, and distributed in a definite and predetermined manner to the various parts of the body. "Ontogeny depends on a gradual process of disintegration of the id of germ-plasm, which splits into smaller and smaller groups of determinants in the development of each individual. . . . Finally, if we neglect possible complications, only *one* kind of determinant remains in each cell, viz. that which has to control that particular cell or group of cells. . . . In this cell it breaks up into its constituent biophores, and gives the cell its inherited specific character." [2] Development is, therefore, essentially evolutionary and not epigenetic; [3] its point of departure is a substance in which all of the adult characters are represented by preformed, prearranged germs; its course is the result of a predetermined harmony in the succession of the qualitative divisions by which the hereditary substance is progressively disintegrated. In order to account for heredity through successive generations, Weismann is obliged to assume that, by means of quantitative or integral division, a certain part of the original germ-plasm is carried on unchanged, and is finally delivered, with its original architecture unaltered, to the germ-nuclei. The power of regeneration is explained, in like manner, as the result of a transmission of unmodified or slightly modified germ-plasm to those parts capable of regeneration.

[1] Essay IV., p. 193, 1885.   [2] *Germ-plasm*, pp. 76, 77.   [3] *l.c.*, p. 15.

X

E. Critique of the Roux-Weismann Theory

From a logical point of view the Roux-Weismann theory is unassailable.   Its fundamental weakness is its *quasi*-metaphysical character, which indeed almost places it outside the sphere of legitimate scientific hypothesis.   Not a single visible phenomenon of cell-divi-

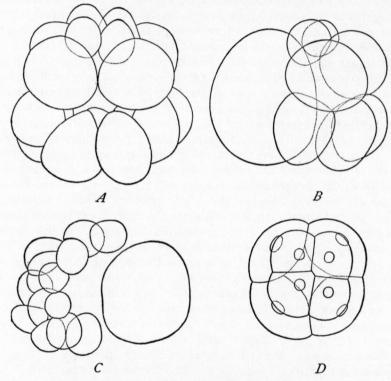

Fig. 132. —Half and whole cleavage in the eggs of sea-urchins.

A. Normal 16-cell stage, showing the four micromeres above (from Driesch, after Selenka). *B.* Half 16-cell stage developed from one blastomere of the 2-cell stage after killing the other by shaking (Driesch). *C.* Half blastula resulting, the dead blastomere at the right (Driesch). *D.* Half-sized 16-cell stage of *Toxopneustes*, viewed from the micromere-pole (the eight lower cells not shown).   This embryo, developed from an isolated blastomere of the 2-cell stage, segmented like an entire normal ovum.

sion gives even a remote suggestion of qualitative division.   All the facts, on the contrary, indicate that the division of the chromatin is carried out with the most exact equality.   The theory of qualitative division was suggested by a totally different order of phenomena, and is an explanation constructed *ad hoc*.   Roux, it is true, was led to the hypothesis through an examination of mitosis ; but it is safe to say that he would never have maintained in the same breath that mitosis is expressly designed for quantitative *and also* for qualitative division, had he fixed his attention on the actual phenomena of mitosis alone. The hypothesis is in fact as complete an *a priori* assumption as any that the history of scholasticism can show, and every fact opposed to it has been met by equally baseless subsidiary hypotheses, which, like their principal, relate to matters beyond the reach of observation.

Such an hypothesis cannot be actually overturned by an appeal to fact. When, however, we make such an' appeal, the improbability of

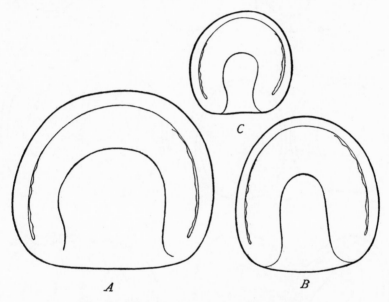

Fig. 133. — Normal and dwarf gastrulas of *Amphioxus*.
A. Normal gastrula. B. Half-sized dwarf, from an isolated blastomere of the 2-cell stage.
C. Quarter-sized dwarf, from an isolated blastomere of the 4-cell stage.

the hypothesis becomes so great that it loses all semblance of reality. It is rather remarkable that Roux himself led the way in this direction. In the course of his observations on the development of a half-embryo from one of the blastomeres of the two-cell stage he determined the significant fact that the half-embryo *afterwards regenerated the missing half, and gave rise to a complete embryo.* Essentially the same result was reached by later observers, both in the frog (Endres, Walter, Morgan) and in a number of other animals, with the important addition that the half-formation is sometimes characteristic of only the earliest stages and may be entirely suppressed. In 1891 Driesch was able to follow out the development of isolated blastomeres of sea-urchin eggs separated by shaking to pieces the two-cell and four-cell stages. Blastomeres thus isolated segment as if still forming part of an entire larva, and give rise to a half- (or quarter-) blastula (Fig. 132).   The opening soon closes, however, to form a

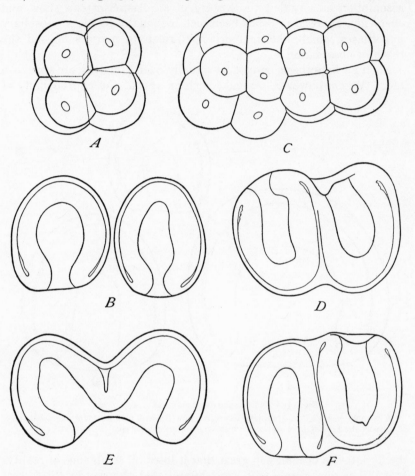

Fig. 134. — Dwarf and double embryos of *Amphioxus*.

A. Isolated blastomere of the 2-cell stage segmenting like an entire egg (cf. Fig, 123, *D*). *B.* Twin gastrulas from a single egg. *C.* Double cleavage resulting from the partial separation, by shaking, of the blastomeres of the 2-cell stage. *D. E. F.* Double gastrulas arising from such forms as the last.

small complete blastula, and the resulting gastrula and Pluteus larva is a perfectly formed dwarf of only half (or quarter) the normal size. Incompletely separated blastomeres gave rise to double embryos like the Siamese twins.   Shortly afterwards the writer obtained similar result in the case of *Amphioxus*, but here *the isolated blastomere seg-*

ments from the beginning like an entire ovum of diminished size (Figs. 133, 124). The same result has since been reached by Morgan in the teleost fishes, and by Zoja in the medusæ. The last-named experimenter was able to obtain perfect embryos not only from blastomeres of the two-cell and four-cell stages, but from eight-cell and even from sixteen-cell stages, the dwarfs in the last case being but $\frac{1}{16}$ the normal size!

These experiments gave a fatal blow to the entire Roux-Weismann theory; for the results showed that the cleavage of the ovum does not in these cases sunder different materials, either nuclear or cytoplasmic, but only splits it up into a number of similar parts, each of which may give rise to an entire body of diminished size.

The theory of qualitative nuclear division has been practically

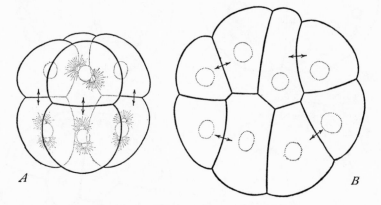

Fig. 135. — Modification of cleavage in sea-urchin eggs by pressure.
A. Normal 8-cell stage of *Toxopneustes*. *B.* Eight-cell stage of *Echinus* segmenting under pressure. Both forms produce normal Plutei.

disproved in another way by Driesch, through the pressure-experiments already mentioned at p. 275. Following the earlier experiments of Pflüger and Roux on the frog's egg, Driesch subjected segmenting eggs of the sea-urchin to pressure, and thus obtained flat plates of cells in which the arrangement of the nuclei differed totally from the normal (Fig. 134); yet such eggs when released from pressure continue to segment, *without rearrangement of the nuclei*, and give rise to perfectly normal larvæ. I have repeated these experiments not only with sea-urchin eggs, but also with those of an annelid (*Nereis*), which yield a very convincing result, since in this case the histological differentiation of the cells appears very early. In the normal development of this animal the archenteron arises from four large cells or macromeres (entomeres), which remain after the successive formation of three quartets of micromeres (ectomeres) and the parent-cell of the

mesoblast.   After the primary differentiation of the germ-layers the
four entomeres do not divide again until a very late period (free-
swimming trochophore), and their substance always retains a characteristic appearance, differing from that of the other blastomeres in
its pale non-granular character and in the presence of large oil-drops.

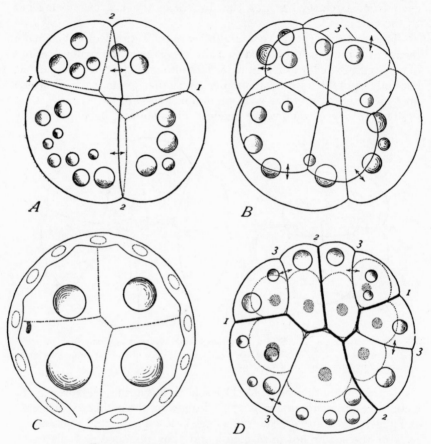

Fig. 136. — Modification of cleavage by pressure in *Nereis*.

A. B. Normal 4- and 8-cell stages. *C.* Normal trochophore larva resulting, with four entoderm-
cells. *D.* Eight-cell stage arising from an egg flattened by pressure; such eggs give rise to trochophores with eight instead of four entoderm-cells. Numerals designate the successive cleavages.

If unsegmented eggs be subjected to pressure, as in Driesch's echinoderm experiments, they segment in a flat plate, all of the cleavages
being vertical. In this way are formed eight-celled plates in which all
of the cells contain oil-drops (Fig. 136, *D*). If they are now released
from the pressure, each of the cells divides in a plane approximately
horizontal, a smaller granular micromere being formed above, leaving

below a larger clear macromere in which the oil-drops remain. The sixteen-cell stage, therefore, consists of eight deutoplasm-laden macromeres and eight protoplasmic micromeres (instead of four macromeres and twelve micromeres, as in the usual development). These embryos developed into free-swimming trochophores containing eight instead of four macromeres, which have the typical clear protoplasm containing oil-drops. In this case there can be no doubt whatever that four of the entoblastic nuclei were normally destined for the first quartet of micromeres (Fig. 136, *B*), from which arise the apical ganglia and the prototroch. Under the conditions of the experiment, however, they have given rise to the nuclei of cells which differ in no wise from the other entoderm-cells. Even in a highly differentiated type of cleavage, therefore, the nuclei of the segmenting egg are not specifically different, as the Roux-Weismann hypothesis demands, but contain the same materials even in cells that undergo the most diverse subsequent fate. But there is, furthermore, very strong reason for believing that this may be true in later stages as well, as Kölliker insisted in opposition to Weismann as early as 1886, and as has been urged by many subsequent writers. The strongest evidence in this direction is afforded by the facts of regeneration; and many cases are known — for instance among the hydroids and the plants—in which even a small fragment of the body is able to reproduce the whole. It is true that the power of regeneration is always limited to a greater or less extent according to the species. But there is no evidence whatever that such limitation arises through specification of the nuclei by qualitative division, and, as will appear beyond, its explanation is probably to be sought in a very different direction.

F. ON THE NATURE AND CAUSES OF DIFFERENTIATION

We have now cleared the ground for a restatement of the problem of development, and an examination of the views opposed to the Roux-Weismann theory. After discarding the hypothesis of qualitative division the problem confronts us in the fóllowing form. If chromatin be the idioplasm in which inheres the sum-total of hereditary forces, and if it be equally distributed at every cell-division, how can its mode of action so vary in different cells as to cause diversity of structure, *i.e. differentiation?* It is perfectly certain that differentiation is an actual progressive transformation of the egg-substance involving both physical and chemical changes, occurring in a definite order, and showing a definite distribution in the regions of the egg. These changes are sooner or later accompanied by the cleavage of the egg into cells whose boundaries may sharply mark the areas of differentiation. What gives these cells their specific character? Why, in the four-cell stage of an annelid egg, should the four cells contribute equally to the formation of the alimentary canal and the cephalic nervous system, while only one of them (the left-hand posterior) gives rise to the nervous system of the trunk-region and to the muscles, connective tissues, and the germ-cells? (Figs. 122, 137, *B*). There cannot be a fixed and necessary relation of cause and effect between the various regions of the egg which these blastomeres represent and the adult parts arising from them; for, as we have seen, these relations may be artificially altered. A portion of the egg which under normal conditions would give rise to only a fragment of the body will, if split off from the rest, give rise to an entire body of diminished size. What then determines the history of such a portion? What influence moulds it now into an entire body, now into a part of a body?

De Vries, in his remarkable essay on *Intracellular Pangenesis* ('89), endeavoured to cut this Gordian knot by assuming that the character of each cell is determined by pangens that migrate from the nucleus into the cytoplasm, and, there becoming active, set up specific changes and determine the character of the cell, this way or that, according to their nature. But what influence guides the migration of the pangens, and so correlates the operations of development? Both Driesch and Oscar Hertwig have attempted to answer this question, though the first-named author does not commit himself to the pangen hypothesis. These writers have maintained that the particular mode of development in a given region or blastomere of the egg is *a result of its relation to the remainder of the mass*, *i.e.* a product of what may be called the intra-embryonic environment. Both at first assumed not only that the nuclei are equivalent, but also that the cytoplasmic regions of the egg are *isotropic, i.e.* primarily composed of the same materials and equivalent in structure. Hertwig insisted that the organism develops as a whole as the result of a formative power pervading the entire mass; that differentiation is but an expression of this power acting at particular points; and that the development of each part is, therefore, dependent on that of the whole.[1] "According to my conception," said Hertwig, "each of the first two blastomeres contains the formative and differentiating forces not simply for the production of a half-body, but for the entire organism; the left blastomere develops into the left half of the body only because it is placed in relation to a right blastomere."[2] Again, in a later paper: — "The egg is a specifically

---

[1] Whitman had strongly urged this view several years before, and a nearly similar conception lay at the bottom of Herbert Spencer's theory of development. Cf. pp. 41, 293.

[2] '92, I, p. 481.

organized elementary organism that develops epigenetically by breaking up into cells and their subsequent differentiation. Since every elementary part (*i.e.* cell) arises through the division of the germ, or fertilized egg, it contains also the germ of the whole,[1] but during the process of development it becomes ever more precisely differentiated and determined by the formation of cytoplasmic products according to its position with reference to the entire organism (blastula, gastrula, etc)."[2]

Driesch expressed the same view with great clearness and precision shortly after Hertwig : — "The fragments (*i.e.* cells) produced by cleavage are completely equivalent or indifferent." "The blasto-

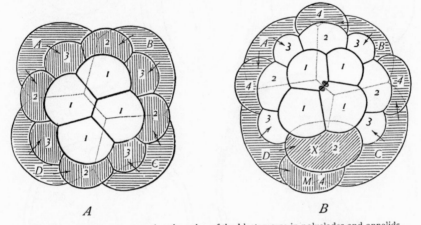

A   B

Fig. 137. — Diagrams contrasting the value of the blastomeres in polyclades and annelids.

A. Plan of cleavage in the polyclade egg (constructed from the figures of Lang). *B.* Corresponding plan of the annelid egg. In both cases the ectoblast is unshaded, with the exception of *X;* the mesoblast is ruled in vertical lines and the entoblast in horizontal. In both, three successive quartets of micromeres are budded forth from the four primary cells *A. B. C. D.* In the polyclade the first quartet is ectoblastic, the second and third mesoblastic. In the annelid all three quartets are ectoblastic, while the mesoblast (*M*) arises from the posterior cell of a fourth quartet of which the remaining three are entoblastic.

meres of the sea-urchin are to be regarded as forming a uniform material, and they may be thrown about, like balls in a pile, without in the least degree impairing thereby the normal power of development."[3] "*The relative position of a blastomere in the whole determines in general what develops from it; if its position be changed, it gives rise to something different;* in other words, *its prospective value is a function of its position.*"[4]

This conclusion undoubtedly expresses a part of the truth, though, as will presently appear, it is too extreme. The relation of the part

---

[1] That is, in the specifically organized chromatin within the nucleus.
[2] '93, p. 793.   [3] Studien IV. p. 25.   [4] Studien IV. p. 39.

to the whole must not, however, be conceived as a merely geometrical or mechanical one; for, in different species of eggs, blastomeres may exactly correspond in origin and relative position, yet have entirely different morphological value.   This is strikingly shown by

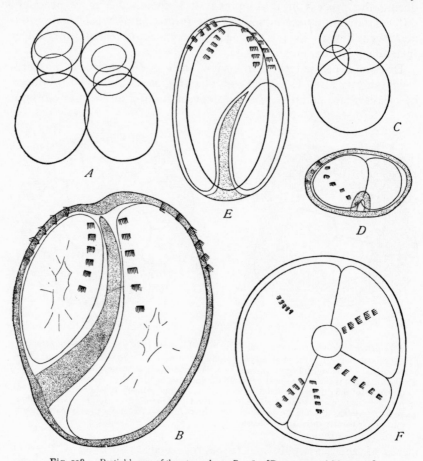

Fig. 138. — Partial larvæ of the ctenophore *Beroë*.   [DRIESCH and MORGAN.]

A. Half 16-cell stage, from an isolated blastomere. *B.* Resulting larva, with four rows of swimming plates and three gastric pouches. *C.* One-fourth 16-cell stage, from an isolated blastomere. *D.* Resulting larva with two rows of plates and two gastric pouches. *E.* Defective larva, with six rows of plates and three gastric pouches, from a nucleated fragment of an unsegmented egg. *F.* Similar larva with five rows of plates, from above.

a comparison of the polyclade egg with that of the annelid or gasteropod (Fig. 137).   In both cases three quartets of micromeres are successively budded off from the four cells of the four-cell stage in exactly the same manner.   The first quartet in both gives rise to ectoderm.   Beyond this point, however, the agreement ceases;

for the second and third quartets form mesoblast in the polyclade, but ectoblast in the annelid and gasteropod! In the latter forms the mesoblast lies in a single cell belonging to a fourth quartet of which the other three cells form entoblast. This shows conclusively that the relation of the part to the whole is of an exceedingly subtle character, and that the nature of the individual blastomere depends, not merely upon its geometrical position, but upon its physiological relation to *the inherited organization* of which it forms a part.

Meanwhile, and subsequently, however, facts were determined that threw doubts on the hypothesis of cytoplasmic isotropy and led Driesch to a profound modification of his views, and in a measure rehabilitated the theory of cytoplasmic localization. Whitman, Morgan, and Driesch himself showed that the cytoplasm of the echinoderm egg is not strictly isotropic, as Hertwig assumed; for the ovum possesses a polarity predetermined before cleavage begins, as proved by the fact that a group of small cells or micromeres always arises at a certain point which may be precisely located before cleavage by reference to the eccentricity of the first cleavage-nucleus.[1] Experiments on the eggs of other animals proved that the predetermination of the cytoplasmic regions may be more extensive. In the egg of the ctenophore, for example, Driesch and Morgan ('95), confirming the earlier observations of Chun, proved that an isolated blastomere of the two- or four-cell stage gives rise not to a whole dwarf body, but to a half- or quarter-body, as Roux had observed in the frog[2] (Fig. 135, *A–D*). But, more than this, these experimenters made the interesting discovery that if a part of the cytoplasm of an *unsegmented* ctenophore-egg were removed, the remainder gave rise to an *incomplete larva, showing certain defects which represent the portions removed* (Fig. 138, *E, F*). Again, Crampton found that in case of the marine gasteropod *Ilyanassa*, isolated blastomeres of two-cell or four-cell stages segmented exactly as if forming part of an entire embryo and gave rise to *fragments* of a larva, not to complete dwarfs, as in the echinoderm (Fig. 139).

These results demonstrate that the ovum *may* show a high degree of cytoplasmic localization and that in such cases cleavage may be in fact a mosaic-work, as Roux maintained in case of the frog. But they also show that the localization, and the resulting mosaic-like cleavage, is not determined by specific differences in the nuclei; for in the ctenophore the fragment of an *unsegmented* egg, though containing an entire nucleus, gives rise to a defective larva, and in *Nereis* the nuclei may be shifted about at will without altering the develop-

---

[1] Cf. Fig. 77.

[2] The larva is, however, not a *strict* partial one, since it makes an abortive attempt to form the normal number of gastric pouches.

ment.   And if the germinal localization is not directly determined by
the nuclei it must here be determined by a pre-organization of the
cytoplasmic substance.   How is this result to be reconciled with the
experiments on *Amphioxus* and the echinoderms, and with the more
general conclusion that the ultimate determining causes of differentia-

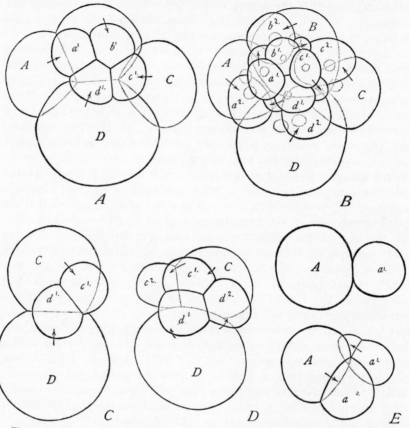

Fig. 139.— Partial development of isolated blastomeres of the gasteropod egg, *Ilyanassa*.
[CRAMPTON.]

A. Normal 8-cell stage. *B.* Normal 16-cell stage. *C.* Half 8-cell stage, from isolated blastomere of the 2-cell stage. *D.* Half 12-cell stage succeeding. *E.* Two stages in the cleavage of an
isolated blastomere of the 4-cell stage ; above a one-fourth 8-cell stage, below a one-fourth 16-cell
stage.

tion are to be sought in the nucleus ?   The difficulty at once disappears when we recall that development and differentiation do not in
any proper sense first begin with the cleavage of the ovum, but long
before this, during its ovarian history.   The primary differentiations
thus established in the cytoplasm form the immediate conditions
to which the later development must conform ; and the difference

between *Amphioxus* on the one hand, and the snail or ctenophore on the other, simply means, I think, that the initial differentiation is less extensive or less firmly established in the one than in the other.

We thus arrive at the central point of my own conception of development, and of Driesch's later views, which were developed in a most able and suggestive though somewhat abstruse manner in his *Analytische Theorie der organischen Entwicklung* ('94), and slightly modified in a later paper published jointly with Morgan ('95, 2). The gist of Driesch's theory is as follows. All the nuclei are equivalent, and all contain the same idioplasm equally distributed to them by mitotic division. Through the influence of this idioplasm the cytoplasm of the egg, or of the blastomeres derived from it, undergoes specific and progressive changes, each change reacting upon the nucleus and thus inciting a new change. These changes differ in different regions of the egg because of pre-existing differences, chemical and physical, in the cytoplasmic structure ; and these form the conditions ("Formbildungsfaktoren") under which the idioplasm operates. Some of these conditions are purely mechanical, such as the shape of the ovum, the distribution of deutoplasm, and the like. Others, and probably the more important, are far more subtle, such as the distribution of different chemical substances in the cytoplasm, and the unknown polarities of the cytoplasmic molecules.

A nearly related conception was developed with admirable clearness by Oscar Hertwig ('94) nearly at the same time. Both Driesch and Hertwig thus retreated in a measure towards the theory of germinal localization in the cytoplasm, which both had at first rejected ; but only to a middle ground which lies between the two extremes of the strict predestination theory and the theory of cytoplasmic isotropy. For these writers now maintain that the initial cytoplasmic localization of the formative conditions is of limited extent and determines only the earlier steps of development. With each forward step new conditions (chemical differentiations and the like) are established which form the basis for the ensuing change, and so on in ever-increasing complexity. This view is substantially the same as that which I have myself urged in several earlier works, and I have pointed out how it enables us to reconcile the apparent contradiction between the partial development of isolated blastomeres of such forms as the ctenophore, on the one hand, with the total development of such forms as *Amphioxus* or the echinoderm, on the other. In the latter case we may suppose the cytoplasmic differentiation to be but feebly established at the beginning, and the blastomeres remain for a time in a plastic state, which enables them on isolation to revert to the condition of the original entire ovum. In the former case the initial differentiation is more extensive or more rigidly fixed, so that

the development of the blastomere is from the beginning hemmed
in by the cytoplasmic conditions, and its powers are correspondingly
limited.   In such cases the cleavage may exhibit more or less of
a mosaic-like character, and the theory of cytoplasmic localization
acquires a real meaning and value.

That we are here approaching the true explanation is indicated by

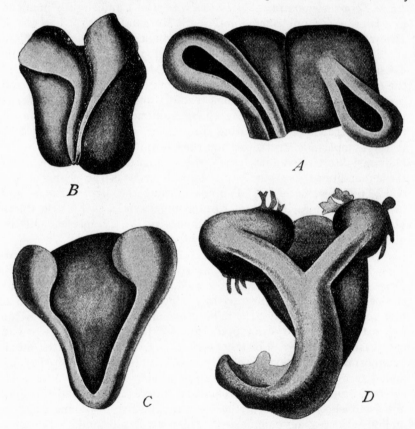

Fig. 140. — Double embryos of frog developed from eggs inverted when in the 2-cell stage.
[O. SCHULTZE.]

A. Twins with heads turned in opposite directions. *B*. Twins united back to back. *C*. Twins
united by their ventral sides. *D*. Double-headed tadpole.

certain very remarkable and interesting experiments on the frog's
egg which prove that each of the first two blastomeres may give rise
either to a half-embryo or to a whole embryo of half size, according
to circumstances, and which indicate, furthermore, that these circumstances lie in a measure in the arrangement of the cytoplasmic
materials.   This most important result, which we owe especially to

Morgan,[1] was reached in the following manner.   Born had shown, in 1885, that if frogs' eggs be fastened in an abnormal position, — *e.g.* upside down, or on the side, — a rearrangement of the egg-material takes place, the heavier deutoplasm sinking towards the lower side, while the nucleus and protoplasm rise.   *A new axis is thus established in the egg*, which has the same relation to the body-axes as in the ordinary development (though the pigment retains its original arrangement).   This proves that in eggs of this character (telolecithal) the distribution of deutoplasm, or conversely of protoplasm, is one of the primary formative conditions of the cytoplasm; and the significant fact is that *by artificially changing this distribution the axis of the embryo is shifted.*   Oscar Schultze ('94) discovered that if the egg be turned upside down when in the two-cell stage, a whole embryo (or half of a double embryo) might arise from each blastomere instead of a half-embryo as in the normal development, and that the axes of these embryos show no constant relation to one another (Fig. 140). Morgan ('95,3) added the important discovery that either a half-embryo or a whole half-sized dwarf might be formed, *according to the position of the blastomere.*   If, after destruction of one blastomere, the other be allowed to remain in its normal position, a half-embryo always results,[2] precisely as described by Roux.   If, on the other hand, the blastomere be inverted, it may give rise either to a half-embryo [3] or to a whole dwarf.[4]   Morgan therefore concluded that the production of whole embryos by the inverted blastomeres was, in part at least, due to a rearrangement or rotation of the egg-materials under the influence of gravity, the blastomere thus returning, as it were, to a state of equilibrium like that of an entire ovum.

This beautiful experiment gives most conclusive evidence that each of the two blastomeres contains all the materials, nuclear and cytoplasmic, necessary for the formation of a whole body; and that these materials may be used to build a whole body or half-body, according to the grouping that they assume.   After the first cleavage takes place, each blastomere is *set*, as it were, for a half-development, but not so firmly that a rearrangement is excluded.

I have reached a nearly related result in the case both of *Amphioxus* and the echinoderms.   In *Amphioxus* the isolated blastomere usually segments like an entire ovum of diminished size.   This is, however, not invariable, for a certain proportion of the blastomeres show a more or less marked tendency to divide as if still forming part of an entire embryo.   The sea-urchin *Toxopneustes* reverses this rule, for the isolated blastomere of the two-cell stage usually shows a perfectly typical half-cleavage, as described by Driesch, but in rare

---

[1] *Anat. Anz.*, X. 19, 1895.   [3] Three cases.
[2] Eleven cases observed.   [4] Nine cases observed.

cases it may segment like an *entire* ovum of half-size (Fig. 132, *D*) and give rise to an entire blastula.[1] We may interpret this to mean that in *Amphioxus* the differentiation of the cytoplasmic substance is at first very slight, or readily alterable, so that the isolated blastomere, as a rule, reverts at once to the condition of the entire ovum.   In the sea-urchin, the initial differentiations are more extensive or more firmly established, so that only exceptionally can they be altered.   In the snail we have the opposite extreme to *Amphioxus*, the cytoplasmic conditions having been so firmly established that they cannot be altered, and the development must, from the outset, proceed within the limits thus set up.

Through this conclusion we reconcile, as I believe, the theories of cytoplasmic localization and mosaic development with the hypothesis of cytoplasmic isotropy.   Primarily the egg-cytoplasm is isotropic in the sense that its various regions stand in no fixed and necessary relation with the parts to which they respectively give rise.   Secondarily, however, it may undergo differentiations through which it acquires a definite regional predetermination which becomes ever more firmly established as development advances.   This process does not, however, begin at the same time, or proceed at the same rate in all eggs. Hence the eggs of different animals may vary widely in this regard at the time cleavage begins, and hence may differ as widely in their power of response to changed conditions.

The origin of the cytoplasmic differentiations existing at the beginning of cleavage has already been considered (p. 285).   If the conclusions there reached be placed beside the above, we reach the following conception.   The primary determining cause of development lies in the nucleus, which operates by setting up a continuous series of specific metabolic changes in the cytoplasm.   This process begins during ovarian growth, establishing the external form of the egg, its primary polarity, and the distribution of substances within it. The cytoplasmic differentiations thus set up form as it were a framework within which the subsequent operations take place, in a more or less fixed course, and which itself becomes ever more complex as development goes forward.   If the cytoplasmic conditions be artificially altered by isolation or other disturbance of the blastomeres, a readjustment may take place and development may be correspondingly altered.   Whether such a readjustment is possible, depends on secondary factors — the extent of the primary differentiations, the physical consistency of the egg-substance, the susceptibility of the protoplasm to injury, and doubtless a multitude of others.

[1] I have observed this only twice.   In both cases the cleavage up to the sixteen-cell stage was exactly like that of the entire egg except that the micromeres were relatively larger, as shown in the figure.

G. The Nucleus in Later Development

The foregoing conception, as far as it goes, gives at least an intelligible view of the more general features of early development and in a measure harmonizes the apparently conflicting results of experiment on various forms. But there are a very large number of facts relating especially to the later stages of differentiation, which it leaves wholly unexplained, and which indicate that the nucleus as well as the cytoplasm may undergo progressive changes of its substance. It has been assumed by most critics of the Roux-Weismann theory that all of the nuclei of the body contain the same idioplasm, and that each therefore, in Hertwig's words, contains the germ of the whole. There are, however, a multitude of well-known facts which cannot be explained, even approximately, under this assumption. The power of a single cell to produce the entire .body is in general limited to the earliest stages of cleavage, rapidly diminishes, and as a rule soon disappears entirely. When once the germ-layers have been definitely separated, they lose entirely the power to regenerate one another save in a few exceptional cases. In asexual reproduction, in the regeneration of lost parts, in the formation of morbid growths, each tissue is in general able to reproduce only a tissue of its own or a nearly related kind. Transplanted or transposed groups of cells (grafts and the like) retain more or less completely their autonomy and vary only within certain well-defined limits, despite their change of environment. All of these statements are, it is true, subject to exception; yet the facts afford an overwhelming demonstration that differentiated cells possess a specific character, that their power of development and adaptability to changed conditions becomes in a greater or less degree limited with the progress of development. How can we explain this progressive specification of the tissue-cells and how interpret the differences in this regard between related species? To these questions the Roux-Weismann theory gives a definite and intelligible answer; namely, that *differentiation sooner or later involves a specification of the nuclear substance which differs in degree in different cases.* When we reflect on the general *rôle* of the nucleus in metabolism and its significance as the especial seat of the formative power, we may well hesitate to deny that this part of Roux's conception may be better founded than his critics have admitted. Nägeli insisted that the idioplasm must undergo a progressive transformation during development, and many subsequent writers, including such acute thinkers as Boveri and Nussbaum, and many pathologists, have recognized the necessity for such an assumption. Boveri's remarkable observations on the nuclei of the primordial germ-cells in

Y

Ascaris demonstrate the truth of this view in a particular case ; for here *all of the somatic nuclei lose a portion of their chromatin, and only the progenitors of the germ-nuclei retain the entire ancestral heritage.* Boveri himself has in a measure pointed out the significance of his discovery, insisting that the specific development of the tissue-cells is conditioned by specific changes in the chromatin that they receive,[1] though he is careful not to commit himself to any definite theory. It hardly seems possible to doubt that in *Ascaris* the limitation of the somatic cells in respect to the power of development arises through a loss of particular portions of the chromatin. One cannot avoid the thought that further and more specific limitations in the various forms of somatic cells may arise through an analogous process, and that we have here a key to the origin of nuclear specification *without recourse to the theory of qualitative division.* We do not need to assume that the unused chromatin is cast out bodily ; for it may degenerate and dissolve, or may be transformed into linin-substance or into nucleoli.

This suggestion is made only as a tentative hypothesis, but the phenomena of mitosis seem well worthy of consideration from this point of view. Its application to the facts of development becomes clearer when we consider the nature of the nuclear " control " of the cell, *i.e.* the action of the nucleus upon the cytoplasm. Strasburger, following in a measure the lines laid down by Nägeli, regards the action as essentially dynamic, *i.e.* as a propagation of molecular movements from nucleus to cytoplasm in a manner which might be compared to the transmission of a nervous impulse. When, however, we consider the *rôle* of the nucleus in synthetic metabolism, and the relation between this process and the morphological formative power, we must regard the question in another light ; and opinion has of late strongly tended to the conclusion that nuclear "control" can only be explained as the result of active exchanges of material between nucleus and cytoplasm. De Vries, followed by Hertwig, assumes a migration of pangens from nucleus to cytoplasm, the character of the cell being determined by the nature of the migrating pangens, and these being, as it were, selected by circumstances (position of the cell, etc.). But, as already pointed out, the pangen hypothesis should be held quite distinct from the purely physiological aspect of the question, and may be temporarily set aside ; for specific nuclear substances may pass from the nucleus into the cytoplasm in an unorganized form. Sachs, followed by Loeb, has advanced the hypothesis that the development of particular organs is determined by specific "formative substances" which incite corresponding forms of metabolic activity, growth, and differentiation.

---

[1] '91, p. 433.

It is but a step from this to the very interesting suggestion of Driesch that the nucleus is a storehouse of ferments which pass out into the cytoplasm and there set up specific activities. Under the influence of these ferments the cytoplasmic organization is determined at every step of the development, and new conditions are established for the ensuing change. This view is. put forward only tentatively as a "fiction" or working hypothesis; but it is certainly full of suggestion. Could we establish the fact that the number of ferments or formative substances in the nucleus diminishes with the progress of differentiation, we should have a comparatively simple and intelligible explanation of the specification of nuclei and the limitation of development. The power of regeneration might then be conceived, somewhat as in the Roux-Weismann theory, as due to a retention of idioplasm or germ-plasm — *i.e.* chromatin — in a less highly modified condition, and the differences between the various tissues in this regard, or between related organisms, would find a natural explanation.

Development may thus be conceived as a progressive transformation of the egg-substance primarily incited by the nucleus, first manifesting itself by specific changes in the cytoplasm, but sooner or later involving in some measure the nuclear substance itself. This process, which one is tempted to compare to a complicated and progressive form of crystallization, begins with the youngest ovarian egg and proceeds continuously until the cycle of individual life has run its course. Cell-division is an accompaniment, but not a direct cause of differentiation. The cell is no more than a particular area of the germinal substance comprising a certain quantity of cytoplasm and a mass of idioplasm in its nucleus. Its character is primarily a manifestation of the general formative energy acting at a particular point under given conditions. When once such a circumscribed area has been established, it may, however, emancipate itself in a greater or less degree from the remainder of the mass, and acquire a specific character so fixed as to be incapable of further change save within the limits imposed by its acquired character.

H. THE EXTERNAL CONDITIONS OF DEVELOPMENT

We have thus far considered only the internal conditions of development which are progressively created by the germ-cell itself. We must now briefly glance at the external conditions afforded by the environment of the embryo. That development is conditioned by the external environment is obvious. But we have only recently come to realize how intimate the relation is; and it has been especially the service of Loeb, Herbst, and Driesch to show how essential a part is played by the environment in the development of specific organic forms. The limits of this work will not admit of any adequate review of the vast array of known facts in this field, for which the reader is referred to the works especially of Herbst. I shall only consider one or two cases which may serve to bring out the general principle that they involve. Every living organism at every stage of its existence reacts to its environment by physiological and morphological changes. The developing embryo, like the adult, is a moving equilibrium—a product of the response of the inherited organization to the external stimuli working upon it. If these stimuli be altered, development is altered. This is beautifully shown by the experiments of Herbst and others on the development of sea-urchins. Pouchet and Chabry showed that if the embryos of these animals be made to develop in sea-water containing no lime-salts, the larva fails to develop not only its calcareous skeleton, but also its ciliated arms, and a larva thus results that resembles in some particulars an entirely different specific form; namely, the Tornaria larva of *Balanoglossus*. This result is not due simply to the lack of necessary material; for Herbst showed that the same result is attained if a slight excess of potassium chloride be added to sea-water containing the normal amount of lime (Fig. 141). In the latter case the specific metabolism of the protoplasm is altered by a particular chemical stimulus, and a new form results.

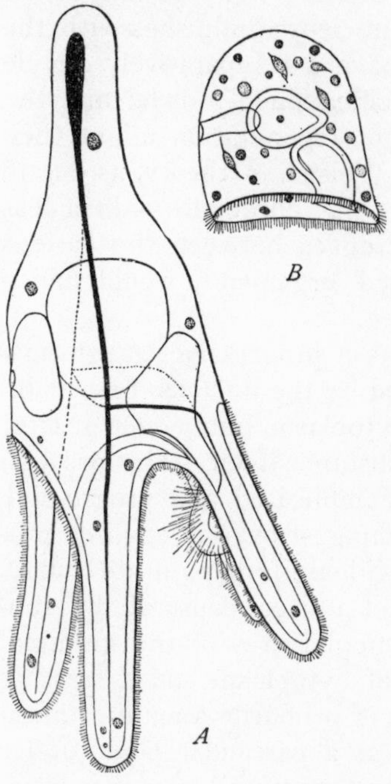

Fig. 141. — Normal and modified larvæ of sea-urchins. [HERBST.]

A. Normal Pluteus (*Strongylocentrotus*). B. Larva (*Sphærechinus*) at the same stage as the foregoing, developed in sea-water containing a slight excess of potassium chloride.

The changes thus caused by slight chemical alterations in the water may be still more profound. Herbst ('92) observed, for example, that when the water contains a very small percentage of lithium chloride, the blastula of sea-urchins fails to invaginate to form a typical gastrula, but *evaginates* to form an hour-glass-shaped larva, one half of which represents the archenteron, the other half the ectoblast. Moreover, a much larger number of the blastula-cells undergo the differentiation into entoblast than in the normal development, the ectoblast sometimes becoming greatly reduced and occasionally disappearing altogether, so that the entire blastula is differentiated into cells having the histological character of the normal entoblast! One of the most fundamental of embryonic differentia-

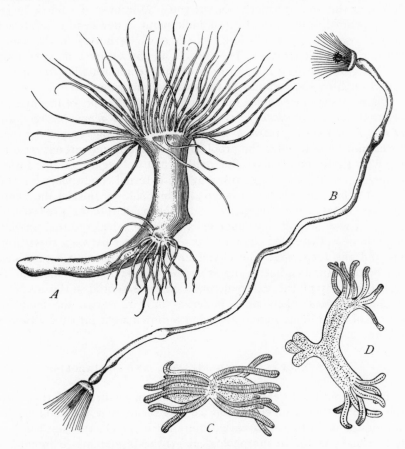

Fig. 142. — Regeneration in cœlenterates (*A. B.* from LOEB; *C. D.* from BICKFORD).

A. Polyp (*Cerianthus*) producing new tentacles from the *aboral* side of a lateral wound. *B.* Hydroid (*Tubularia*) generating a head at each end of a fragment of the stem suspended in water. *C. D.* Similar generation of heads at both ends of short pieces of the stem, in *Tubularia*.

tions is thus shown to be intimately conditioned by the chemical environment.

The observations of botanists on the production of roots and other structures as the result of local stimuli are familiar to all. Loeb's interesting experiments on hydroids gave a similar result ('91). It has long been known that *Tubularia*, like many other hydroids, has the power to regenerate its "head" — *i.e.* hypostome, mouth, and ten-tacles — after decapitation.   Loeb proved that in this case the power to form a new head is conditioned by the environment.   For if a *Tubularia* stem be cut off at both ends and inserted in the sand upside down, *i.e.* with the oral end buried, a new head is regen-erated at the free (formerly aboral) end.   Moreover, if such a piece be suspended in the water by its middle point, a new head is produced at *each end* (Fig. 142); while if both ends be buried in the sand, neither end regenerates.   This proves in the clearest manner that in this case the power to form a definite complicated structure is called forth by the stimulus of the external environment.

These cases must suffice for our purpose.   They prove incontesta-bly that *normal development is in a greater or less degree the response of the developing organism to normal conditions ;* and they show that we cannot hope to solve the problems of development without reckon-ing with these conditions.   But neither can we regard specific forms of development as *directly caused* by the external conditions ; for the egg of a fish and that of a polyp develop, side by side, in the same drop of water, under identical conditions, each into its predestined form.   Every step of development is a physiological reaction, involv-ing a long and complex chain of cause and effect between the stimu-lus and the response.   The character of the response is determined not by the stimulus, but by the *inherited organization.*   While, there-fore, the study of the external conditions is essential to the analysis of embryological phenomena, it serves only to reveal the mode of action of the idioplasm and gives but a dim insight into its ultimate nature.

I.   Development, Inheritance, and Metabolism

In bringing the foregoing discussion into more direct relation with the general theory of cell-action we may recall that the cell-nucleus appears to us in two apparently different *rôles.*   On the one hand, it is a primary factor in morphological synthesis and hence in inheri-tance, on the other hand an organ of metabolism especially concerned with the constructive process.   These two functions we may with Claude Bernard regard as but different phases of one process.   The building of a definite cell-product, such as a muscle-fibre, a nerve-process, a cilium, a pigment-granule, a zymogen-granule, is in the last analysis the result of a specific form of metabolic activity, as we may conclude from the fact that such products have not only a definite physical and morphological character, but also a definite chemical character.   In its physiological aspect, therefore, inheritance is the recurrence, in successive generations, of like forms of metabolism ;

and this is effected through the transmission from generation to generation of a specific substance or idioplasm which we have seen reason to identify with chromatin. This remains true however we may conceive the morphological nature of the idioplasm — whether as a microcosm of invisible germs or pangens, as conceived by De Vries, Weismann, and Hertwig, as a storehouse of specific ferments as Driesch suggests, or as complex molecular substance grouped in micellæ as in Nägeli's hypothesis. It is true, as Verworn insists, that the cytoplasm is essential to inheritance; for without a specifically organized cytoplasm the nucleus is unable to set up specific forms of synthesis. This objection, which has already been considered from different points of view, both by De Vries and Driesch, disappears as soon as we regard the egg-cytoplasm as *itself a product of the nuclear activity;* and it is just here that the general *rôle* of the nucleus in metabolism is of such vital importance to the theory of inheritance. If the nucleus be the formative centre of the cell, if nutritive substances be elaborated by or under the influence of the nucleus while they are built into the living fabric, then the specific character of the cytoplasm is determined by that of the nucleus, and the contradiction vanishes. In accepting this view we admit that the cytoplasm of the egg is, in a measure, the substratum of inheritance, but it is so only by virtue of its relation to the nucleus, which is, so to speak, the ultimate court of appeal. The nucleus cannot operate without a cytoplasmic field in which its peculiar powers may come into play; but this field is created and moulded by itself. Both are necessary to *development;* the nucleus alone suffices for the *inheritance* of specific possibilities of development.

J. Preformation and Epigenesis. The Unknown Factor in Development

We have now arrived at the furthest outposts of cell-research; and here we find ourselves confronted with the same unsolved problems before which the investigators of evolution have made a halt. For we must now inquire what is the guiding principle of embryological development that correlates its complex phenomena and directs them to a definite end. However we conceive the special mechanism of development, we cannot escape the conclusion that the power behind it is involved in the structure of the germ-plasm inherited from foregoing generations. What is the nature of this structure and how has it been acquired? To the first of these questions we have as yet no certain answer. The second question is merely the general problem of evolution stated from the standpoint of the cell-theory.

The first question raises once more the old puzzle of preformation or epigenesis. The pangen hypothesis of De Vries and Weismann recognizes the fact that development is epigenetic in its external features; but like Darwin's hypothesis of pangenesis, it is at bottom a theory of preformation, and Weismann expresses the conviction that an epigenetic development is an impossibility.[1] He thus explicitly adopts the view, long since suggested by Huxley, that "the process which in its superficial aspect is epigenesis appears in essence to be evolution in the modified sense adopted in Bonnet's later writings; and development is merely the expansion of a potential organism or 'original preformation' according to fixed laws."[2] Hertwig ('92, 2), while accepting the pangen hypothesis, endeavours to take a middle ground between preformation and epigenesis, by assuming that the pangens (idioblasts) represent only *cell-characters*, the traits of the multicellular body arising epigenetically by permutations and combinations of these characters. This conception certainly tends to simplify our ideas of development in its outward features, but it does not explain why cells of different characters should be combined in a definite manner, and hence does not reach the ultimate problem of inheritance.

What lies beyond our reach at present, as Driesch has very ably urged, is to explain the orderly rhythm of development — the coordinating power that guides development to its predestined end. We are logically compelled to refer this power to the inherent organization of the germ, but we neither know nor can we even conceive what this organization is. The theory of Roux and Weismann demands for the orderly distribution of the elements of the germ-plasm a prearranged system of forces of absolutely inconceivable complexity. Hertwig's and De Vries's theory, though apparently simpler, makes no less a demand; for how are we to conceive the power which guides the countless hosts of migrating pangens throughout all the long and complex events of development? The same difficulty confronts us under any theory we can frame. If with Herbert Spencer we assume the germ-plasm to be an aggregation of like units, molecular or supra-molecular, endowed with predetermined polarities which lead to their grouping in specific forms, we but throw the problem one stage further back, and, as Weismann himself has pointed out,[3] substitute for one difficulty another of exactly the same kind.

The truth is that an explanation of development is at present beyond our reach. The controversy between preformation and

[1] *Germ-plasm*, p. 14.

[2] *Evolution, Science and Culture*, p. 296.

[3] *Germinal Selection*, January, 1896, p. 284.

epigenesis has now arrived at a stage where it has little meaning apart from the general problem of physical causality. What we know is that a specific kind of living substance, derived from the parent, tends to run through a specific cycle of changes during which it transforms itself into a body like that of which it formed a part ; and we are able to study with greater or less precision the mechanism by which that transformation is effected and the conditions under which it takes place. But despite all our theories we no more know how the properties of the idioplasm involve the properties of the adult body than we know how the properties of hydrogen and oxygen involve those of water. So long as the chemist and physicist are unable to solve so simple a problem of physical causality as this, the embryologist may well be content to reserve his judgment on a problem a hundredfold more complex.

The second question, regarding the historical origin of the idio-plasm, brings us to the side of the evolutionists. The idioplasm of every species has been derived, as we must believe, by the modifica-tion of a pre-existing idioplasm through variation, and the survival of the fittest. Whether these variations first arise in the idioplasm of the germ-cells, as Weismann maintains, or whether they may arise in the body-cells and then be reflected back upon the idioplasm, is a question on which, as far as I can see, the study of the cell has not thus far thrown a ray of light. Whatever position we take on this question, the same difficulty is encountered; namely, the origin of that co-ordinated *fitness*, that power of active adjustment between internal and external relations, which, as so many eminent biological thinkers have insisted, overshadows every manifestation of life. The nature and origin of this power is the fundamental problem of biology. When, after removing the lens of the eye in the larval salamander, we see it restored in perfect and typical form by regeneration from the posterior layer of the iris,[1] we behold an adaptive response to changed conditions of which the organism can have had no antece-dent experience either ontogenetic or phylogenetic, and one of so marvellous a character that we are made to realize, as by a flash of light, how far we still are from a solution of this problem.[2] It may be true, as Schwann himself urged, that the adaptive power of living beings differs in degree only, not in kind, from that of unor-ganized bodies. It is true that we may trace in organic nature long and finely graduated series leading upward from the lower to the higher forms, and we must believe that the wonderful adaptive mani-festations of the more complex forms have been derived from simpler conditions through the progressive operation of natural causes. But

---

[1] See Wolff, '95, and Müller, '96.

[2] See Wolff, '94, for an admirably clear and forcible discussion of this case.

when all these admissions are made, and when the conserving action of natural selection is in the fullest degree recognized, we cannot close our eyes to two facts : first, that we are utterly ignorant of the manner in which the idioplasm of the germ-cell can so respond to the play of physical forces upon it as to call forth an adaptive variation ; and second, that the study of the cell has on the whole seemed to widen rather than to narrow the enormous gap that separates even the lowest forms of life from the inorganic world.

I am well aware that to many such a conclusion may appear reactionary or even to involve a renunciation of what has been regarded as the ultimate aim of biology. In reply to such a criticism I can only express my conviction that the magnitude of the problem of development, whether ontogenetic or phylogenetic, has been underestimated ; and that the progress of science is retarded rather than advanced by a premature attack upon its ultimate problems. Yet the splendid achievements of cell-research in the past twenty years stand as the promise of its possibilities for the future, and we need set no limit to its advance. To Schleiden and Schwann the present standpoint of the cell-theory might well have seemed unattainable. We cannot foretell its future triumphs, nor can we repress the hope that step by step the way may yet be opened to an understanding of inheritance and development.

LITERATURE. IX

Boveri, Th.— Ein geschlechtlich erzeugter Organismus ohne mütterliche Eigenschaften : *Sitz.-Ber. d. Ges. f. Morph. und Phys. in München*, V. 1889. See also *Arch. f. Entwm.* 1895.

Brooks, W. K. — The Law of Heredity. *Baltimore*, 1883.

Driesch, H. — Analytische Theorie der organischen Entwicklung. *Leipzig*, 1894.

Herbst, C. — Uber die Bedeutung der Reizphysiologie für die kausale Auffassung von Vorgängen in der tierischen Ontogenese : *Biol. Centralb.*, XIV., XV. 1894-95.

Hertwig, O. — Altere und neuere Entwicklungs-theorieen. *Berlin*, 1892.

Id. — Urmund und Spina Bifida : *Arch. mik. Anat.*, XXXIX. 1892.

Id. — Über den Werth der ersten Furchungszellen für die Organbildung des Embryo : *Arch. mik. Anat.*, XLII. 1893.

Id. — Zeit und Streitfragen der Biologie. *Berlin*, 1894.

His, W. — Unsere Körperform und das physiologische Problem ihrer Entstehung. *Leipzig*, 1874.

Loeb, J. — Untersuchungen zur physiologischen Morphologie : I. Heteromorphosis. *Würzburg*, 1891. II. Organbildung und Wachsthum. *Würzburg*, 1892.

Id. — Some Facts and Principles of Physiological Morphology : *Wood's Holl Biol. Lectures.* 1893.

Nägeli, C. — Mechanisch-physiologische Theorie der Abstammungslehre. *München u. Leipzig*, 1884.

Roux, W. — Uber die Bedeutung der Kernteilungsfiguren. *Leipzig*, 1883.

Roux, W.—Über das künstliche Hervorbringen halber Embryonen durch Zerstörung einer der beiden ersten Furchungskugeln, etc.: *Virchow's Archiv*, 114. 1888.

Sachs, J. — Stoff und Form der Pflanzenorgane : *Ges. Abhandlungen*, II. 1893.

Weismann, A. — Essays upon Heredity, First Series. *Oxford*, 1891.

Id. — Essays upon Heredity, Second Series. *Oxford*, 1892.

Id. — Aussere Einflüsse als Entwicklungsreize. *Jena*, 1894.

Whitman, C. O. — Evolution and Epigenesis : *Wood's Holl Biol. Lectures.* 1894.

Wilson, Edm. B. — On Cleavage and Mosaic-work : *Arch. für Entwicklungsm.*, III. 1. 1896.

GLOSSARY

[Obsolete terms are enclosed in brackets. The name and date refer to the first use of the word; subsequent changes of meaning are indicated in the definition.]

Achro′matin (see **Chromatin**), the non-staining substance of the nucleus, as opposed to chromatin; comprising the ground-substance and the linin-network. (FLEMMING, 1880.)

[Akaryo′ta] (see **Karyota**), non-nucleated cells. (FLEMMING, 1882.)

Ale′cithal (ά-priv.; λέκιθος, the yolk of an egg), having little or no yolk (applied to eggs). (BALFOUR, 1880.)

Amito′sis (see **Mitosis**), direct or amitotic nuclear division; mass-division of the nuclear substance without the formation of chromosomes and amphiaster. (FLEMMING, 1882.)

Am′phiaster (ἀμφί, on both sides; ἀστήρ, a star), the achromatic figure formed in mitotic cell-division, consisting of two asters connected by a spindle. (FOL, 1877.)

Amphipy′renin (see **Pyrenin**), the substance of the nuclear membrane. (SCHWARZ, 1887.)

Amy′loplasts (ἄμυλον, starch; πλαστός, πλάσσειν, form), the colourless starch-forming plastids of plant-cells. (ERRARA, 1882.)

An′aphase (ἀνά, back or again), the later period of mitosis during the divergence of the daughter-chromosomes. (STRASBURGER, 1884.)

Aniso′tropy (see **Isotropy**), having a predetermined axis or axes (as applied to the egg). (PFLÜGER, 1883.)

Antherozo′ïd, the same as **Spermatozoïd**.

Anti′podal cone, the cone of astral rays opposite to the spindle-fibres. (VAN BENEDEN, 1883.)

Archiam′phiaster (ἀρχι = first, + amphiaster), the amphiaster by which the first or second polar body is formed. (WHITMAN, 1878.)

Ar′choplasma or **Archoplasm** (ἄρχων, a ruler), the substance from which the attraction-sphere, the astral rays and the spindle-fibres are developed, and of which they consist. (BOVERI, 1888.)

As′ter (ἀστήρ, a star). 1. The star-shaped structure surrounding the centrosome. (FOL, 1877.) [2. The star-shaped group of chromosomes during mitosis (see **Karyaster**). (FLEMMING, 1892.)]

[As′trocœle] (ἀστήρ, a star; κοῖλος, hollow), a term somewhat vaguely applied to the space in which the centrosome lies. (FOL, 1891.)

As′trosphere (see **Centrosphere**). 1. The central mass of the aster, exclusive of the rays, in which the centrosome lies. Equivalent to the "attraction-sphere" of Van Beneden. (FOL, 1891; STRASBURGER, 1892.) 2. The entire aster exclusive of the centrosome. Equivalent to the "astral sphere" of Mark. (BOVERI, 1895.)

Attraction-sphere (see **Centrosphere**), the central mass of the aster from which the rays proceed. Also the mass of "archoplasm," derived from the aster, by which the centrosome is surrounded in the resting cell. (VAN BENEDEN, 1883.)

[**Au′toblast**] (αὐτός, self), applied by Altmann to bacteria and other minute organisms, conceived as independent solitary "bioblasts." (1890.)

Axial filament, the central filament, probably contractile, of the spermatozoön-flagellum. (EIMER, 1874.)

Basichro′matin (see **Chromatin**), the same as chromatin in the usual sense. That portion of the nuclear network stained by basic aniline dyes. (HEIDENHAIN, 1894.)

Bi′oblast (βίος, life; βλαστός, a germ), the hypothetical ultimate supra-molecular vital unit. Equivalent to *plasome*, etc. First used by Beale. Afterwards identified by Altmann as the "granulum."

Bi′ogen (βίος, life; -γενής, producing), equivalent to *plasome*, etc. (VERWORN, 1895.)

Bi′ophores (βίος, life; -φόρος, bearing), the ultimate supra-molecular vital units. Equivalent to the *pangens* of De Vries, the *plasomes* of Wiesner, etc. (WEISMANN, 1893.)

Biva′lent, applied to chromatin-rods representing two chromosomes joined end to end. (HÄCKER, 1892.)

Cell-plate (see **Mid-body**), the equatorial thickening of the spindle-fibres from which the partition-wall arises during the division of plant-cells. (STRASBURGER, 1875.)

Cell-sap, the more liquid ground-substance of the nucleus. [KÖLLIKER, 1865; more precisely defined by R. HERTWIG, 1876.]

Central spindle, the primary spindle by which the centrosomes are connected, as opposed to the contractile mantle-fibres surrounding it. (HERMANN, 1891.)

Centriole, a term applied by Boveri to a minute body or bodies ("Central-korn") within the centrosome. In some cases not to be distinguished from the centrosome. (BOVERI, 1895.)

Centrodes′mus (κέντρον, centre; δεσμός, a band), the primary connection between the centrosomes, forming the beginning of the central spindle. (HEIDENHAIN, 1894.)

Centrole′cithal (κέντρον, centre; λέκιθος, yolk), that type of ovum in which the deutoplasm is mainly accumulated in the centre. (BALFOUR, 1880.)

Cen′trosome (κέντρον, centre; σῶμα, body), a cell-organ generally regarded as the active centre of cell-division and in this sense as the dynamic centre of the cell. Under its influence arise the asters and spindle (amphiaster) of the mitotic figure. (BOVERI, 1888.)

Cen′trosphere, used in this work as equivalent to the "astrosphere" of Strasburger; the central mass of the aster from which the rays proceed and within which lies the centrosome. The attraction-sphere. [STRASBURGER, 1892; applied by him to the "astrosphere" and centrosome taken together.]

Chloroplas′tids (χλωρός, green; πλαστός, form), the green plastids or chlorophyll-bodies of plant and animal cells. (SCHIMPER, 1883.)

Chro′matin (χρῶμα, colour), the deeply staining substance of the nuclear network and of the chromosomes, consisting of nuclein or nucleic acid. (FLEMMING, 1880.)

Chro′matophore (χρῶμα, colour; -φόρος, bearing), a general term applied to the colored plastids of plant and animal cells, including chloroplastids and chromoplastids. (SCHAARSCHMIDT, 1880; SCHMITZ, 1882.)

Chro′matoplasm (χρῶμα, colour; πλάσμα, anything formed or moulded), the substance of the chromatoplasts and other plastids. (STRASBURGER, 1882.)

Chro'momere (χρῶμα, colour; μέρος, a part), the individual chromatin-granules of which the chromosomes are made up. Identified by WEISMANN as the "id." (FOL, 1891.)

Chromoplas'tids (χρῶμα, colour; πλαστός, form), the coloured plastids or pigment-bodies other than the chloroplasts, in plant-cells. (SCHIMPER, 1883.)

Chro'mosomes (χρῶμα, colour; σῶμα, body), the deeply staining bodies into which the chromatic nuclear network resolves itself during mitotic cell-division. (WALDEYER, 1888.)

Cleavage-nucleus, the nucleus of the fertilized egg, resulting from the union of egg-nucleus and sperm-nucleus. (O. HERTWIG, 1875.)

Cortical zone, the outer zone of the centrosphere. (VAN BENEDEN, 1887.)

Cyano'philous (κύανος, blue; φιλεῖν, to love), having an especial affinity for blue or green dyes. (AUERBACH.)

Cy'taster (κύτος, hollow (a cell); ἀστήρ, star), the same as **Aster,** 1. See **Karyaster.** (FLEMMING, 1882.)

[Cy'toblast] (κύτος, hollow (a cell); βλαστός, germ). 1. The cell-nucleus. (SCHLEIDEN, 1838.) 2. One of the hypothetical ultimate vital units (bioblasts or "granula") of which the cell is built up. (ALTMANN, 1890.) 3. A naked cell or "protoblast." (KÖLLIKER.)

[Cytoblaste'ma] (see **Cytoblast**), the formative material from which cells were supposed to arise by "free cell-formation." (SCHLEIDEN, 1838.)

Cytochyle'ma (κύτος, hollow (a cell); χυλός, juice), the ground-substance of the cytoplasm as opposed to that of the nucleus. (STRASBURGER, 1882.)

Cy'tode (κύτος, hollow (a cell); εἶδος, form), a non-nucleated cell. (HACKEL, 1866.)

Cytodie'resis (κύτος, hollow (a cell); διαίρεσις, division), the same as **Mitosis.** (CARNOY, 1885.)

Cytohy'aloplasma (κύτος, hollow (a cell); ὕαλος, glass; πλάσμα, anything formed), the substance of the cytoreticulum in which are embedded the microsomes; opposed to nucleohyaloplasma. (STRASBURGER, 1882.)

Cy'tolymph (κύτος, hollow (a cell); lympha, clear water), the cytoplasmic ground-substance. (HÄCKEL, 1891.)

Cytomi'crosomes (see **Microsome**), microsomes of the cytoplasm; opposed to nucleomicrosomes. (STRASBURGER, 1882.)

Cytomi'tome (κύτος, hollow (a cell); μίτωμα, from μίτος, thread), the cytoplasmic as opposed to the nuclear thread-work. (FLEMMING, 1882.)

Cytoretic'ulum, the same as **Cytomitome.** (STRASBURGER, 1882.)

Cy'tosome (κύτος, hollow (a cell); σῶμα, body,) the cell-body or cytoplasmic mass as opposed to the nucleus. (HÄCKEL, 1891.)

Der'matoplasm (δέρμα, skin), the living protoplasm asserted to form a part of the cell-membrane in plants. (WIESNER, 1886.)

Der'matosomes (δέρμα, skin; σῶμα, body), the plasomes which form the cell-membrane. (WIESNER, 1886.)

Determinant, a hypothetical unit formed as an aggregation of biophores, determining the development of a single cell or independently variable group of cells. (WEISMANN, 1891.)

[Deuthy'alosome] (δεύτ(ερος), second; see **Hyalosome**), the nucleus remaining in the egg after formation of the first polar body. (VAN BENEDEN, 1883.)

Deu'toplasm (δεύτ(ερος), second; πλάσμα, anything formed), yolk, lifeless food-matters deposited in the cytoplasm of the egg; opposed to "protoplasm." (VAN BENEDEN, 1870.)

Directive bodies, the polar bodies. (FR. MÜLLER, 1848.)

Directive sphere, the attraction-sphere. (GUIGNARD, 1891.)

Dispermy, the entrance of two spermatozoa into the egg.

Dispi'reme (see **Spireme**), that stage of mitosis in which each daughter-nucleus has given rise to a spireme. (FLEMMING, 1882.)

Dy'aster (δυάς, two; see **Aster**, 2), the double group of chromosomes during the anaphases of cell-division. (FLEMMING, 1882.)

Egg-nucleus, the nucleus of the egg after formation of the polar bodies and before its union with the sperm-nucleus. Equivalent to the "female pronucleus" of VAN BENEDEN. (O. HERTWIG, 1875.)

Enchyle'ma (ἐν, in; χυλός, juice). 1. The more fluid portion of protoplasm, consisting of "hyaloplasma." (HANSTEIN, 1882.) 2. The ground-substance (cytolymph) of cytoplasm as opposed to the reticulum. (CARNOY, 1883.)

Ener'gid, the cell-nucleus together with the cytoplasm lying within its sphere of influence. (SACHS, 1892.)

Equatorial plate, the group of chromosomes lying at the equator of the spindle during mitosis. (VAN BENEDEN, 1875.)

Erythro'philous (ἐρυθρός, red; φιλεῖν, to love), having an especial affinity for red dyes. (AUERBACH.)

Ga'mete (γαμέτη, wife; γαμέτης, husband), one of two conjugating cells. Usually applied to the unicellular forms.

Gem'mule (see **Pangen**), one of the ultimate supra-molecular germs of the cell assumed by Darwin. (DARWIN, 1868.)

[Ge'noblasts] (γένος, sex; βλαστός, germ), a term applied by Minot to the mature germ-cells. The female genoblast (egg, or "thelyblast") unites with the male (spermatozoön or "arsenoblast") to form an hermaphrodite or indifferent cell. (MINOT, 1877.)

Germinal spot, the nucleolus of the germinal vesicle. (WAGNER, 1836.)

Germinal vesicle, the nucleus of the egg before formation of the polar bodies. (PURKINJE, 1825.)

Germ-plasm, the same as idioplasm. (WEISMANN.)

Heterole'cithal (ἕτερος, different; λέκιθος, yolk), having unequally distributed deutoplasm (includes telolecithal and centrolecithal). (MARK, 1892.)

Heterotyp'ical mitosis (ἕτερος, different; see **Mitosis**), that mode of mitotic division in which the daughter-chromosomes remain united by their ends to form rings. (FLEMMING, 1887.)

[Holoschi'sis] (ὅλος, whole; σχίζειν, to split), direct nuclear division. Amitosis. (FLEMMING, 1882.)

Homole'cithal (ὁμός, the same, uniform; λέκιθος, yolk), equivalent to alecithal. Having little deutoplasm, equally distributed, or none. (MARK, 1892.)

Homœotyp'ical mitosis (ὅμοιος, like; see **Mitosis**), a form of mitosis occurring in the spermatocytes of the salamander, differing from the usual type only in the shortness of the chromosomes and the irregular arrangement of the daughter-chromosomes. (FLEMMING, 1887.)

Hy'aloplasma (ὕαλος, glass; πλάσμα, anything formed). 1. The ground-substance of the cell as distinguished from the granules or microsomes. [HANSTEIN, 1880.] 2. The ground-substance as distinguished from the reticulum or "spongioplasm." (LEYDIG, 1885.) 3. The exoplasm or peripheral protoplasmic zone in plant-cells. (PFEFFER.)

Hy'alosomes (ὕαλος, glass; σῶμα, body), nucleolar-like bodies but slightly stained by either nuclear or plasma stains. (LUKJANOW, 1888.)

[Hy'groplasma] (ὑγρός, wet; πλάσμα, something formed), the more liquid part of protoplasm as opposed to the firmer stereoplasm. (NÄGELI, 1884.)

Id, the hypothetical structural unit resulting from the successive aggregation of biophores and determinants. Identified by Weismann as the chromomere, or chromatin-granule. (WEISMANN, 1891.)

Idant, the hypothetical unit resulting from the successive aggregation of biophores, determinants, and ids. Identified by Weismann as the chromosome. (WEISMANN, 1891.)

Id'ioblasts (ἴδιος, one's own, βλαστός, germ), the hypothetical ultimate units of the cell; the same as biophores. (O. HERTWIG, 1893.)

Id'ioplasm (ἴδιος, one's own; πλάσμα, a thing formed), equivalent to the germ-plasm of Weismann. The substance, now generally identified with chromatin, which by its inherent organization involves the characteristics of the species. The physical basis of inheritance. (NÄGELI, 1884.)

Id'iosome (ἴδιος, one's own; σῶμα, body), the same as idioblast or plasome. (WHITMAN, 1893.)

Interfilar substance, the ground-substance of protoplasm as opposed to the thread-work. (FLEMMING, 1882.)

Interzonal fibres ("Filaments reunissants" of Van Beneden. "Verbindungs-fasern" of Flemming and others). Those spindle-fibres that stretch between the two groups of daughter-chromosomes during the anaphase. Equivalent in some cases to the central spindle. (MARK, 1881.)

Iso'tropy (ἴσος, equal; τροπή, a turning), the absence of predetermined axes (as applied to the egg). (PFLÜGER, 1883.)

[Ka'ryaster] (κάρυον, nut, nucleus; see **Aster**, 2), the star-shaped group of chromosomes in mitosis. Opposed to cytaster. (FLEMMING, 1882.)

Karyenchy'ma (κάρυον, nut, nucleus; ἐν, in; χυμός, juice), the "nuclear sap." (FLEMMING, 1882.)

Karyokine'sis (κάρυον, nut, nucleus; κίνησις, change, movement), the same as mitosis. (SCHLEICHER, 1878.)

[Karyoly'ma], the "karyolytic" (mitotic) figure. (AUERBACH, 1876.)

Ka'ryolymph. The nuclear sap. (HÄCKEL, 1891.)

[Karyo'lysis] (κάρυον, nut, nucleus; λύσις, dissolution), the supposed dissolution of the nucleus during cell-division. (AUERBACH, 1874.)

[Karyoly'tic figure] (see **Karyolysis**), a term applied by Auerbach to the mitotic figure in living cells. Believed by him to result from the dissolution of the nucleus. (AUERBACH, 1874.)

Karyomi'crosome (see **Microsome**), the same as nucleo-microsome.

Ka'ryomite, the same as chromosome [? SCHIEFFERDECKER].

Karyomi'tome (κάρυον, nut, nucleus; μίτωμα, from μίτος, a thread), the nuclear as opposed to the cytoplasmic thread-work. (FLEMMING, 1882.)

Karyomito'sis (κάρυον, nut, nucleus; see **Mitosis**), mitosis. (FLEMMING, 1882.)

Ka'ryon (κάρυον, nut, nucleus), the cell-nucleus. (HÄCKEL, 1891.)

Ka'ryoplasm (κάρυον, nut, nucleus; πλάσμα, a thing formed), nucleoplasm. The nuclear as opposed to the cytoplasmic substance. (FLEMMING, 1882.)

Ka'ryosome (κάρυον, nut, nucleus; σῶμα, body). 1. Nucleoli of the "net-knot" type, staining with nuclear dyes, as opposed to plasmosomes or true nucleoli. (OGATA, 1883.) 2. The same as chromosome. (PLATNER, 1886.) 3. Caryosome. The cell-nucleus. (WATASÉ, 1894.)

[Karyo'ta] (κάρυον, nut, nucleus), nucleated cells. (FLEMMING, 1882.)

Karyothe'ca (κάρυον, nut, nucleus; θήκη, case, box), the nuclear membrane. (HÄCKEL, 1891.)

Ki'noplasm (κινεῖν, to move; πλάσμα, a thing formed), equivalent to archoplasm; opposed by Strasburger to the "trophoplasm" or nutritive plasm. (STRASBURGER, 1892.)

[Lanthanin] (λανθάνειν, to conceal), equivalent to oxychromatin. (HEIDENHAIN, 1892.)

z

Leucoplas'tids (λευκός, white; πλαστός, form), the colourless plastids of plant-cells from which arise the starch-formers (amyloplastids), chloroplastids, and chromoplastids. (SCHIMPER, 1883.)

Li'nin (linum, a linen thread), the substance of the "achromatic" nuclear reticulum. (SCHWARZ, 1887.)

Maturation, the final stages in the development of the germ-cells. More specifically, the processes by which the reduction of the number of chromosomes is effected.

Metakine'sis (see **Metaphase**) (μετά, beyond (*i.e.* further); κίννησις, movement), the middle stage of mitosis, when the chromosomes are grouped in the equatorial plate. (FLEMMING, 1882.)

Metanu'cleus, a term applied to the egg-nucleus after its extrusion from the germinal vesicle. (HÄCKER, 1892.)

Met'aphase, the middle stage of mitosis during which occurs the splitting of the chromosomes in the equatorial plate. (STRASBURGER, 1884.)

Met'aplasm (μετά, after, beyond; πλάσμα, a thing formed), a term collectively applied to the lifeless inclusions (deutoplasm, starch, etc.) in protoplasm as opposed to the living substance. (HANSTEIN, 1880.)

Micel'la, one of the ultimate supra-molecular units of the cell. (NÄGELI, 1884.)

Microcen'trum, the dynamic centre of the cell, consisting of one or more centrosomes. (HEIDENHAIN, 1894.)

Mi'cropyle (μικρός, small; πύλη, orifice), the aperture in the egg-membrane through which the spermatozoön enters. [First applied by TURPIN, in 1806, to the opening through which the pollen-tube enters the ovule. t. ROBERT BROWN.]

Mi'crosome (μικρός, small; σῶμα, body), the granules as opposed to the ground-substance of protoplasm. (HANSTEIN, 1880.)

Middle-piece, that portion of the spermatozoön lying behind the nucleus at the base of the flagellum. (SCHWEIGGER-SEIDEL, 1865.)

Mid-body ("Zwischenkörper"), a body or group of granules, probably comparable with the cell-plate in plants, formed in the equatorial region of the spindle during the anaphases of mitosis. (FLEMMING, 1890.)

Mi'tome (μίτωμα, from μίτος, a thread), the reticulum or thread-work as opposed to the ground-substance of protoplasm. (FLEMMING, 1882.)

[Mitoschi'sis] (μίτος, thread; σχίζειν, to split), indirect nuclear division; mitosis. (FLEMMING, 1882.)

Mito'sis (μίτος, a thread), indirect nuclear division typically involving: *a*, the formation of an amphiaster; *b*, conversion of the chromatin into a thread (spireme); *c*, segmentation of the thread into chromosomes; *d*, splitting of the chromosomes. (FLEMMING, 1882.)

Mi'tosome (μίτος, a thread; σῶμα, body), a body derived from the spindle-fibres of the secondary spermatocytes, giving rise, according to PLATNER, to the middle-piece and the tail-envelope of the spermatozoön. Equivalent to the Nebenkern of La Valette St. George. (PLATNER, 1889.)

Nebenkern (Paranucleus), a name originally applied by Bütschli (1871) to an extranuclear body in the spermatid; afterwards shown by La Valette St. George and Platner to arise from the spindle-fibres of the secondary spermatocyte. Since applied to many forms of cytoplasmic bodies (yolk-nucleus, etc.) of the most diverse nature.

Nuclear plate. 1. The equatorial plate. (STRASBURGER, 1875.) 2. The partition-wall which sometimes divides the nucleus in amitosis.

Nucleic acid, a complex organic acid, rich in phosphorus, and an essential constituent of chromatin.

Nuclein, the chemical basis of chromatin; a compound of nucleic acid and albumin. (MIESCHER, 1874.)

Nucleo-albumin, a nuclein having a relatively high percentage of albumin. Distinguished from nucleo-proteids by containing paranucleic acid which yields no xanthin-bodies.

Nucleochyl'ema (χυλός, juice), the ground-substance of the nucleus as opposed to that of the cytoplasm. (STRASBURGER, 1882.)

Nucleohy'aloplasma (see **Hyaloplasm**), the achromatic substance (linin) in which the chromatin-granules are suspended. (STRASBURGER, 1882.)

Nucleomi'crosomes (see **Microsome**), the nuclear (chromatin) granules as opposed to those of the cytoplasm. (STRASBURGER, 1882.)

Nu'cleoplasm. 1. The reticular substance of the (egg-) nucleus. (VAN BENEDEN, 1875.) 2. The substance of the nucleus as opposed to that of the cell-body or cytoplasm. (STRASBURGER, 1882.)

Nucleo-pro'teid, a nuclein having a relatively high percentage of albumin. May be split into albumin and true nucleic acid, the latter yielding xanthin-bodies.

Œdematin (οἴδημα, a swelling), the granules or microsomes of the nuclear ground-substance. (REINKE, 1893.)

O'öcyte (**Ovocyte**), (ᾠόν, egg; κύτος, hollow (a cell)), the ultimate ovarian egg before formation of the polar bodies. The primary oöcyte divides to form the first polar body and the secondary oöcyte. The latter divides to form the second polar body and the mature egg. (BOVERI, 1891.)

Oögen'esis, **Ovogenesis** (ᾠόν, egg; γένεσις, origin), the genesis of the egg after its origin by division from the mother-cell. Often used more specifically to denote the process of reduction in the female.

Oögo'nium, **Ovogonium** (ᾠόν, egg; γονή, generation). 1. The primordial mother-cell from which arises the egg and its follicle. (PFLÜGER.) 2. The descendants of the primordial germ-cell which ultimately give rise to the oöcytes or ovarian eggs. (BOVERI, 1891.)

Oökine'sis (ᾠόν, egg; κίνησις, movement), the mitotic phenomena of the egg during maturation and fertilization. (WHITMAN, 1887.)

O'vocentre, the egg-centrosome during fertilization. (FOL, 1891.)

Oxychro'matin (ὀξύς, acid; see **Chromatin**), that portion of the nuclear substance stained by acid aniline dyes. Equivalent to "linin" in the usual sense. (HEIDENHAIN, 1894.)

Pangen'esis (πᾶς (παν-), all; γένεσις, production), the theory of gemmules, according to which hereditary traits are carried by invisible germs thrown off by the individual cells of the body. (DARWIN, 1868.)

Pangens (πᾶς (παν-), all; -γενής, producing), the hypothetical ultimate supra-molecular units of the idioplasm, and of the cell generally. Equivalent to gemmules, micellæ, idioblasts, biophores, etc. (DE VRIES, 1889.)

Panmeri'stic (παν, all; μέρος, part), relating to an ultimate protoplasmic structure consisting of independent units. See **Pangen**.

Parachro'matin (see **Chromatin**), the achromatic nuclear substance (linin of Schwarz) from which the spindle-fibres arise. (PFITZNER, 1883.)

Parali'nin (see **Linin**), the nuclear ground-substance or nuclear sap. (SCHWARZ, 1887.)

Parami'tome (see **Mitome**), the ground-substance or interfilar substance of protoplasm, opposed to mitome. (FLEMMING, 1892.)

Paranu'clein (see **Nuclein**), the substance of true nucleoli or plasmosomes. Pyrenin of Schwarz. (O. HERTWIG, 1878.) Applied by Kossel to "nucleins" derived from the cytoplasm. These are compounds of albumin and paranucleic acid which yields no xanthin-bodies.

Par'aplasm (παρά, beside; πλάσμα, something formed), the less active portion of the cell-substance. Originally applied by Kupffer to the cortical region of the cell (exoplasm), but now often applied to the ground-substance. (KUPFFER, 1875.)

Per'iplast (περί, around; πλαστός, form), a term somewhat vaguely applied to the attraction-sphere. The term daughter-periplast is applied to the centrosome. (VEJDOVSKÝ, 1888.)

Plas'mosome (πλάσμα, something formed (*i.e.* protoplasmic); σῶμα, body), the true nucleolus, distinguished by its affinity for acid anilines and other " plasma-stains." (OGATA, 1883.)

Pla'some (πλάσμα, a thing formed; σῶμα, body), the ultimate supra-molecular vital unit. See **Biophore, Pangen.** (WIESNER, 1890.)

Plas'tid (πλαστός, form). 1. A cell, whether nucleated or non-nucleated. (HÄCKEL, 1866.) 2. A general term applied to permanent cell-organs (chloroplasts, etc.) other than the nucleus and centrosome. (SCHIMPER, 1883.)

Plas'tidule, the ultimate supra-molecular vital unit. (ELSSBERG, 1874; HÄCKEL, 1876.)

Plas'tin, a term of vague meaning applied to a substance related to the nucleo-proteids and nucleo-albumins constituting the linin-network (Zacharias) and the cytoreticulum (Carnoy). (REINKE and RODEWALD, 1881.)

Pluriva'lent (*plus*, more; *valere*, to be worth), applied to chromatin-rods that have the value of more than one chromosome *sensu strictu*. (HACKER, 1892.)

Polar bodies (Polar globules), two minute cells segmented off from the ovum before union of the germ-nuclei. (Disc. by CARUS, 1824; so named by ROBIN, 1862.)

Polar corpuscle, the centrosome. (VAN BENEDEN, 1876.)

Polar rays (Polradien), a term sometimes applied to all of the astral rays as opposed to the spindle-fibres, sometimes to the group of astral rays opposite to the spindle-fibres.

Pole-plates (End-plates), the achromatic spheres or masses at the poles of the spindle in the mitosis of Protozoa, probably representing the attraction-spheres. (R. HERTWIG, 1877.)

Polyspermy, the entrance into the ovum of more than one spermatozoön.

Prochro'matin (see **Chromatin**), the substance of true nucleoli, or plasmosomes. Equivalent to paranuclein of O. Hertwig. (PFITZNER, 1883.)

Pronuclei, the germ-nuclei during fertilization; *i.e.*, the egg-nucleus (female pro-nucleus) after formation of the polar bodies, and the sperm-nucleus (male pro-nucleus) after entrance of the spermatozoön into the egg. (VAN BENEDEN, 1875.)

[Prothy'alosome] (see **Hyalosome**), an area in the germinal vesicle (of *Ascaris*) by which the germinal spot is surrounded, and which is concerned in formation of the first polar body. (VAN BENEDEN, 1883.)

Pro'toblast (πρῶτος, first; βλαστός, a germ), a naked cell, devoid of a membrane. (KÖLLIKER.)

Pro'toplasm (πρῶτος, first; πλάσμα, a thing formed or moulded). 1. The living substance of the cell, comprising cytoplasm and karyoplasm. (PURKYNĔ, 1840; H. VON MOHL, 1846.) 2. The cytoplasm as opposed to the karyoplasm.

Pro'toplast (πρῶτος, first; πλαστός, formed). 1. The protoplasmic body of the cell, including nucleus and cytoplasm, regarded as a unit. Nearly equivalent to the energid of Sachs. (HANSTEIN, 1880.) 2. Used by some authors synony-mously with plastid.

[Pseudochro'matin] (see **Chromatin**), the same as prochromatin. (PFITZNER, 1886.)

Pseudonu'clein (see **Nuclein**), the same as the paranuclein of Kossel. (HAM-
MARSTEN, 1894.)

Pseudo-reduction, the preliminary halving of the number of chromatin-rods as a
prelude to the formation of the tetrads and to the actual reduction in the number
of chromosomes in maturation. (RÜCKERT, 1894.)

Pyre'nin (πυρήν, the stone of a fruit; *i.e.* relating to the nucleus), the substance
of true nucleoli. Equivalent to the paranuclein of Hertwig. (SCHWARZ, 1887.)

Pyre'noid (πυρήν, the stone of a fruit; like a nucleus), colourless plastids (leuco-
plastids), occurring in the chromatophores of lower plants, forming centres for
the formation of starch. (SCHMITZ, 1883.)

Reduction, the halving of the number of chromosomes in the germ-nuclei during
maturation.

Sertoli-cells, the large, digitate, supporting, and nutritive cells of the mammalian
testis to which the developing spermatozoa are attached. (Equivalent to "sper-
matoblast" as originally used by VON EBNER, 1871.)

Sper'matid (σπέρμα, seed), the final cells which are converted without further
division into spermatozoa; they arise by division of the secondary spermatocytes
or "Samenmütterzellen." (LA VALETTE ST. GEORGE, 1886.)

Sper'matoblasts (σπέρμα, seed; βλαστός, germ), a word of vague meaning,
originally applied to the supporting cell or Sertoli-cell, from which a group of
spermatozoa was supposed to arise. By various later writers used synonymously
with spermatid. (VON EBNER, 1871.)

Sper'matocyst (σπέρμα, seed; κύστις, bladder), originally applied to a group of
sperm-producing cells ("spermatocytes"), arising by division from an "Ursamenzelle" or "spermatogonium." (LA VALETTE ST. GEORGE, 1876.)

Sper'matocyte (σπέρμα, seed; κύτος, hollow (a cell)), the cells arising from the
spermatogonia. The *primary spermatocyte* arises by growth of one of the last
generation of spermatogonia. By its division are formed two *secondary spermatocytes*, each of which gives rise to two spermatids (ultimately spermatozoa).
(LA VALETTE ST. GEORGE, 1876.)

[**Spermatogem'ma**] (σπέρμα, seed; *gemma*, bud), nearly equivalent to spermato-
cyst. Differs in the absence of a surrounding membrane. [In mammals,
LA VALETTE ST. GEORGE, 1878.]

Spermatogen'esis (σπέρμα, seed; γένεσις, origin), the phenomena involved in
the formation of the spermatozoön. Often used more specifically to denote the
process of reduction in the male.

Spermatogo'nium ("Ursamenzelle") (σπέρμα, seed; γονή, generation), the
descendants of the primordial germ-cells in the male. Each ultimate spermatogonium typically gives rise to four spermatozoa. (LA VALETTE ST.
GEORGE, 1876.)

Spermatome'rites (σπέρμα, seed; μέρος, a part), the chromatin-granules into
which the sperm-nucleus resolves itself after entrance of the spermatozoön. (In
Petromyzon, BÖHM, 1887.)

Sper'matosome (σπέρμα, seed; σῶμα, body), the same as spermatozoön. (LA
VALETTE ST. GEORGE, 1878.)

Spermatozo'ïd (see **Spermatozoön**), the ciliated paternal germ-cell in plants.
The word was first used by von Siebold as synonymous with spermatozoön.

Spermatozo'ön (σπέρμα, seed; ζῷον, animal), the paternal germ-cell of animals.
(LEEUWENHOEK, 1677.)

Sperm-nucleus, the nucleus of the spermatozoön; more especially applied to it after
entrance into the egg before its union with the egg-nucleus. In this sense
equivalent to the "male pronucleus" of Van Beneden. (O. HERTWIG, 1875.)

Sper'mocentre, the sperm-centrosome during fertilization. (FOL, 1891.)

Spi′reme (σπείρημα, a thing wound or coiled; a skein), the skein or " Knäuel" stage of the nucleus in mitosis, during which the chromatin appears in the form of a thread, continuous or segmented. (FLEMMING, 1882.)

Spon′gioplasm (σπογγίον, a sponge; πλάσμα, a thing formed), the cytoreticulum. (LEYDIG, 1885.)

Ste′reoplasm (στερεός, solid), the more solid part of protoplasm as opposed to the more fluid " hygroplasm." (NÄGELI, 1884.)

Substantia hyalina, the protoplasmic ground-substance or " hyaloplasm." (LEYDIG, 1885.)

Substantia opaca, the protoplasmic reticulum or " spongioplasm." (LEYDIG, 1885.)

Te′loblast (τέλος, end; βλαστός, a germ), large cells situated at the growing end of the embryo (in annelids, etc.), which bud forth rows of smaller cells. (WHITMAN, WILSON, 1887.)

Telole′cithal (τέλος, end; λέκιθος, yolk), that type of ovum in which the yolk is mainly accumulated in one hemisphere. (BALFOUR, 1880.)

Te′lophases, Telokine′sis (τέλος, end), the closing phases of mitosis, during which the daughter-nuclei are re-formed. (HEIDENHAIN, 1894.)

To′noplasts (τόνος, tension; πλαστός, form), plastids from which arise the vacuoles in plant-cells. (DE VRIES, 1885.)

Trophoplasm (τροφή, nourishment; πλάσμα). 1. The nutritive or vegetative substance of the cell, as distinguished from the idioplasm. (NÄGELI, 1884.) 2. The active substance of the cytoplasm other than the " kinoplasm " or archoplasm. (STRASBURGER, 1892.)

Tro′phoplasts (τροφή. nourishment; πλαστός, form), a general term, nearly equivalent to the " plastids " of Schimper, including " anaplasts " (amyloplasts), " autoplasts " (chloroplasts), and chromoplasts. (A. MEYER, 1882–83.)

Yolk-nucleus, a word of vague meaning applied to a cytoplasmic body, single or multiple, that appears in the ovarian egg. [Named " Dotterkern " by CARUS, 1850.]

Zy′gote or **Zy′gospore** (ζυγόν, a yoke), the cell produced by the fusion of two conjugating cells or gametes in some of the lower plants.

GENERAL LITERATURE-LIST

THE following list includes only the titles of works actually referred to in the text and those immediately related to them. For more complete bibliography the reader is referred to the literature-lists in the special works cited, especially the following. For reviews of the early history of the cell-theory see Remak's *Untersuchungen* ('50-'55), Huxley on the *Cell-theory* ('53), and Tyson's *Cell-doctrine* ('78). An exhaustive review of the earlier literature on protoplasm, nucleus, and cell-division will be found in Flemming's *Zellsubstanz* ('82), and a later review of theories of protoplasmic structure in Bütschli's *Protoplasma* ('92). The earlier work on mitosis and fertilization is very thoroughly reviewed in Whitman's *Clepsine* ('78), Fol's *Hénogenie* ('79), and Mark's *Limax* ('81). For more recent general literature-lists see especially Hertwig's *Zelle und Gewebe* ('93), Yves Delage ('95), Henneguy's *Cellule* ('96), and the admirable reviews by Flemming, Boveri, Rückert, Roux, and others in Merkel and Bonnet's *Ergebnisse* ('91-'94).

The titles are arranged in alphabetical order, according to the system adopted in Minot's *Human Embryology*. Each author's name is followed by the date of publication (the first two digits being omitted, except in case of works published before the present century), and this by a single number to designate the paper, in case two or more works were published in the same year. For example, **Boveri, Th., '87, 2**, denotes the second paper published by Boveri in 1887.

In order to economize space, the following abbreviations are used for the journals most frequently referred to : —

ABBREVIATIONS

A. A. Anatomischer Anzeiger.
A. B. Archives de Biologie.
A. A. P. Archiv für Anatomie und Physiologie.
A. m. A. Archiv für mikroscopische Anatomie.
A. Entm. Archiv für Entwicklungsmechanik.
B. C. Biologisches Centralblatt.
C. R. Comptes Rendus.
J. M. Journal of Morphology.
J. Z. Jenaische Zeitschrift.
M. A. Müller's Archiv.
M. J. Morphologisches Jahrbuch.
Q. J. Quarterly Journal of Microscopical Science.
Z. A. Zoologischer Anzeiger.
Z. w. Z. Zeitschrift für wissenschaftliche Zoologie.

ACQUA, '91. Contribuzione alla conoscenza della cellula vegetale : *Malpighia*, *V.* — **Altman, R., '86.** Studien über die Zelle, I. : *Leipzig.* — **Id., '87.** Die Genese der Zellen : *Leipzig.* — **Id., '89.** Über Nucleinsäure : *A. A. P.*, p. 524. — **Id., '90, '94.** Die Elementarorganismen und ihre Beziehung zu den Zellen : *Leipzig.* — **Amelung, E., '93.** Über mittlere Zellgrösse : *Flora*, p. 176. — **Arnold, J., '79.**

Über feinere Struktur der Zellen, etc. : *Virchow's Arch.*, 1879. (See earlier papers.) — **Auerbach, L.**, '74. Organologische Studien : *Breslau.* — **Id.**, '91. Über einen sexuellen Gegensatz in der Chromatophilie der Keimsubstanzen : *Sitzungsber. der Konigl. preuss. Akad. d. Wiss. Berlin*, XXXV.

VON BAER, C. E., '28, '37. Über Entwickelungsgeschichte der Thiere. Beobachtung und Reflexion : I. *Königsberg*, 1828 ; II. 1837. — **Id.**, '34. Die Metamorphose des Eies der Batrachier : *Müller's Arch.* — **Balbiani, E. G.**, '64. Sur la constitution du germe dans l'œuf animal avant la fécondation : *C. R.*, LVIII. — **Id.**, '76. Sur les phénomènes de la division du noyau cellulaire : *C. R*, XXX., October, 1876. — **Id.**, '81. Sur la structure du noyau des cellules salivares chez les larves de Chironomus : *Z. A.*, 1881, Nos. 99, 100. — **Id.**, '89. Recherches expérimentales sur la merotomie des Infusoires ciliés : *Recueil Zool. Suisse*, January, 1889. — **Id.**, '91, 1. Sur les régénérations successives du peristome chez les Stentors et sur le rôle du noyau dans ce phénomène : *Z. A.*, 372, 373. — **Id.**, '91, 2. Sur la structure et division du noyau chez les Spirochona gemmipara : *Ann. d. Micrographie.* **Id.**, '93. Centrosome et Dotterkern : *Journ. de l'anat. et de la physiol.*, XXIX. — — **Balfour, F. M.**, '80. Comparative Embryology : 1. 1880. — **Ballowitz, '88–'91.** Untersuchungen über die Struktur der Spermatozoen : 1. (birds) *A. m. A.*, XXXII., 1888 ; 2. (insects) *Z. w. Z.*, LX., 1890 ; 3. (fishes, amphibia, reptiles) *A. m. A.* XXXVI., 1890 ; 4. (mammals) *Z. w. Z.*, 1891. — **Id.**, '89. Fibrilläre Struktur und Contractilität : *Arch. ges. Phys.*, XLVI. — **Id.**, '91, 2. Die innere Zusammensetzung des Spermatozoënkopfes der Säugetiere : *Centralb. f. Phys.*, V. — **Id.**, '95. Die Doppelspermatozoa der Dytisciden : *Z. w. Z.*, XLV., 3. — **Van Bambeke, C.**, '93. Élimination d'éléments nucléaires dans l'œuf ovarien de Scorpæna scrofa : *A. B.*, XIII. 1. — **De Bary**, '58. Die Conjugaten. — **Id.**, '62. Über den Bau und das Wesen der Zelle : *Flora*, 1862. — **Id.**, '64. Die Mycetozoa : 2d Ed., *Leipzig.* — **Barry, M.** Spermatozoa observed within the Mammiferous Ovum : *Phil. Trans.*, 1843. — **Beale, Lionel S.**, '61. On the Structure of Simple Tissues of the Human Body : *London.* — **Béchamp and Estor**, '82. De la constitution élémentaire des tissues : *Montpellier.* — **Belajeff, '94, 1.** Zur Kenntniss der Karyokinese bei den Pflanzen : *Flora*, 1894, Ergänzungsheft. — **Id.**, '94, 2. Über Bau und Entwicklung der Spermatozoiden der Pflanzen : *Flora*, LIV. — **Benda, C.**, '87. Untersuchungen über den Bau des funktionirenden Samenkenkälchens einiger Säugethiere : *A. m. A.* — **Id.**, '93. Zellstrukturen und Zelltheilungen des Salamanderhodens : *Verh. d. Anat. Ges.*, 1893. — **Van Beneden, E.**, '70. Recherches sur la composition et la signification de l'œuf : *Mém. cour. de l'Ac. roy. d. S. de Belgique*, 1870. — **Id.**, '75. La maturation de l'œuf, la fécondation et les premières phases du développement embryonnaire des mammifères d'après des recherches faites chez le lapin : *Bull. Ac. roy. de Belgique*, XI. — **Id.**, '76, 1. Recherches sur les Dicyémides : *Bull. Acad. Roy. Belgique*, XLI., XLII. — **Id.**, '76, 2. Contribution à l'histoire de la vésicule germinative et du premier noyau embryonnaire : *Ibid.*, XLI. ; also *Q. J.*, XVI. — **Id.**, '83. Recherches sur la maturation de l'œuf, la fécondation et la division cellulaire : *A. B.*, IV. — **Van Beneden and Julin, '84, 1.** La segmentation chez les Ascidiens et ses rapports avec l'organisation de la larve : *Ibid.*, V. — **Id.**, '84, 2. La spermatogenèse chez l'Ascaride mégalocéphale : *Bull. Acad. Roy. Belgique*, 3me ser., VII. — **Van Beneden, E., et Neyt, A.**, '87. Nouvelles recherches sur la fécondation et la division mitosique chez l'Ascaride mégalocéphale : *Ibid.*, 1887. — **Bergh, R. S.**, '94. Vorlesungen über die Zelle und die einfachen Gewebe : *Wiesbaden.* — **Id.**, '95. Über die relativen Theilungspotenzen einiger Embryonalzellen : *A. Entm.*, II., 2. — **Bernard, Claude.** Leçons sur les Phénomènes de la Vie : 1st Ed. 1878, 2d Ed. 1885, *Paris.* — **Berthold, G.**, '86. Studien über Protoplasma-mechanik : *Leipzig.* — **Bickford, E. E.**,

'94. Notes on Regeneration and Heteromorphosis of Tubularian Hydroids : *J. M.*, IX., 3. — **Biondi, D.**, '85. Die Entwicklung der Spermatozoiden : *A. m. A.*, XXV. — **Blanc, H.**, '93. Étude sur la fécondation de l'œuf de la truite : *Ber. Naturforsch. Ges. zu Freiburg*, VIII. — **Blochmann, F.**, '87, 2. Über die Richtungskörper bei Insekteneiern : *M. J.*, XII. — **Id.**, '88. Über die Richtungskörper bei unbefruchtet sich entwickelnden Insekteneiern : *Verh. naturh. med. Ver. Heidelberg*, N. F., IV., 2. — **Id.**, '89. Über die Zahl der Richtungskörper bei befruchteten und unbefruchteten Bieneneiern : *M. J.* — **Id.**, '94. Über die Kerntheilung bei Euglena : *B. C.*, XIV. — **Böhm, A.**, '88. Über Reifung und Befruchtung des Eies von Petromyzon Planeri : *A. m. A.*, XXXII. — **Id.**, '91. Die Befruchtung des Forelleneies : *Sitz.-Ber. d. Ges. f. Morph. u. Phys. München*, VII. — **Boll, Fr.**, '76. Das Princip des Wachsthums : *Berlin.* — **Bonnet, C.**, 1762. Considerations sur les Corps organisés : *Amsterdam.* — **Born, G.**, '85. Über den Einfluss der Schwere auf das Froschei : *A. m. A.*, XXIV. — **Id.**, '94. Die Structur des Keimbläschens im Ovarialei von Triton tæniatus : *A. m. A.*, XLIII. — **Bourne, G. C.**, '95. A Criticism of the Cell-theory ; being an answer to Mr. Sedgwick's Article on the Inadequacy of the Cellular Theory of Development : *Q. J.*, XXXVIII., 1. — **Boveri, Th.**, '86. Über die Bedeutung der Richtungskörper : *Sitz.-Ber. Ges. Morph. u. Phys. München*, II. — **Id.**, '87, 1. Zellenstudien, Heft I. : *J. Z.*, XXI. — **Id.**, '87, 2. Über die Befruchtung der Eier von *Ascaris megalocephala* : *Sitz.-Ber. Ges. Morph. Phys. München*, III. — **Id.**, '87, 2. Über den Anteil des Spermatozoön an der Teilung des Eies : *Sitz.-Ber. Ges. Morph. Phys. München*, III., 3. — **Id.**, '87, 3. Über Differenzierung der Zellkerne während der Furchung des Eies von Ascaris meg. : *A. A.*, 1887. — **Id.**, '88, 1. Über partielle Befruchtung : *Sitz.-Ber. Ges. Morph. Phys. München*, IV., 2. — **Id.**, '88, 2. Zellenstudien, II. : *J. Z.*, XXII. — **Id.**, '89. Ein geschlechtlich erzeugter Organismus ohne mütterliche Eigenschaften : *Sitz.-Ber. Ges. Morph. Phys. München*, V. Trans. in *Am. Nat.*, March, '93. — **Id.**, '90. Zellenstudien, Heft III. : *J. Z.*, XXIV. — **Id.**, '91. Befruchtung : *Merkel und Bonnet's Ergebnisse*, I. — **Id.**, '95, 1. Über die Befruchtungs-und Entwicklungsfähigkeit kernloser Seeigel-Eier, etc. : *A. Entm.*, II., 3. — **Id.**, '95, 2. Über das Verhalten der Centrosomen bei der Befruchtung des Seeigeleies, nebst allgemeinen Bemerkungen über Centrosomen und Verwandtes : *Verh. d. Physikal.-med. Gesellschaft zu Würzburg*, N. F., XXIX., 1. — **Braem, F.**, '93. Des Prinzip der organbildenden Keimbezirke und die entwicklungsmechanischen Studien von H. Driesch : *B. C.*, XIII., 4, 5. — **Brandt, H.**, '77. Über Actinosphærium Eichhornii : *Dissertation, Halle*, 1877. — **Brass, A.**, '83-4. Die Organisation der thierischen Zelle : *Halle.* — **Brauer, A.**, '92. Das Ei von Branchipus Grubii von der Bildung bis zur Ablage : *Abh. preuss. Akad. Wiss.*, '92. — **Id.**, '93, 1. Zur Kenntniss der Reifung des parthenogenetisch sich entwickelnden Eies von Artemia Salina : *A. m. A.*, XLIII. — **Id.**, '93, 2. Zur Kenntniss der Spermatogenese von Ascaris megalocephala : *A. m. A.*, XLII. — **Id.**, '94. Über die Encystierung von Actinosphærium Eichhornii : *Z. w. Z.*, LVIII., 2. — **Braus, '95.** Über Zellteilung und Wachstum des Tritoneies : *J. Z.*, XXIX. — **Brooks, W. K.**, '83. The Law of Heredity : *Baltimore.* — **Brown, H. H.**, '85. On Spermatogenesis in the Rat : *Q. J.*, XXV. — **Brown, Robert**, '33. Observations on the Organs and Mode of Fecundation in Orchideæ and Asclepiadeæ : *Trans. Linn. Soc.*, 1833. — **Brunn, M. von**, '89. Beiträge zur Kenntniss der Samenkörper und ihrer Entwickelung bei Vögeln und Säugethieren : *A. m. A.*, XXXIII. — **Brücke, C.**, '61. Die Elementarorganismen : *Wiener Sitzber.*, XLIV., 1861. — **Bürger, O.**, '91. Über Attractionssphären in den Zellkörpern einer Leibesflüssigkeit : *A. A.*, VI. — **Id.**, 92. Was sind die Attractionssphären und ihre Centralkörper ? *A. A.*, 1892. — **De Bruyne, C.**, '95. La sphère attractive dans les cellules fixes du tissu conjonctif : *Bull. Acad. Sc. de Belgique*, XXX. —

Bütschli, O., '73. Beiträge zur Kenntniss der freilebenden Nematoden : *Nova acta acad. Car. Leopold,* XXXVI. — **Id., '75.** Vorläufige Mitteilungen über Untersuchungen betreffend die ersten Entwickelungsvorgänge im befruchteten Ei von Nematoden und Schnecken : *Z. w. Z.,* XXV. — **Id., '76.** Studien über die ersten Entwickelungsvorgänge der Eizelle, die Zellteilung und die Konjugation der Infusorien : *Abh. des Senckenb. Naturforscher-Ges.,* X. — **Id., '91.** Über die sogenannten Centralkörper der Zellen und ihre Bedeutung : *Verh. Naturhist. Med. Ver. Heidelberg,* 1891. — **Id., '92, 1.** Über die künstliche Nachahmung der Karyokinetischen Figuren : *Ibid.,* N. F., V. — **Id., '92, 2.** Untersuchungen über mikroskopische Schäume und das Protoplasma (full review of literature on protoplasmic structure) : *Leipzig (Engelmann).* — **Id., '94.** Vorläufige Bericht über fortgesetzte Untersuchungen an Gerinnungsschäumen, etc. : *Verh. Naturhist. Ver. Heidelberg,* V.

CALKINS, G. N., '95, 1. Observations on the Yolk-nucleus in the Eggs of Lumbricus : *Trans. N. Y. Acad. Sci.,* June, 1895. — **Id., '95, 2.** The Spermatogenesis of Lumbricus : *J. M.,* XI., 2. — **Carnoy, J. B., '94.** La biologie cellulaire : *Liège.* — **Id., '85.** La cytodiérèse des Arthropodes : *La Cellule,* I. — **Id., '86.** La cytodiérèse de l'œuf : *La Cellule,* III. — **Id., '86.** La vésicule germinative et les globules polaires chez quelques Nématodes : *La Cellule,* III. — **Id., '86.** La segmentation de l'œuf chez les Nématodes : *La Cellule,* III., 1. — **Calberla, E., '78.** Der Befruchtungsvorgang beim Ei von Petromyzon Planeri : *Z. w. Z.,* XXX. — **Campbell, D. H., '88–9.** On the Development of Pilularia globulifera : *Ann. Bot.,* II. — **Castle, W. E., '96.** The Early Embryology of Ciona intestinalis : *Bull. Mus. Comp. Zoöl.,* XXVII., 7. — **Chabry, L., '87.** Contributions à l'embryologie normale et pathologique des ascidies simples : *Paris,* 1887. — **Chittenden, R. H., '94.** Some Recent Chemico-physiological Discussions regarding the Cell : *Ann. Nat.,* XXVIII., Feb., 1894. — **Chun, C., '90.** Über die Bedeutung der direkten Zelltheilung : *Sitzb. Schr. Physik.-Ökon. Ges. Königsberg,* 1890. — **Id., '92, 1.** Die Dissogonie der Rippenquallen : *Festschr. f. Leuckart, Leipzig,* 1892. — **Id., '92, 2.** (In Roux, '92, p. 55) : *Verh. d. Anat. Ges.,* VI., 1892. — **Clapp, C. M., '91.** Some Points in the Development of the Toad-Fish : *J. M.,* V. — **Clarke, J. Jackson, '95.** Observations on various Sporozoa : *Q. J.,* XXXVII., 3. — **Cohn, Ferd., '51.** Nachträge zur Naturgeschichte des Protococcus pluvialis : *Nova Acta,* XXII. — **Conklin, E. G., '94.** The Fertilization of the Ovum : *Biol. Lect., Marine Biol. Lab., Wood's Holl, Boston,* 1894. — **Id., '96.** Cell-size and Body-size : *Rept. of Am. Morph. Soc., Science,* III., Jan. 10, 1896. — **Crampton, H. E., '94.** Reversal of Cleavage in a Sinistral Gasteropod : *Ann. N. Y. Acad. Sci.,* March, 1894. — **Crampton and Wilson, '96.** Experimental Studies on Gasteropod Development (H. E. Crampton). Appendix on Cleavage and Mosaic-Work (E. B. Wilson) : *A. Entm.,* III., 1.

DELAGE, YVES, '95. La Structure du Protoplasma et les Théories sur l'hérédité et les grands Problèmes de la Biologie Générale : *Paris,* 1895. — **Demoor, J., '95.** Contribution à l'étude de la physiologie de la cellule (indépendance fonctionelle du protoplasme et du noyau) : *A. B.,* XIII. — **Dogiel, A. S., '90.** Zur Frage über das Epithel der Harnblase : *A. m. A.,* XXXV. — **Driesch, H.** Entwicklungsmechanische Studien ; I., II., 1892, *Z. w. Z.,* LIII. ; III.–VI., 1893, *Ibid.,* LV. ; VII.–X., 1893 : *Mitt. Zoöl. St. Neapel,* XI., 2. — **Id., '94.** Analytische Theorie der organischen Entwicklung : *Leipzig.* — **Id., '95, 1.** Von der Entwickelung einzelner Ascidienblastomeren : *A. Entm.,* I., 3. — **Driesch and Morgan, '95, 2.** Zur Analysis der ersten Entwickelungs stadien des Ctenophoreneies : *Ibid.,* II., 2. — **Drüner, L., '94.** Zur Morphologie der Centralspindel : *J. Z.,* XXVIII. (XXI.). — **Id., '95.** Studien über den Mechanismus der Zelltheilung : *Ibid.,* XXIX., 2. — **Düsing, C., '84.** Die Regulierung des Geschlechtsverhältnisses : *Jena,* 1884.

VON EBNER, V., '71. Untersuchungen über den Bau der Samencanälchen und die Entwicklung der Spermatozoiden bei den Säugethieren und beim Menschen: *Inst. Phys. u. Hist. Graz.*, 1871 (*Leipzig*). — **Id., 88.** Zur Spermatogenese bei den Säugethieren: *A. m. A.*, XXXI. — **Ehrlich, P.**, '79. Über die specifischen Granulationen des Blutes: *A. A. P.* (*Phys.*), 1879, p. 573. — **Eismond, J.**, '95. Einige Beiträge zur Kenntniss der Attraktionssphären und der Centrosomen: *A. A.*, X. — **Endres and Walter**, '95. Anstichversuche an Eiern von Rana fusca: *A. Entm.*, II., 1. — **Engelmann, T. W.**, '80. Zur Anatomie und Physiologie der Flimmerzellen: *Arch. ges. Phys.*, XXIII. — **von Erlanger, R.**, '96, 1. Die neuesten Ansichten über die Zelltheilung und ihre Mechanik: *Zoöl. Centralb.*, III., 2. — **Id.**, '96, 2. Zur Befruchtung des Ascariseies nebst Bemerkungen über die Struktur des Protoplasmas und des Centrosomes: *Z. A.*, XIX. — **Id.**, '96, 3. Neuere Ansichten über die Struktur des Protoplasmas: *Zoöl. Centralb.*, III., 8, 9. — **Errara**, '86. Eine fundamentale Gleichgewichtsbedingung organischen Zellen: *Ber. Deutsch. Bot. Ges.*, 1886. — **Id.**, '87. Zellformen und Seifenblasm: *Tagebl. der 60 Versammlung deutscher Naturforscher und Aerzte zu Wiesbaden*, 1887.

FARMER, J. B., '93. On nuclear division of the pollen-mother-cell of Lilium Martagon: *Ann. Bot.*, VII., 27. — **Id.**, '94. Studies in Hepaticæ: *Ibid.*, VIII., 29. — **Id.**, '95, 1. Über Kernteilung in Lilium-Antheren, besonders in Bezug auf die Centrosomenfrage: *Flora*, 1895, p. 57. — **Farmer and Moore**, '95. On the essential similarities existing between the heterotype nuclear divisions in animals and plants: *A. A.*, XI., 3. — **Fick, R.**, '93. Über die Reifung und Befruchtung des Axolotleies: *Z. w. Z.*, LVI., 4. — **Fiedler, C.**, '91. Entwickelungsmechanische Studien an Echinodermeneier: *Festschr. Nägeli u. Kölliker*, Zurich, 1891. — **Field, G. W.**, '95. On the Morphology and Physiology of the Echinoderm Spermatozoön: *J. M.*, XI. — **Fischer, A.**, '94. Zur Kritik der Fixierungsmethoden der Granula: *A. A.*, IX., 22. — **Id.** '95. Neue Beiträge zur Kritik der Fixierungsmethoden: *Ibid.*, X. — **Flemming, W.**, '79. Beiträge zur Kenntniss der Zelle und ihre Lebenserscheinungen, I.: *A. m. A.*, XVI. — **Id.**, '79. Über das Verhalten des Kerns bei der Zelltheilung, etc.: *Virchow's Arch.*, LXXVII. — **Id.**, '80. Beiträge zur Kenntniss der Zelle und ihrer Lebenserscheinungen, II.: *A. m. A.*, XIX. — **Id.**, '81. Beiträge zur Kenntnis der Zelle und ihrer Lebenserscheinungen, III.: *Ibid.*, XX. — **Id.**, '82. Zellsubstanz, Kern und Zellteilung: *Leipzig*, 1882. — **Id.**, '87. Neue Beiträge zur Kenntnis der Zelle: *A. m. A.*, XXIX. — **Id.**, '88. Weitere Beobachtungen über die Entwickelung der Spermatosomen bei Salamandra maculosa: *Ibid.*, XXXI. — **Id.**, '91–4. Zelle, I.–IV.: *Ergebn. Anat. u. Entwicklungsgesch.* (*Merkel and Bonnet*), 1891–94. — **Id.**, '91, 1. Attraktionssphären u. Centralkörper in Gewebs- u. Wanderzellen: *A. A.* — **Id.**, '91, 2. Neue Beiträge zur Kenntnis der Zelle, II. Teil: *A. m. A.*, XXXVII. — **Id.**, '95, 1. Über die Struktur der Spinalganglienzellen: *Verhandl. der anat. Gesellschaft in Basel*, 17 April, 1895, p. 19. — **Id.**, '95, 2. Zur Mechanik der Zelltheilung: *A. m. A.*, XLVI. — **Floderus, M.**, '96. Über die Bildung der Follikelhüllen bei den Ascidien: *Z. w. Z.*, LXI., 2. — **Fol, H.**, '73. Die erste Entwickelung des Geryonideies: *J. Z.*, VII. — **Id.**, '75. Études sur le développement des Mollusques. — **Id.**, '77. Sur le commencement de l'hénogenie chez divers animaux: *Arch. Sci. Nat. et Phys. Genève*, LVIII. See also *Arch. Zool. Exp.*, VI. — **Id.**, '79. Recherches sur la fécondation et la commencement de l'hénogenie; *Mém. de la Soc. de physique et d'hist. nat., Genève*, XXVI. — **Id.**, '91. Le Quadrille des Centres. Un episode nouveau dans l'histoire de la fécondation: *Arch. des sci. phys. et nat.*, 15 *Avril*, 1891; also, *A. A.*, 9–10. 1891. — **Foot, K.**, '94. Preliminary Note on the Maturation and Fertilization of Allolobophora: *J. M.*, IX., 3, '94. — **Id.**, '96. Yolk-nucleus and Polar Rings: *Ibid.*, XII., 1. — **Frenzel, J.**, '93. Die Mitteldarmdrüse des Flusskrebses und die amitotische Zelltheilung: *A. m. A.*,

XLI. — **Fromman, C.**, '65. Über die Struktur der Bindesubstanzzellen des Rückenmarks: *Centrl. f. med. Wiss.*, III., 6. — Id., '75. Zur Lehre von der Structur der Zellen : *J. Z.*, IX. (earlier papers cited). — Id., '84. Untersuchungen über Struktur, Lebenserscheinungen und Reactionen thierischer und pflanzlicher Zellen: *J. Z.*, XVII.

GALEOTTI, GINO, '93. Über experimentelle Erzeugung von Unregelmässigkeiten des karyokinetischen Processes : *Bei. zur patholog. Anat. u. z. Allg. Pathol.*, XIV., 2, *Jena, Fischer,* 1893. — **Gardiner, W.**, '83. Continuity of Protoplasm in Vegetable Cells : *Phil. Trans.*, CLXXIV. — **Garnault**, '88, '89. Sur les phénomènes de la fécondation chez Helix aspera et Arion empiricorum : *Zool. Anz.*, XI., XII. — **Geddes and Thompson.** The Evolution of Sex. — **Gegenbaur, C.**, '54. Beiträge zur näheren Kenntniss der Schwimmpolypen : *Z. w. Z.*, V. — **Van Gehuchten, A.,** '90. Recherches histologiques sur l'appareil digestif de la larve de la Ptychoptera contaminata : *La Cellule*, VI. — **Giard, A.,** '77. Sur la signification morphologique des globules polaires : *Revue scientifique*, XX. — Id., '90. Sur les globules polaires et les homologues de ces éléments chez les infusoires ciliés : *Bulletin scientifique de la France et de la Belgique*, XXII. — **Grobben, C.,** '78. Beiträge zur Kenntniss der männlichen Geschlechtsorgane der Dekapoden : *Arb. Zool. Inst. Wien*, I. — **Gruber, A.,** '84. Über Kern und Kerntheilung bei den Protozoen : *Z. w. Z.*, XL. — Id., 85. Über künstliche Teilung bei Infusorien : *B. C.*, IV., 23; V., 5. — Id., '86. Beiträge zur Kenntniss der Physiologie und Biologie der Protozoen : *Ber. Naturf. Ges. Freiburg*, I. — Id., '93. Mikroscopische Vivisektion : *Ber. d. Naturf. Ges. zu Freiburg*, VII., I — **Guignard, L.,** '89. Développement et constitution des Anthérozoides : *Rev. gen. Bot.*, I. — Id., '91, 1. Nouvelles études sur la fécondation : *Ann. d. Sciences Nat. Bot.*, XIV. — Id., '91, 2. Sur l'existence des " sphères attractives " dans les cellules végétales : *C. R.*, 9 Mars.

HABERLANDT, G., '87. Über die Beziehungen zwischen Funktion und Lage des Zellkerns : *Fischer*, 1887. — **Häckel, E.,** '66. Generelle Morphologie. — Id., '91. Anthropogenie, 4th ed., *Leipzig*, 1891. — **Häcker, V.,** '92, 1. Die Furchung des Eies von Æquorea Forskalea : *A. m. A.*, XL. — Id., '92, 2. Die Eibildung bei Cyclops und Camptocanthus : *Zool. Jahrb.*, V. — Id., '92, 3. Die heterotypische Kerntheilung im Cyclus der generativen Zellen : *Ber. naturf. Ges. Freiburg*, VI. — Id., '93. Das Keimbläschen, seine Elemente und Lageveränderungen : *A. m. A.*, XLI. — Id., '94. Über den heutigen Stand der Centrosomenfrage : *Verhandl. d. deutschen Zool. Ges.*, 1894, p. 11. — Id., '95, 1. Die Vorstadien der Eireifung : *A. m. A.*, XLV., 2. — Id., '95, 2. Zur Frage nach dem Vorkommen der Schein-Reduktion bei den Pflanzen : *Ibid.*, XLVI. Also *Ann. Bot.*, IX. — Id., '95, 3. Über die Selbständigkeit der väterlichen und mütterlichen Kernsbestandtheile während der Embryonalentwicklung von Cyclops : *A. m. A.*, XLVI., 4. — **Hallez, P.,** '86. Sur la loi de l'orientation de l'embryon chez les insectes : *C. R.*, 103, 1886. — **Halliburton, W. D.,** '91. A Text-book of Chemical Physiology and Pathology : *London.* — Id., '93. The Chemical Physiology of the Cell : (*Gould-stonian Lectures*) *Brit. Med. Journ.* — **Hammar, J. A.,** '96. Über einen primären Zusammenhang zwischen den Furchungszellen des Seeigeleies : *A. m. A.*, XLVII., I. — **Hammarsten, O.,** '94. Zur Kenntniss der Nucleo-proteids : *Zeit. Phys. Chem.*, XIX. — Id., '95. Lehrbuch der physiologischen Chemie, 3e Ausgabe : *Wiesbaden*, 1895. — **Hansemann, D.,** '91. Karyokinese und Cellularpathologie : *Berl. Klin. Wochenschrift*, No. 42. — Id., '93. Spezificität, Altruismus und die Anaplasie der Zellen : *Berlin*, 1893. — **Hanstein, J.,** '80. Das Protoplasma als Träger der pflanzlichen und thierischen Lebensverrichtungen . *Heidelberg.* — **Harvey, Wm., 1651.** Exercitationes de Generatione Animalium : *London.* Trans.

in *Sydenham Soc.*, X., 1847. — **Hartog, M. M.**, '91. Some Problems of Reproduction, etc : *Q. J.*, XXXIII. — **Hatschek, B.**, '87. Über die Bedeutung der geschlechtlichen Fortpflanzung : *Prager Med. Wochenschrift*, XLVI. — **Id.**, '88. Lehrbuch der Zoologie. — **Heidenhain, M.**, '93. Über Kern und Protoplasma : *Festchr. z. 50-Jähr. Doctorjub. von v. Kölliker : Leipzig.* — **Id.**, '94. Neue Untersuchungen über die Centralkörper und ihre Beziehungen zum Kern und Zellenprotoplasma : *A. m. A.*, XLIII. — **Id.**, '95. Cytomechanische Studien : *A. Entm.*, I., 4. — **Heitzmann, J.**, '73. Untersuchungen über das Protoplasma : *Sitzb. d. k. Acad. Wiss. Wien*, LXVII. — **Id.**, '83. Mikroscopische Morphologie des Thierkörpers im gesunden und kranken Zustande : *Wien*, 1883. — **Henking, H.** Untersuchungen über die ersten Entwicklungsvorgänge in den Eiern der Insekten, I., II., III. : *Z. w. Z.*, XLIX., LI., LIV., 1890–1892. — **Henle, J.**, '41. Allgemeine Anatomie : *Leipzig.* — **Henneguy, L. F.**, '91. Nouvelles recherches sur la division cellulaire indirecte : *Journ. Anat. et Physiol.*, XXVII. — **Id.**, '93. Le Corps vitellin de Balbiani dans l'œuf des Vértébres : *Ibid.*, XXIX. — **Id.**, '96. Leçons sur la cellule : *Paris.* — **Hensen, V.**, '81. Physiologie der Zeugung : *Hermann's Physiologie*, VI. — **Herbst, C.** Experimentelle Untersuchungen über den Einfluss der veränderten chemischen Zusammensetzung des umgebenden Mediums auf die Entwicklung der Thiere, I. : *Z. w. Z.*, LV., 1892 ; II., *Mitt. Zool. St. Neapel*, XI., 1893 ; III.–VI., *Arch. Entm.*, II., 4, 1896. — **Id.**, '94, '95. Über die Bedeutung der Reizphysiologie für die Kausale Auffassung von Vorgängen in der tierischen Ontogenese : *Biol. Centralb.*, XIV., XV., 1894, 1895. — **Herla, V.**, '93. Étude des variations de la mitose chez l'ascaride mégalocéphale : *A. B.*, XIII. — **Herlitzka, A.**, '95. Contributo allo studio della capacità evolutiva dei due primi blastomeri nell' uove di Tritone : *A. Entm.*, II., 3. — **Hermann, F.**, '89. Beiträge zur Histologie des Hodens : *A. m. A.*, XXXIV. — **Id.**, '91. Beitrag zur Lehre von der Entstehung der karyokinetischen Spindel : *Ibid.*, XXXVII. — **Id.**, '92. Urogenitalsystem, Struktur und Histiogenese der Spermatozoen : *Merkel und Bonnet's Ergebnisse*, II. — **Hertwig, O.**, '75. Beiträge zur Kenntnis der Bildung, Befruchtung und Teilung des tierischen Eies, I. : *M. J.*, I. — **Id.**, '77. Beiträge. etc., II. : *Ibid.*, III. — **Id.**, '78. Beiträge, etc., III. : *Ibid.*, IV. — **Id.**, '84. Das Problem der Befruchtung und der Isotropie des Eies, eine Theorie der Vererbung : *J. Z.*, XVIII. — **Id.**, '90, 1. Vergleich der Ei- und Samenbildung bei Nematoden. Eine Grundlage für celluläre Streitfragen : *A. m. A.*, XXXVI. — **Id , '90, 2.** Experimentelle Studien am tierischen Ei vor, während und nach der Befruchtung : *J. Z.*, 1890. — **Id.**, '92, 1. Urmund und Spina Bifida : *A. m. A.*, XXXIX. — **Id.**, '92, 2. Aeltere und neuere Entwicklungs-theorieen : *Berlin.* — **Id.**, '93, 1. Über den Werth der ersten Furchungszellen für die Organbildung des Embryo : *A. m. A.*, XLII. — **Id.**, 93, 2. Die Zelle und die Gewebe : *Fischer, Jena*, 1893. — **Id.**, '94. Zeit und Streitfragen der Biologie : *Berlin.* — **Hertwig, O. and R.**, '86. Experimentelle Untersuchungen über die Bedingungen der Bastardbefruchtung : *J. Z*, XIX. — **Id.**, '87. Über den Befruchtungs- und Teilungsvorgang des tierischen Eies unter dem Einfluss äusserer Agentien : *Ibid.*, XX. — **Hertwig, R.**, '77. Über den Bau und die Entwicklung der Spirochona gemmipara : *Ibid.*, XI. — **Id.**, '84. Die Kerntheilung bei Actinosphærium Eichhorni : *Ibid.*, XVII. — **Id.**, '88. Über Kernstruktur und ihre Bedeutung für Zellteilung und Befruchtung : *Ibid.*, IV., 1888. — **Id.**, '89. Über die Konjugation der Infusorien : *Abh. der bayr. Akad. d. Wiss.*, II., Cl., XVII. — **Id.**, '92. Über Befruchtung und Conjugation : *Verh. deutsch. Zool. Ges., Berlin.* — **Id.**, '95. Über Centrosoma und Centralspindel : *Sitz.-Ber. Ges. Morph. und Phys., München*, 1895, Heft I. — **Heuser, E.**, '84. Beobachtung über Zelltheilung : *Bot. Cent.* — **Hill, M. D.**, '95. Notes on the Fecundation of the Egg of *Sphærechinus granularis* and on the Maturation and Fertilization of the Egg of *Phallusia mammillata* : *Q. J.*, XXXVIII. — **His, W**,

'74. — Unsere Körperform und das physiologische Problem ihrer Entstehung: *Leipzig.* — **Hofer, B.**, '89. Experimentelle Untersuchungen über den Einfluss des Kerns auf das Protoplasma: *J. Z.*, XXIV. — **Hofmeister,** '67. Die Lehre von der Pflanzenzelle: *Leipzig,* 1867. — **Holl, M.,** '90. Über die Reifung der Eizelle des Huhns: *Sitzb. Acad. Wiss. Wien.,* XCIX., 3. — **Hooke, Robt.,** 1665. Micrographia, or some physiological Descriptions of minute Bodies by magnifying Glasses: *London.* — **Hoyer, H.,** '90. Über ein für das Studium der "direkten" Zelltheilung vorzüglich geeignetes Objekt: *A. A.,* V. — **Humphrey, J. E.,** '94. Nucleolen und Centrosomen: *Ber. deutschen bot. Ges.,* XII., 5. — **Id.,** '95. On some Constituents of the Cell: *Ann. Bot.,* IX. — **Huxley, T. H.,** '53. Review of the Cell-theory: *Brit. and Foreign Med.-Chir. Review,* XII. — **Id.,** '78. Evolution in Biology, *Enc. Brit.,* 9th ed., 1878; *Science and Culture,* N. Y., 1882.

ISHIKAWA, M., '91. Vorläufige Mitteilungen über die Konjugationserscheinungen bei den Noctiluceen: *Z. A.,* No. 353, 1891. — **Id.,** '94. Studies on Reproductive Elements: II., *Noctiluca miliaris,* Sur., its Division and Spore-formation; *Journ. College of Sc. Imp. Univ. Japan,* VI.

JENSEN, O. S., '83. Recherches sur la spermatogenèse: *A. B.,* IV. — **Johnson, H. P.,** '92. Amitosis in the embryonal envelopes of the Scorpion: *Bull. Mus. Comp. Zoöl.,* XXII., 3. — **Jordan, E. O.,** '93. The Habits and Development of the Newt: *J. M.,* VIII., 2. — **Jordan and Eycleshymer,** '94. On the Cleavage of Amphibian Ova: *J. M.,* IX., 3, 1894. — **Julin, J.,** '93, 1. Structure et développement des glandes sexuelles, ovogénèse, spermatogenèse et fécondation chez Styleopsis grossularia: *Bull. Sc. de France et de Belgique.,* XXIV. — **Id.,** '93, 2. Le corps vitellin de Balbiani et les éléments des Métazoaires qui correspondent au Macronucléus des Infusoires ciliés: *Bull. Sc. de France et de Belgique,* XXIV.

KEUTEN, J., '95. Die Kerntheilung von *Euglena viridis* Ehr: *Z. w. Z.,* LX. — **Kienitz-Gerloff, F.,** '91. Review and Bibliography of Researches on Protoplasmic Connection between adjacent Cells: in *Bot. Zeitung,* XLIX. — **Klebahn,** '92. Die Befruchtung von Œdigonium: *Zeit. wiss. Bot.,* XXIV. — **Id.** Die Keimung von Closterium und Cosmarium: *Jahrb. f. wiss. Bot.,* XXII. — **Klebs, G.,** '84. Über die neueren Forschungen betreffs der Protoplasmaverbindungen benachbarter Zellen: *Bot. Zeit.,* 1884. — **Id.,** '87. Über den Einfluss des Kerns in der Zelle: *B. C.,* VII. — **Klein, E.,** '78-9. Observations on the Structure of Cells and Nuclei: *Q. J.,* XVIII., XIX. — **von Kölliker, A.,** '41. Beiträge zur Kenntnis der Geschlechtsverhältnisse und der Samenflüssigkeit wirbelloser Tiere: *Berlin.* — **Id.,** '44. Entwicklungsgeschichte der Cephalopoden: *Zürich.* — **Id.,** '85. Die Bedeutung der Zellkerne für die Vorgänge der Vererbung: *Z. w. Z.,* XLII. — **Id.,** '86. Das Karyoplasma und die Vererbung, eine Kritik der Weismann'schen Theorie von der Kontinuität des Keimplasmas: *Z. w. Z.,* XLIII. — **Id.,** '89. Handbuch der Gewebelehre, 6th ed.: *Leipzig.* — **Korschelt, E.,** '89. Beiträge zur Morphologie und Physiologie des Zell-Kernes: *Zool. Jahrb. Anat. u. Ontog.,* IV. — **Id.,** '93. Über Ophryotrocha puerilis: *Z. w. Z.,* LIV. — **Id.,** '95. Über Kerntheilung, Eireifung und Befruchtung bei *Ophryotrocha puerilis*: *Z. w. Z.,* LX. — **Kossel, A.,** '91. Über die chemische Zusammensetzung der Zelle: *Arch. Anat. u. Phys.* — **Id.,** '93. Über die Nucleinsäure: *Ibid.,* 1893. — **von Kostanecki, '91.** Über Centralspindelkörperchen bei karyokinetischer Zellteilung: *Anat. Hefte,* 1892, dat. 91. — **Kostanecki and Wierzejski,** '96. Über das Verhalten der sogenannten achromatischen Substanzen im befruchteten Ei: *A. m. A.,* XLII., 2. — **Kühne, W.,** '64. Untersuchungen über das Protoplasma und die Contractilität. — **Kupffer,**

C., '75. Über Differenzierung des Protoplasma an den Zellen thierischer Gewebe: *Schr. natur. Ver. Schles.-Holst.*, I., 3. — **Id.**, '90. Die Entwicklung von Petromyzon Planeri: *A. m. A.*, XXXV.

LAMEERE, A., '90. Recherches sur la reduction karyogamique: *Bruxelles.* — **Lauterborn, R.**, '93. Über Bau und Kerntheilung der Diatomeen: *Verh. d. Naturh. Med. Ver. in Heidelberg*, 1893. — **Id.**, '95. Protozoenstudien. Kern- und Zellteilung von Ceratium hirundinella O. F. M.: *Z. w. Z.*, XLIX. — **La Valette St. George**, '65. Ueber die Genese der Samenkörper: *A. m. A.*, I. — **Id.**, '67. Über die Genese der Samenkörper, II., (Terminology): *A. m. A.*, III. — **Id.**, '76. — Die Spermatogenese bei den Amphibien: *Ibid.*, XII. — **Id.**, '78. Die Spermatogenese bei den Säugethieren und dem Menschen: *Ibid.*, XV. — **Id.** Spermatologische Beiträge, I.-V.: *A. m. A.*, XXV., XXVII., XXVIII., and XXX., 1885-87. — **Lankester, E. Ray**, '77. Notes on Embryology and Classification: *London.* — **Lavdovsky, M.**, '94. Von der Entstehung der chromatischen und achromatischen Substanzen in den tierischen und pflanzlichen Zellen: *Merkel und Bonnet's Anat. Hefte*, IV., 13. — **von Lenhossék, M.**, '95. Centrosom und Sphäre in den Spinalganglien des Frosches; *A. m. A.*, XLVI. — **Leydig, Fr.** '54. Lehrbuch der Histologie des Menschen und der Thiere: *Frankfurt.* — **Id.**, '85. — Zelle und Gewebe, *Bonn.* — **Id.**, '89. Beiträge zur Kenntniss des thierischen Eies im unbefruchteten Zustande: *Spengel's Jahrb. Anat. Ont.*, III. — **Lilienfeld, L.**, '92, '93. Über die Verwandschaft der Zellelemente zu gewissen Farbstoffen: *Verh. Phys. Ges., Berlin*, 1892-3. — **Id.**, '93. Über die Wahlverwandtschaft der Zellelemente zu Farbstoffen: *A. A. P.*, 1893. — **Lillie, F. R.**, '95. The Embryology of the Unionidæ: *J. M.*, X. — **Id.**, '96. On the Limit of Size in the Regeneration of Stentor: *Rept. Am. Morph. Soc. Science.*, III., Jan. 10, 1896. — **Loeb, J.**, '91-2. Untersuchungen zur physiologischen Morphologie. I. Heteromorphosis: *Würzburg*, 1891. II. Organbildung und Wachsthum: *Würzburg*, 1892. — **Id.**, '93. Some Facts and Principles of physiological Morphology: *Wood's Holl Biol. Lectures*, 1893. — **Id.**, '94. Über die Grenzen der Theilbarkeit der Eisubstanz: *A. ges. P.*, LIX., 6, 7. — **Löwit, M.**, '91. Über amitotische Kerntheilung: *B. C.*, XI. — **Lukjanow**, '91. Grundzüge einer allgemeinen Pathologie der Zelle: *Leipzig.* — **Lustig and Galeotti**, '93. Cytologische Studien über pathologische menschliche Gewebe: *Beitr. Path. Anat.*, XIV.

MACALLUM, A. B., '91. Contribution to the Morphology and Physiology of the Cell: *Trans. Canad. Inst.*, I., 2. — **McMurrich, J. P.**, '86. A Contribution to the Embryology of the Prosobranch Gasteropods: *Studies Biol. Lab. Johns Hopkins Univ.*, III. — **Id.**, '95. Embryology of the Isopod Crustacea: *J. M.*, XI., 1. — **Maggi, L.**, '78. I plastiduli nei ciliati ed i plastiduli liberamente viventi: *Atti. Soc. Ital. Sc. Nat. Milano*, XXI. (also later papers). — **Malfatti, H.**, '91. — Beiträge zur Kenntniss der Nucleine: *Zeit. Phys. Chem.*, XVI. — **Mark, E. L.**, '81. Maturation, Fecundation and Segmentation of Limax campestris: *Bull. Mus. Comp. Zoöl. Harvard College*, VI. — **Maupas, M.**, '88. Recherches expérimentales sur la multiplication des Infusoires ciliés: *Arch. Zool. Exp.*, 2me série, VI. — **Id.**, '89. Le rejeunissement karyogamique chez les Ciliés: *Ibid.*, 2me série, VII. — **Id.**, '91. Sur le déterminisme de la sexualité chez l'Hydatina senta: *C. R., Paris.* — **Mead, A. D.**, '95. Some observations on maturation and fecundation in Chætopterus pergamentaceus Cuv.: *J. M.*, X., 1. — **Merkel, F.**, '71. Die Stützzellen des menschlichen Hodens: *Müller's Arch.* — **Mertens, H.**, '93. Recherches sur la signification du corps vitellin de Balbiani dans l'ovule des Mammiféres et des Oiseaux: *A. B.*, XIII. — **Metschnikoff, E.**, '66. Embryologische Studien an Insecten: *Z. w. Z.*, XVI. — **Meves, F.**, '91. Über amitotische Kernteilung in den Spermatogonien des Salamanders, und das Verhalten der Attraktionssphären bei derselben: *A. A.*, 1891, No. 22. — **Id.**, '94. Über eine Metamorphose der Attraktionssphäre in den Spermatogonien von Salamandra maculosa: *A. m. A.*, XLIV. — **Id.**, '95. Über die Zellen des Sesambeines der Achillessehne des Frosches (*Rana temporaria*) und über ihre Centralkörper: *Ibid.*, XLV. — **Meyer, O.**, '95. Celluläre Untersuchungen an Nematodeneiern: *J. Z.*, XXIX. (XXII.). — **Mikosch**, '94. Über Struktur im pflanzlichen Protoplasma: *Verhandl. d. Ges. deutscher Naturf. und Ärzte*, 1894; *Abteil f. Pflanzenphysiologie u. Pflanzenanatomie.* — **Minot, C. S.**, '77. Recent Investigations of Embryologists: *Proc. Bost. Soc. Nat. Hist.*, XIX. — **Id.**, '79. Growth as a Function of Cells: *Ibid.*, XX. — **Id.**, '82. Theorie der Genoblasten: *B. C.*, II., 12. See also *Am. Nat.*, February, 1880. — **Id.**, '87. Theorie der Genoblasten: *B. C.*, II., 12, 1887; also, *Proc. Bost. Soc. Nat. Hist.*, XIX., 1877. — **Id.**, '91. Senescence and Rejuvenation: *Journ. Phys.*, XII., 2. — **Id.**, '92. Human Embryology: *New York.* — **von Mohl, Hugo**, '46. Über die Saftbewegung im Innern der Zellen: *Bot. Zeitung.* — **Moore, J. E. S.**, '93. Mammalian Spermatogenesis: *A. A.*, VIII. — **Id.**, '95. On the Structural Changes in the Reproductive Cells during the Spermatogenesis of Elasmobranchs: *Q. J.*, XXXVIII. — **Morgan, T. H.**, '93. Experimental Studies on Echinoderm Eggs: *A. A.*, IX., 5, 6. — **Id.**, '95, 1. Studies of the "Partial" Larvæ of Sphærechinus: *A. Entm.*, II., 1. — **Id.**, 95, 2. Experimental Studies on Teleost-eggs: *A. A.*, X., 19. — **Id.**, '95, 3. Half-embryos and Whole-embryos from one of the first two Blastomeres of the Frog's Egg: *Ibid.*, X., 19. — **Id.**, '95, 4. The Fertilization of non-nucleated Fragments of Echinoderm-eggs: *Arch. Entm.*, II., 2. — **Id.**, '95, 5. The Formation of the Fish-embryo: *J. M.*, X., 2. — **Id.**, '96, 1. On the Production of artificial archoplasmic Centres: *Rept. of the Am. Morph. Soc., Science*, III., January 10, 1896. — **Id.**, '96, 2. The Number of Cells in Larvæ from Isolated Blastomeres of Amphioxus: *Arch. Entm.*, III., 2. — **Müller, E.**, '96. Über die Regeneration der Augenlinse nach Exstirpation derselben bei Triton: *A. m. A.*, XLVII., 1.

NÄGELI, C., '84. Mechanisch-physiologische Theorie der Abstammungslehre: *München u. Leipzig*, 1884. — **Nägeli und Schwendener**, '67. Das Mikroskop. (See later editions.) *Leipzig.* — **Newport, G.** On the Impregnation of the Ovum in the Amphibia: *Phil. Trans.*, 1851, 1853, 1854. — **Nussbaum, M.**, '80. Zur Differenzierung des Geschlechts im Tierreich: *A. m. A.*, XVIII. — **Id.**, '84, 1. Über Spontane und Künstliche Theilung von Infusorien: *Verh. d. naturh. Ver. preuss. Rhineland*, 1884. — **Id.**, '84, 2. Über die Veränderungen der Geschlechtsproducte bis zur Eifurchung: *A. m. A.*, XXIII. — **Id.**, '85. — Über die Teilbarkeit der lebendigen Materie, I.: *A. m. A.*, XXVI. — **Id.**, '94. Die mit der Entwickelung fortschreitende Differenzierung der Zellen: *Sitz.-Ber. d. niederrhein. Gesellschaft f. Natur- u. Heilkunde, Bonn*, 5 Nov., 1894; also *B. C.*, XVI., 2, 1896.

OGATA, '83. Die Veränderungen der Pancreaszellen bei der Secretion: *A. A. P.* — **Oppel, A.**, '92. Die Befruchtung des Reptilieneies: *A. m. A*, XXXIX. — **Overton, C. E.**, '88. Über den Conjugationsvorgang bei Spirogyra: *Ber. deutsch. Bot. Ges.*, VI. — **Id.**, '89. Beitrag zur Kentniss der Gattung Volvox: *Bot. Centrb.*, XXXIX. — **Id.**, '93. Über die Reduktion der Chromosomen in den Kernen der Pflanzen: *Vierteljahrschr. naturf. Ges. Zürich*, XXXVIII. Also *Ann. Bot.*, VII., 25.

PALADINO, G., '90. I ponti intercellulari tra l' uovo ovarico e le cellule follicolari, etc.: *A. A.*, V. — **Palla**, '90. Beobachtungen über Zellhautbildung an des Zellkerns beraubten Protoplasten. *Flora*, 1890. — **Pfitzner, W.**, '82. Über den feineren Bau der bei der Zelltheilung auffretenden fadenförmigen Differenzierungen des Zellkerns: *M. J.*, VII. — **Id.**, '83. Beiträge zur Lehre vom Baue des Zellkerns und seinen Theilungserscheinungen: *A. m. A.*, XXII. — **Pflüger, E.**, '83. Über den Einfluss der Schwerkraft auf die Theilung der Zellen: I., *Arch. ges. Phys.*, XXXI.; II., *Ibid.*, XXXII.; abstract in *Biol. Centb.*, III., 1884. — **Id.**, '84. Über die Einwirkung der Schwerkraft und anderer Bedingungen auf die Richtung der Zelltheilung: *Arch. ges. Phys.*, XXXIV. — **Id.**, '89. Die allgemeinen Lebenserscheinungen: *Bonn.* — **Platner, G.**, '86. Über die Befruchtung von *Arion empiricorum*: *A. m. A.*, XXXVII. — **Id.**, '89, 1. Über die Bedeutung der Richtungskörperchen: *B. C.*, VIII. — **Id.**, '89, 2. Beiträge zur Kenntniss der Zelle und ihrer Teilungserscheinungen, I.–VI.: *A. m. A.*, XXXIII. — **Poirault and Raciborski**, '96. Über konjugate Kerne und die konjugate Kerntheilung: *B. C.*, XVI., 1. — **Prenant**, '94. Sur le corpuscule central: *Bull. Soc. Sci.*, *Nancy*, 1894. — **Preusse, F.**, '95. Über die amitotische Kerntheilung in den Ovarien der Hemipteren: *Z. w. Z.*, LIX., 2. — **Prévost and Dumas**, '24. Nouvelle théorie de la géneration: *Ann. Sci. Nat.*, I., II. — **Pringsheim, N.**, '55. Über die Befruchtung der Algen: *Monatsb. Berl. Akad.*, 1855–6. — **Purkyně**: *Jahrb. f. wiss. Kritik*, 1840.

RABL, C., '85. Über Zellteilung: *M. J.*, X. — **Id.**, '89, 1. Über Zelltheilung: *A. A.*, IV. — **Id.**, '89, 2. Über die Prinzipien der Histologie: *Verh. Anat. Ges.*, III. — **vom Rath, O.**, '91. Über die Bedeutung der amitotischen Kernteilung im Hoden: *Zoöl. Anz.*, XIV. — **Id.**, '92. Zur Kenntniss der Spermatogenese von *Gryllotalpa vulgaris*: *A. m. A.*, XL. — **Id.**, '93. Beiträge zur Spermatogenese von Salamandra: *Z. w. Z.*, LVII. — **Id.**, '94. Über die Konstanz der Chromosomenzahl bei Tieren: *B. C.*, XIV., 13. — **Id.**, '95, 1. Neue Beiträge zur Frage der Chromatinreduction in den Samen- und Eireife: *A. m. A.*, XLVI. — **Id.**, '95, 2. Über den feineren Bau der Drüsenzellen des Kopfes von Anilocra, etc.: *Z. w. Z.*, LX., 1. — **Rauber, A.**, '83. Neue Grundlegungen zur Kentniss der Zelle: *M. J.*, VIII. — **Rawitz, B.**, '95. Centrosoma und Attraktionsphäre in der ruhenden Zelle des Salamanderhodens: *A. m. A.*, XLIV., 4. — **Reinke, Fr.** '94. Zellstudien. I., *A. m. A.*, XLIII.; II., *Ibid.*, XLIV., 1894. — **Id.**, '95. Untersuchungen über Befruchtung und Furchung des Eies der Echinodermen: *Sitz.-Ber. Akad. d. Wiss. Berlin*, 1895, June 20. — **Reinke and Rodewald**, '81. Studien über das Protoplasma: *Untersuch. aus d. bot. Inst. Göttingen*, II. — **Remak, R.**, '41. Über Theilung rother Blutzellen beim Embryo: *Med. Ver. Zeit.*, 1841. — **Id.**, '50–5., Untersuchungen über die Entwicklung der Wirbelthiere: *Berlin*, 1850–55. — **Id.**, '58. Über die Theilung der Blutzellen beim Embryo: *Müllers Arch.*, 1858. — **Retzius, G.**, '89. Die Intercellularbrücken des Eierstockeies und der Follikelzellen: *Verh. Anat. Ges.*, 1889. — **Rhumbler, L.**, '93. Über Entstehung und Bedeutung der in den Kernen vieler Protozoen und im Keimbläschen von Metazoen vorkommenden Binnenkörper (Nucleolen): *Z. w. Z.*, LVI. — **Rompel**, '94. Kentrochona Nebaliae n. g. n. sp., ein neues Infusor aus der Familie der Spirochoninen. Zugleich ein Beitrag zur Lehre von der Kernteilung und dem Centrosoma: *Z. w. Z.*, LVIII., 4. — **Rosen**, 92. Über tinctionelle Unterscheidung verschiedener Kernbestandtheile und der Sexual-kerne: *Cohn's Beitr. z. Biol. d. Pflanzen*, V. — **Id.**, '94. Neueres über die Chromatophilie der Zellkerne: *Schles. Ges. väterl. Kult*, 1894. — **Roux, W.**, '83, 1. Über die Bedeutung der Kernteilungsfiguren: *Leipzig.* — **Id.**, '83, 2. Über die Zeit der Bestimmung der Hauptrichtungen des Froschembryo: *Leipzig.* — **Id.**, '85. Über die Bestimmung der Hauptrichtungen des Froschembryos im Ei, und über die erste Theilung des Froscheies: *Breslauer ärtzl. Zeitg.*, 1885. — **Id.**, '87. Bestimmung der medianebene des Froschembryo durch die Kopulationsrichtung des Eikernes und des Spermakernes: *A. m. A.*, XXIX. — **Id.**, '88. Über das künstliche Hervorbringen halber Embryonen durch Zerstörung einer der beiden ersten Furchungskugeln, etc.: *Virchow's Archiv*, 114. — **Id.**, '90. Die Entwickelungsmechanik der Organismen. *Wien*, 1890. — **Id.**, '92, 1. Entwickelungsmechanik : *Merkel and Bonnet, Erg.*, II. — **Id.**, '92, 2. Über das entwickelungsmechanische Vermögen jeder der beiden ersten Furchungszellen des Eies : *Verh. Anat. Ges.*, VI. — **Id.**, '93, 1. Über Mosaikarbeit und neuere Entwickelungshypothesen : *An. Hefte*, Feb., 1893. — **Id.**, '93, 2. Über die Spezifikation der Furchungzellen, etc.: *B. C.*, XIII., 19-22. — **Id.**, '94, 1. Über den "Cytotropismus" der Furchungszellen des Grasfrosches : *Arch. Entm.*, I., 1, 2. — **Id.**, '94, 2. Aufgabe der Entwickelungsmechanik, etc.: *Arch. Entm.*, I., 1. Trans. in *Biol. Lectures, Wood's Holl*, 1894. — **Rückert, J.**, '91. Zur Befruchtung des Selachiereies : *A. A.*, VI. — **Id.**, '92, 1. Zur Entwicklungsgeschichte des Ovarialeies bei Selachiern : *A. A.*, VII. — **Id.**, '92, 2. Über die Verdoppelung der Chromosomen im Keimbläschen des Selachiereies : *Ibid.*, VIII. — **Id.**, '93, 2. Die Chromatinreduktion der Chromosomenzahl im Entwicklungsgang der Organismen : *Merkel and Bonnet, Erg.*, III. — **Id.**, '94. Zur Eireifung bei Copepoden : *An. Hefte.* — **Id.**, '95, 1. Zur Kenntniss des Befruchtungsvorganges : *Sitsb. Bayer. Akad. Wiss.*, XXVI., 1. — **Id.**, '95, 2. Zur Befruchtung von *Cyclops strenuus : A. A.*, X., 22. — **Id.**, '95, 3. Über das Selbständigbleiben der väterlichen und müterlichen Kernsubstanz während der ersten Entwicklung des befruchteten Cyclops-Eies : *A. m. A.*, XLV., 3. — **Rüge, G.**, '89. Vorgänge am Eifollikel der Wirbelthiere : *M. J.*, XV. — **Ryder, J. A.**, '83. — The microscopic Sexual Characteristics of the Oyster, etc.: *Bull. U. S. Fish. Comm.*, March 14, 1883. Also, *Ann. Mag. Nat. Hist.*, XII., 1883.

SABATIER, A., '90. De la Spermatogenèse chez les Locustides ; *Comptes Rend.*, CXI., '90. — **Sachs., J.**, '82. Vorlesungen über Pflanzen-physiologie ; *Leipzig.* — **Id.** Über die Anordnung der Zellen in jüngsten Pflanzentheile : *Arb. Bot. Inst. Würzburg*, II. — **Id.**, '92. Physiologische Notizen, II., Beiträge zur Zellentheorie : *Flora*, 1892, Heft I. — **Id.**, '93. Stoff und Form der Pflanzen-organe ; *Gesammelte Abhandlung*, II., 1893. — **Id.**, '95. Physiologische Notizen, IX., weitere Betrachtungen über Energiden und Zellen : *Flora*, LXXXI., 2. — **Sala, L.**, '95. Experimentelle Untersuchungen über die Reifung und Befruchtung der Eier bei *Ascaris megalocephala ; A. m. A.*, XL. — **Sargant, Ethel**, '95. Some details of the first nuclear Division in the Pollen-mother-cells of *Lilium martagon ; Journ. Roy. Mic. Soc.*, 1895, part 3. — **Schäfer, E. A.**, '91. General Anatomy or Histology : in *Quain's Anatomy*, I., 2, 10th ed., London. — **Schaudinn, F.**, '95. Über die Theilung von *Amœba binucleata* Gruber : *Sitz.-Ber. Ges. Naturforsch., Freunde, Berlin*, Jahrg. 1895, No. 6. — **Id.**, '96. Über den Zeugungskreis von *Paramœba Eilhardi : Sitz.-Ber. Ges. Naturforsch., Freunde, Berlin*, 1896, Jan. 13. — **Schewiakoff, W.**, '88. Über die karyokinetische Kerntheilung der *Euglypha alveolata : M. J.*, XIII. — **Schiefferdecker and Kossel**, '91. Die Gewebe des Menschlichen Körpers : *Braunschweig.* — **Schimper**, '85. Untersuchungen über die Chlorophyllkörper, etc.: *Zeitsch. wiss. Bot.*, XVI. — **Schleicher, W.**, '78. Die Knorpelzelltheilung. Ein Beitrag zur Lehre der Theilung von Gewebezellen : *Centr. med. Wiss. Berlin*, 1878. Also *A. m. A.*, XVI, 1879. — **Schleiden, M. J.**, '38. Beiträge zur Phytogenesis : *Müller's Archiv*, 1838. [Trans. in Sydenham Soc., XII.: London, 1847.] — **Schloter, G.**, '94. Zur Morphologie der Zelle : *A. m. A.*, XLIV., 2. — **Schmitz**, '84. Die Chromatophoren der Algen. — **Schneider, A.**, '73. Untersuchungen über Plathelminthen : *Jahrb. d. oberhess. Ges. f. Natur - Heilkunde*, XIV., *Giessen.* — **Schneider, C.**, '91. Untersuchungen über die Zelle : *Arb. Zool. Inst. Wien*, IX., 2. — **Schottländer, J.**, '88. Über Kern und Zelltheilungsoorgänge in dem Endothel der entzündeten Hornhaut : *A. m. A.*, XXXI. — **Schultze, Max**, '61. Über Muskelkörperchen und das was man eine Zelle zu nennen hat :

Arch. Anat. Phys., 1861. — **Schultze, O.**, '87. Untersuchungen über die Reifung und Befruchtung des Amphibien-eies: *Z. w. Z.*, XLV. — **Id.**, '94. Die künstliche Erzeugung von Doppelbildungen bei Froschlarven, etc.: *Arch. Entm.*, I., 2. — **Schwann, Th.**, '39. Mikroscopische Untersuchungen über die Uebereinstimmung in der Structur und dem Wachsthum der Thiere und Pflanzen: *Berlin*. [Trans. in *Sydenham Soc.*, XII.: *London*, 1847.] — **Schwarz, Fr.**, '87. Die Morphologische und chemische Zusammensetzung des Protoplasmas: *Breslau.* — **Schweigger-Seidel, O.**, '65. Über die Samenkörperchen und ihre Entwickelung: *A. m. A.*, I. — **Sedgwick, A.**, '85-8. The Development of the Cape Species of Peripatus, I.-VI.: *Q. J.*, XXV.-XXVIII. — **Id.**, '94. On the Inadequacy of the Cellular Theory of Development, etc.: *Q. J.*, XXXVII., I. — **Seeliger, O.**, '94. Giebt es geschlechtlicherzeugte Organismen ohne mütterliche Eigenschaften?: *A. Ent.*, I., 2. — **Selenka, E.**, '83. Die Keimblätter der Echinodermen: *Studien über Entwick.*, II, *Wiesbaden*, 1883. — **Sertoli, E.**, '65. Dell' esistenza di particolori cellule ramificate dei canaliculi seminiferi del testicolo umano: *Il Morgagni.* — **Siedlecki, M.**, '95. Über die Struktur und Kerntheilungsvorgänge bei den Leucocyten der Urodelen: *Anz. Akad. Wiss., Krakau*, 1895. — **Sobotta, J.**, '95. Die Befruchtung und Furchung des Eies der Maus: *A. m. A.*, XL. — **Solger, B.**, '91. Die radiären Strukturen der Zellkorper im Zustand der Ruhe und bei der Kerntheilung: *Berl. Klin. Wochenschr.*, XX., 1891. — **Spallanzani, 1786.** Expériences pour servir à l'histoire de la generation des animaux et des plantes: *Geneva.* — **Strasburger, E.**, '75. Zellbildung und Zelltheilung: 1st ed., *Jena*, 1875. — **Id.**, '77. Über Befruchtung und Zelltheilung: *J. Z.*, XI. — **Id.**, '80. Zellbildung und Zellteilung: 3d ed. — **Id.**, '82. Über den Theilungsvorgang der Zellkerne und das Verhältniss der Kerntheilung zur Zelltheilung: *A. m. A.*, XXI. — **Id.**, '84, 1. Die Controversen der indirecten Zelltheilung: *Ibid.*, XXIII. — **Id.**, '84, 2. Neue Untersuchungen über den Befruchtungsvorgang bei den Phanerogamen, als Grundlage für eine Theorie der Zeugung: *Jena*, 1884. — **Id.**, '88. Über Kern- und Zellteilung im Pflanzenreich, nebst einem Anhang über Befruchtung: *Jena.* — **Id.**, '89. Über das Wachsthum vegetabilischer Zellhäute: *Hist. Bei.*, II., *Jena.* — **Id.**, '91. Das Protoplasma und die Reizbarkeit: *Rektoratsrede, Bonn*, Oct. 18, 1891. *Jena, Fischer.* — **Id.**, '92. Histologische Beiträge, Heft IV.: Das Verhalten' des Pollens und die Befruchtungsvorgänge bei den Gymnospermen, Schwärmsporen, pflanzliche Spermatozoiden und das Wesen der Befruchtung: *Fischer, Jena*, 1892. — **Id.**, '93. 1. Über die Wirkungssphäre der Kerne und die Zellengrösse: *Hist. Beitr.*, V. — **Id.**, '93, 2. Zu dem jetzigen Stande der Kern- und Zelltheilungsfragan: *A. A.*, VIII., p. 177. — **Id.**, '94. Über periodische Reduktion der Chromosomenzahl im Entwicklungsgang der Organismen: *B. C.*, XIV. — **Id.**, '95. Karyokinetische Probleme: *Jahrb. f. wiss. Botanik*, XXVIII., I. — **Van der Stricht, O.**, '92. Contribution à l'étude de la sphère attractive: *A. B.*, XII., 4. — **Id.**, '95, 1. La maturation et la fécondation de l'œuf d'Amphioxus lanceolatus: *Bull. Acad. Roy. Belgique*, XXX., 2. — **Id.**, '95, 2. De l'origine de la figure achromatique de l'ovule en mitose chez le Thysanozoon Brocchi: *Verhandl. d. anat. Versamml. in Strassburg*, 1895, p. 223. — **Id.**, '95, 3. Contributions à l'étude de la forme, de la structure et de la division du noyau: *Bull. Acad. Roy. Sc. Belgique*, XXIX. — **Stricker, S.**, '71. Handbuch der Lehre von den Geweben: *Leipzig.* — **Stuhlmann, Fr.**, '86. Die Reifung des Arthropodeneies nach Beobachtungen an Insekten, Spinnen, Myriopoden und Peripatus: *Ber. Naturf. Ges. Freiburg*, I. — **Swaen and Masquelin**, '83. Etude sur la Spermatogenèse: *A. B.*, IV.

THOMA, R., '96. Text-book of General Pathology and Pathological Anatomy: Trans. by A. Bruce, *London.* — **Thomson, Allen.** Article "Generation" in Todd's Cyclopedia. — **Id.** Article "Ovum" in Todd's Cyclopedia. — **Tyson, James**, '78. The Cell-doctrine: 2d ed., *Philadelphia.*

USSOW, M., '81.   Untersuchungen über die Entwickelung der Cephalopoden : *Arch. Biol.*, II.

VEJDOVSKÝ, F., '88.   Entwickelungsgeschichtliche Untersuchungen, Heft I. : Reifung, Befruchtung und Furchung des Rhynchelmis-Eies : *Prag*, 1888. — **Verworn, M. '88.**   Biologische Protisten-studien : *Z. w. Z.*, XLVI. — **Id.**, **'89.** — Psychophysiologische Protisten-studien : *Jena.* — **Id.**, **'91.**   Die physiologische Bedeutung des Zellkerns : *Pflüger's Arch. f. d. ges. Physiol.*, LI. — **Id.**, **'95.**   Allgemeine Physiologie : *Jena.* — **Virchow, R.**, **'55.**   Cellular-Pathologie : *Arch. Path. Anat. Phys.*, VIII., 1. — **Id.**, **'58.**   Die Cellularpathologie in ihrer Begründung auf physiologische und pathologische Gewebelehre : *Berlin*, 1858. — **De Vries, H.**, **'89.**   Intracelluläre Pangenesis : *Jena.*

WALDEYER, W., **'70.**   Eierstock und Ei : *Leipzig.* — **Id.**, **'87.**   Bau und Entwickelung der Samenfäden : *Verh. d. Anat. Leipzig*, 1887. — **Id.**, **'88.**   Über Karyokinese und ihre Beziehungen zu den Befruchtungsvorgängen : *A. m. A.*, XXXII. [Trans. in *Q. J.*] — **Id.**, **'95.**   Die neueren Ansichten über den Bau und das Wesen der Zelle : *Deutsch. Med. Wochenschr.*, No. 43, ff., Oct. ff., 1895. — **Warneck, N. A.**, **'50.**   Ueber die Bildung und Entwickelung des Embryos bei Gasteropoden : *Bull. Soc. Imp. Nat. Moscou*, XXIII., 1. — **Watasé, S.**, **'91.**   Studies on Cephalopods ; I., Cleavage of the Ovum : *J. M.*, IV., 3. — **Id.**, **'92.**   On the Phenomena of Sex-differentiation : *Ibid.*, VI., 2, 1892. — **Id.**, **'93, 1.**   On the Nature of Cell-organization : *Wood's Holl Biol. Lectures*, 1893. — **Id.**, **'93, 2.**   Homology of the Centrosome : *J. M.*, VIII., 2. — **Id.**, **'94.**   Origin of the centrosome : *Biological Lectures, Wood's Holl*, 1894. — **Weismann, A.**, **'83.**   Über Vererbung : *Jena.* — **Id.**, **'85.**   Die Kontinuität des Keimplasmas als Grundlage einer Theorie der Vererbung : *Jena.* — **Id.**, **'86, 1.**   Richtungskörper bei parthenogenetischen Eiern : *Zool. Anz.*, No. 233. — **Id.**, **'86, 2.**   Die Bedeutung der sexuellen Fortpflanzung für die Selektionstheorie : *Jena.* — **Id.**, **'87.**   Über die Zahl der Richtungskörper und über ihre Bedeutung für die Vererbung : *Jena.* — **Id.**, **'91, 1.**   Essays upon Heredity, First Series : *Oxford.* — **Id.**, **'91, 2.**   Amphimixis, oder die Vermischung der Individuen : *Jena, Fischer.* — **Id.**, **'92.**   Essays upon Heredity, Second Series : *Oxford*, 1892. — **Id.**, **'93.**   The Germ-plasm : *New York.* — **Id.**, **'94.**   Aeussere Einflüsse als Entwicklungsreize : *Jena.* — **Wheeler, W. M.**, **'89.**   The Embryology of *Blatta Germanica* and *Doryphora decemlineata* : *J. M.*, III. — **Id.**, **'93.**   A Contribution to Insect-embryology : *Ibid.*, VIII. 1. — **Id.**, **'95.**   The Behavior of the Centrosomes in the Fertilized Egg of *Myzostoma glabrum* : *Ibid.*, X. — **Whitman, C. O.**, **'78.**   The Embryology of Clepsine : *Q. J.*, XVIII. — **Id.**, **'87.**   The Kinetic Phenomena of the Egg during Maturation and Fecundation : *J. M.*, I., 2. — **Id.**, **88.**   The Seat of Formative and Regenerative Energy : *Ibid.*, II. — **Id.**, **'93.**   The Inadequacy of the Cell-theory of Development : *Wood's Holl Biol. Lectures*, 1893. — **Id.**, **94.**   Evolution and Epigenesis : *Ibid.*, 1894. — **Wiesner, J.**, **'92.**   Die Elementarstruktur und das Wachstum der lebenden Substanz : *Wien.* — **Wilcox, E. V.**, **'95.**   Spermatogenesis of Caloptenus and Cicada : *Bull. of the Museum of Comp. Zool., Harvard College*, Vol. XXVII., Nr. 1. — **Will, L.**, **'86.**   Die Entstehung des Eies von Colymbetes : *Z. w. Z.*, XLIII. — **Wilson, Edm. B.**, **'92.**   The Cell-lineage of *Nereis* : *J. M.*, VI., 3. — **Id.**, **'93.**   Amphioxus and the Mosaic Theory of Development : *Ibid.*, VIII , 3. — **Id.**, **'94.**   The Mosaic Theory of Development : *Wood's Holl Biol. Lect.*, 1894. — **Id.**, **'95, 1.**   Atlas of Fertilization and Karyokinesis : *New York, Macmillan.* — **Id.**, **'95, 2.**   Archoplasm, Centrosome, and Chromatin in the Sea-urchin Egg : *J. M.*, XI. — **Id.**, **'96.**   On Cleavage and Mosaic-work : *A. Entm.*, III., 1. — **Wilson and Mathews, '95.**   Maturation, Fertilization, and Polarity in the Echinoderm Egg : *J. M.*, X., 1. — **Wolff, Caspar**

Friedrich, 1759. Theoria Generationis. — **Wolff, Gustav, '94.** Bemerkungen zum Darwinismus mit einem experimentellen Beitrag zur Physiologie der Entwicklung: *B. C.,* XIV., 17. — **Id., '95.** Die Regeneration der Urodelenlinse: *Arch. Entm.,* I., 3. — **Wolters, M., '91.** Die Conjugation und Sporenbildung bei Gregarinen: *A. m. A.,* XXXVII.

ZACHARIAS, O., '85. Über die amöboiden Bewegungen der· Spermatozoen von Polyphemus pediculus: *Z. w. Z.,* XLI. — **Zacharias, E., '93, 1.** Über die chemische Beschaffenheit von Cytoplasma und Zellkern: *Ber. deutsch. bot. Ges.,* II., 5. — **Id., '93, 2.** Über Chromatophilie: *Ibid.,* 1893. — **Id., '95.** Über das Verhalten des Zellkerns in wachsenden Zellen: *Flora,* 81, 1895. — **Id., '94.** Über Beziehungen des Zellenwachstums zur Beschaffenheit des Zellkerns: *Berichte der deutschen botan. Gesellschaft,* XII., 5. — **Ziegler, E., '88.** Die neuesten Arbeiten über Vererbung und Abstammungslehre und ihre Bedeutung für die Pathologie: *Beitr. zur path. Anat.,* IV. — **Id., '92.** Lehrbuch der allgemeinen pathologischen Anatomie und Pathogenese, 7th ed.: *Jena.* — **Ziegler, H. E., '87.** Die Entstehung des Blutes bei Knochenfischenembryonen: *A. m. A.* — **Id., '91.** Die biologische Bedeutung der amitotischen Kerntheilung im Tierreich: *B. C.,* XI. — **Id., '94.** Über das Verhalten der Kerne im Dotter der meroblastischen Wirbelthiere: *Ber. Naturf. Ges. Freiburg,* 1894. — **Id., '95.** Untersuchungen über die Zelltheilung: *Verhandl. d. deutsch. Zool. Ges.,* 1895. — **Ziegler and vom Rath.** Die amitotische Kerntheilung bei den Arthropoden: *B. C.,* XI. — **Zimmermann, A., '93, 1.** Beiträge zur Morphologie und Physiologie der Pflanzenzelle: *Tübingen.* — **Zimmermann, K. W., '93. 2.** Studien über Pigmentzellen, etc: *A. m. A.,* XLI. — **Zoja, R., '95, 1.** Sullo sviluppo dei blastomeri isolati dalle uova di alcune meduse: *A. Entm.,* I., 4; II., 1; II., IV. — **Id., '95, 2.** Sulla independenza della cromatina paterna e materna nel nucleo delle cellule embrionali: *A. A.,* XI., 10.

INDEX OF AUTHORS

Geddes and Thompson, theory of sex, 90.
Van Gehuchten, spireme-nuclei, 25; nuclear polarity, 26; muscle-fibre, 34.
Giard, polar bodies, 177.
Gilson, spireme-nuclei, 26.
Graf, nephridial cells, 32.
Griffin, fertilization, centrosomes in *Thalassema*, 143, 144; structure of centrosome, 235.
Grobben, spermatozoa, 105.
Gruber, diffused nuclei, 23, 26; regeneration in *Stentor*, 248.
Guignard, mitosis in plants, 59, 78; spermatozoïds, 107; fertilization in plants, 157, 159, 161; reduction, 195; centrosome, 224.

Haacke, gemmæ, 22.
Haberlandt, position of nuclei, 252.
Häckel, inheritance, 5; cell-organization, 21, 22, 210; epithelium, 40; cell-state, 41.
Häcker, polar spindles of *Ascaris*, 58; bivalent chromosomes, 61, 62; nucleolus, 91, 93; primordial germ-cells, 110, 112; germ-nuclei, 156, 193, 194, 219; reduction in copepods, 189, 191; polar bodies, 280.
Hallez, promorphology of ovum, 283.
Halliburton, proteids, 239; nuclein, 240, 241.
Hamm, discovery of spermatozoön, 7, 130.
Hammar, cell-bridges, 43.
Hammarsten, proteids, 239.
Hansemann, pathological mitoses, 67, 68.
Hanstein, metaplasm, 15; microsomes, 21.
Hartsoeker, spermatozoön, 7.
Harvey, inheritance, 5; epigenesis, 6.
Hatschek, cell-polarity, 39, 40; fertilization, 130.
Heidenhain, nucleus, 24, 25; basichromatin and oxychromatin, 27, 244; cell-polarity, 39; position of centrosome, 40; leucocytes, 72, 73; theory of mitosis, 74; amitosis, 81; staining-reactions, 127, 144; nuclear microsomes, 223; microcentrum, 227; asters, 234; position of spindle, 277.
Heider, insect-egg, 96.
Heitzmann, theory of organization, 42; nucleus and cytoplasm, 214.
Henking, fertilization, 124, 136; insect-egg, 96; tetrads, 188; reduction, 201.
Henle, granules, 21.
Henneguy, deutoplasm, 117.
Hensen, rejuvenescence, 129.
Herbst, development and environment, 324.
Herla, independence of chromosomes, 156, 219.

Hermann, spermatogonia, 16; central spindle, 52, 74, 76; division of chromatin, 78; spermatozoön, 123–126; staining-reactions, 127; centrosome, 224.
Herrick, spermatozoön, 105.
Hertwig, O., 1, 5, 7, 15, 21; idioblasts, 22; cell-division, 46; bivalent chromosomes, 61; pathological mitoses, 67; theory of mitosis, 75; rejuvenescence, 129; fertilization, 132; middle-piece, 135; polyspermy, 140; paths of germ-nuclei, 153; maturation, 175, 180–182; polar bodies, 177; inheritance, 257, 302; laws of cell-division, 276; cleavage-planes, 282; theory of development, 312, 317, 322, 328.
Hertwig, O. and R., origin of centrosome, 64; egg-fragments, 145; polyspermy, 148.
Hertwig, R., mitosis in Protozoa, 63, 64, 67; central spindle, 74; amphiasters in unfertilized eggs, 159, 226; conjugation, 167; reduction in Infusoria, 199.
Hill, fertilization, 135, 143, 157; centrosphere, 235.
His, germinal localization, 297.
Hofer, regeneration in *Amœba*, 249.
Hoffman, micropyle, 148.
Hofmeister, cell-division and growth, 293.
Hooke, R., cell, 13.
Hoyer, amitosis, 81.
Humphrey, centrosome, 225.
Huxley, protoplasm, 3; germ, 5, 295; fertilization, 129, 171; evolution and epigenesis, 328.

Ishikawa, *Noctiluca*, mitosis, 65, 67; conjugation, 168.

Jordan, deutoplasm and yolk-nucleus, 116, 119; first cleavage-plane, 282.
Julin, fertilization in *Styleopsis*, 142.

Karsten, centrosome, 225.
Keuten, mitosis in *Euglena*, 64.
Klebahn, conjugation and reduction in desmids, 199.
Klebs, pathological mitosis, 67, 68; cell-membrane, 251.
Klein, nuclear membrane, 28; theory of mitosis, 70, 230; amitosis, 84; nucleus and cytoplasm, 214; asters, 230.
von Kölliker, 1, 5, 7, 9, 13; epithelium, 40; cell-division, 45; spermatozoön, 98, 122; inheritance, 257, 302; development, 311.
Korschelt, nucleus, 25; amitosis, 81, 83; movements and position of nuclei, 92, 254–256; insect-egg, 96; nurse-cells, 113,

INDEX OF SUBJECTS